COPING WITH DELIBERATE RELEASE

INTERNATIONAL CENTRE FOR HUMAN AND PUBLIC AFFAIRS

General Editors: M. C. P. Morales and R. von Schomberg

Series A: Human Rights, Development and Environment

Series B: Social Studies of Science and Technology

SERIES B: SOCIAL STUDIES OF SCIENCE AND TECHNOLOGY

VOLUME 2

The titles published in this series

1. René von Schomberg (ed.): *Contested Technology. Ethics, Risk and Public Debate.* 1995
    ISBN 90-802139-2-6

2. Ad van Dommelen (ed.): *Coping with Deliberate Release. The Limits of Risk Assessment.* 1996
    ISBN 90-802139-4-2

3. Peter Wheale: *The Social Management of Biotechnology.* 1996

The titles published in the series A: Human Rights, Development and Environment

1. Patricia Morales (ed.): *Indigineous Peoples, Human Rights and Global Interdependence.* 1994
    ISBN 90-802139-1-8

2. Patricia Morales (ed.): *Towards Global Human Rights.* 1996
    ISBN 90-802139-3-4

COPING WITH DELIBERATE RELEASE

THE LIMITS OF RISK ASSESSMENT

edited by

AD VAN DOMMELEN

Free University of Amsterdam, The Netherlands

INTERNATIONAL CENTRE FOR HUMAN AND PUBLIC AFFAIRS

TILBURG / BUENOS AIRES

CIP-DATA KONINKLIJKE BIBLIOTHEEK, DEN HAAG

Coping

Coping with deliberate release: the limits of risk
assessment / ed. by Ad van Dommelen. - Tilburg [etc]:
International Centre for Human and Public Affairs
With Index.
ISBN 90-802139-4-2
Subject headings: biotechnology / genetic engineering /
risk assessment.

Published by the International Centre for Human and Public Affairs
Pastoor Smitsstraat 25,
5014 RH Tilburg
The Netherlands

Telephone/fax number: +31-13-5360751

Cover design: Theo Heldens
Cover illustration: Hugo van den Berg, 'Pandora' (adapted from J.W. Waterhouse)

Printed in the Netherlands

Acknowledgements

Most chapters of this book were presented in an earlier form in sessions on 'Quality of Risk Assessment: Theory, Practice and Politics of Deliberate Release', during the biennial meeting of the *International Society for the History, Philosophy and Social Studies of Biology* (ISHPSSB), 19-23 July 1995, in Leuven, Belgium. I thank Linnda Caporael, as a program officer of this meeting, for making these sessions possible. Along the road from draft papers to final chapters there are many people to acknowledge. I am indebted to the authors who contributed to this volume for their congenial cooperation and their diligent revising of earlier drafts. Philip Regal, René von Schomberg and Wim van der Steen have been very supportive and stimulating from the inception to the completion of this book. I thank Les Levidow for suggesting the title of the book. Hugo van den Berg managed to bring 'Pandora' to life on the cover. I thank Thea Laan for her technical support. My colleagues in the Department of Theoretical Biology at the Free University of Amsterdam provided an inspiring environment. This work was supported by the Netherlands Organization for Scientific Research (NWO).

The editor, January 1996

Contents

ACKNOWLEDGEMENTS 5

INTRODUCTION 9
Ad van Dommelen

Part I – Limits of Risk Assessment: Scientific Backgrounds

1. Metaphysics in Genetic Engineering: Cryptic Philosophy and
   Ideology in the 'Science' of Risk Assessment 15
   Philip Regal

2. Risk Assessment of Genetically Engineered Microorganisms:
   From Genetic Reductionism to Ecological Modeling 33
   Sheldon Krimsky

3. The Impact of Background Models on the Quality of Risk
   Assessment as Exemplified by the Discussion on
   Genetically Modified Organisms 47
   Ad van Dommelen

4. Politics and Science in Risk Assessment 63
   Manuela Jäger and Beatrix Tappeser

5. Species as Natural Kinds that Express Distinctive Natures:
   The Case for a Moratorium on Deliberate Release 73
   Brian Goodwin

Part II – Limits of Risk Assessment: Regulatory Practice

6. Bounding the Risk Assessment of a Herbicide-Tolerant Crop 81
   Les Levidow, Susan Carr, René von Schomberg and David Wield

7. Political Problems – Genetically Engineered Solutions:
   The Socio-technical Translations of Fox Rabies 103
   Ruth McNally

8. The Oxford Baculovirus Controversy – Safely Testing Safety? 121
   Les Levidow

9. Deliberate Release of Genetically Modified Organisms:
Applying the Precautionary Principle   137
Soemini Kasanmoentalib

10. The Laborious Transition to a Discursive Policy Process on the
Release of Genetically Modified Organisms   147
René von Schomberg

Part III – Limits of Risk Assessment: Political Conditions

11. Outlooks on the Public Information and Participation in the
Context of the European Biotechnology Directives 90/219/EEC
and 90/220/EEC   159
Piet Schenkelaars

12. On How the People can Become 'The Prince':
Machiavellian Advice to NGOs on GMOs   177
Peter Wheale and Ruth McNally

13. Lacking Scientific Knowledge or Lacking the Wisdom and
Culture of Not-Knowing   195
Christine von Weizsäcker

14. Risk Communication and the Ethos of Democracy   207
Christoph Rehmann-Sutter and Adrian Vatter

15. Public Acceptance and Risks of Biotechnology   227
Darryl Macer

ABOUT THE AUTHORS   247

INDEX   253

Editor's Introduction

History repeats itself in unexpected ways. In 1859 Thomas Austin imported 24 rabbits into Australia to provide some hunting. Now the Australians have to deal with an estimated 200 to 300 million of them. But a recent new release may be going to revert this invasion. In October 1995 two dead rabbits were found on the mainland of Australia, not far from Wardang Island where an experiment involving the release of a lethal rabbit virus was going on. It turned out the virus had left the containment of the island and reached the mainland, probably with the Australian bushfly acting as a vector for the virus. Two months later the death toll of rabbits on the mainland is an estimated 7 million, with the virus travelling as fast as 8 kilometres a day (*New Scientist*: 21 October and 9 December, 1995).

Now, instead of worrying about the presence of rabbits in Australia, there is cause for concern about their disappearance from wildlife. For the moment, scientists can only speculate about the social, ecological and economic consequences. The rabbit calicivirus was found in 1984 in China and is not a product of genetic engineering. The example makes it clear, however, that tinkering with nature is a complex affair, affecting society and the natural environment.

Few technologies have been documented in their development so well as recombinant DNA technology has been since its inception in the early 1970s. Saying that something is well-documented is not the same as saying that it is well-understood in its consequences, however. The dawning of modern biotechnology has created a complex new 'landscape' of emerging scientific, social and political issues. We cannot just wait for problems to materialize in this new socio-political landscape, because our responses may come too late then. Instead, we must actively uncover and analyse its intricacies and pitfalls, and consider if we can help the new biotechnological culture get a proper shape. The contributions in this book are all dedicated to this cause.

The focus of this volume is on our capacity to assess and foresee risks that applications of modern biotechnology may bear for society and nature. How good can we expect ourselves to perform in the face of this challenge? The answer to this question cannot be simple. One thing is clear at least: the surest way to jeopardize our future society is to underestimate the complexity of its present technological culture. To cope with the challenges of modern biotechnology, we must explore the limits of our risk assessments. The application of rDNA technology that is central in all the following investigations is the planned release into the environment of genetically engineered organisms. There is no easy way of understanding the impacts and consequences that the development of this technology may have to our lives.

Important and difficult issues that need to be addressed in parallel with the technological developments of genetic engineering are matters such as public participation, sustainability, biosafety, insurance, patenting and labelling. The aim of this book is to contribute to creating a more adequate view on aspects of biosafety and its regulation. It is important to note that the practice of risk assessment did not arise out of a well-developed capability to predict hazards, but came into being because of the urgent practical need to understand the scope of our enterprises.

The different chapters of this volume can be seen as a concerted attempt to map promises and perils in the emerging landscape of scientific, social and political problems that come along with modern biotechnology. If we want to be able to move around freely in this new terrain, we must take time to examine its panoramas and morasses. The chapters are arranged under three general headings, although their subjects and perspectives overlap. The limits of risk assessment are studied with regard to the 'Scientific Backgrounds' (Part I), the 'Regulatory Practice' (Part II), and the 'Political Conditions' (Part III) of deliberate release.

In the first part of this book, Philip Regal uncovers hidden philosophies and world views that colour much of the 'science' and thinking that pertains to the benefits and risks of genetic engineering. He calls for careful analyses of the rhetoric that is being used as society enters the era of biotechnology, with its powerful impact on human institutions, economic patterns, life-styles, and values. Sheldon Krimsky probes into the scientific difficulties of making prospective risk assessments. His analysis explores the theoretical limitations of using microcosms to predict the behaviour of genetically engineered organisms in the natural environment. Ad van Dommelen draws attention to the host of methodological pitfalls that challenge our reasoning in debates on risk assessment. His analysis emphasizes the importance of being explicit and critical about the underlying theoretical models on the basis of which we construe our arguments. Manuela Jäger and Beatrix Tappeser have brought together scientific evidence that undermines the appeasement strategies of 'molecular politics'. They report unnerving results about the survival, spread, persistence, integration and activation of genetically engineered organisms and their DNA. Brian Goodwin, in his chapter, challenges the idea that species are purely functional entities that have arisen by historical contingency. He argues that the results of gene transfer are intrinsically unpredictable because of genome fluidity and the destabilising effects of gene transfers from one species to another.

In the second part, on limits of risk assessment in the regulatory practice, Les Levidow, Susan Carr, René von Schomberg and David Wield analyse how the European Union handled a proposal for market approval of a herbicide-tolerant crop, oilseed rape. Their case study relates limitations of the practice of risk assessment to national political cultures. Ruth McNally unravels the underlying rationale of one of the largest authorised open field releases of genetically engineered organisms anywhere in the world, which aimed to immunise foxes against infection with rabies virus. Looking through the lens of the 'sociology of translation', she makes a critical reconstruction to show that the relation between problem and solution is dubious in this case. Les Levidow investigates the controversy in Britain over the intentional release of a baculovirus with a gene inserted to kill moth larvae more quickly. His analysis uncovers limits of risk assessment in the form of methodological indeterminacy, difficulties in the design of adequate simulations, and the 'teleology' of predefined performance criteria of genetically engineered organisms. Soemini Kasanmoentalib examines the relationship between the precautionary principle and scientific uncertainty and ignorance. She concludes that the existing regulatory system cannot be regarded as rigorously precautionary, because the existence of uncertainties is not sufficiently acknowledged. René von Schomberg discusses the possibility of moving to a discursive policy process. Considering the Dutch practice of risk assessment procedures, he sees indications that we are now entering a phase of a societal embedding of biotechnology.

Finally, in the third part of this book, on the limits of risk assessment with respect to political conditions, Piet Schenkelaars reports about European regulations on risks in biotechnology and points out the important difference between 'acceptance' and 'acceptability'. He makes a comparison of existing provisions for public information and participation in the different countries and concludes that fora at the national and European level are needed to judge from the viewpoint of 'acceptability'. Peter Wheale and Ruth McNally put together their insights and experience to formulate advice to non-governmental organisations on how best to approach issues about the deliberate release of genetically modified organisms. In a Machiavellian style they suggest practical strategies to foster a democratically controlled technology. Christine von Weizsäcker critically contrasts technology-centered risk assessment with problem-oriented comparison of different technological options. She argues that our present culture does not adequately match efforts in technology with efforts in comparative technology assessment. Christoph Rehmann-Sutter and Adrian Vatter argue that we need innovative politics to improve risk communication. To ensure qualified rights of public participation for those highly affected by technological risks we must adjust democratic procedures. Darryl Macer reports on his descriptive approach to bioethics. His survey findings support the call for public involvement in the process of risk definition and assessment.

All these studies contribute to the important object of making the picture or map that we have of the challenging new 'problem landscape' that is brought about by modern biotechnology as adequate as possible. Without a reliable map of this complex landscape we may not be able to find our way into a benevolent future.

Part I

Limits of Risk Assessment: Scientific Backgrounds

1

Metaphysics in Genetic Engineering: Cryptic Philosophy and Ideology in the 'Science' of Risk Assessment

Philip Regal

1. Introduction

There has been much concern that organisms that have been modified with powerful recombinant DNA techniques might sometimes be dangerous. Could it be unsafe to eat a particular 'transgenic' or 'genetically engineered' fruit or grain, for example?

It is the question of *ecological* risks, though, that has been intensively discussed by scientists and government agencies for over a decade. This concern has been greatest because if dangerous new forms of life begin to reproduce in nature and spread, it is improbable that they could be recalled. Humans have been helpless to stop non-indigenous rogue species that have gone out of control and caused enormous economic damage, for example, such as fire-ants, zebra mussels, or killer bees in the Western Hemisphere, or Chinese mitten crabs in Europe.

There has been more or less a consensus among those scientists who have published analyses of ecological risks that most genetically engineered organisms (GEOs) should be ecologically safe, though a minority could cause great problems. Yet after years of analysis and discussion, the scientific community is still divided over what this generality should imply for regulatory oversight.

Industry and DNA research scientists tend to argue that careful oversight would cost them too much time and money, especially considering that the chances are that most laboratories are doing safe work. Their world is one of intense competition. And, despite the tens of billions of dollars that have been invested to develop biotechnology, many companies have difficulties raising enough venture capital even to stay in business. They argue that even a careful regulatory system could not guarantee complete safety.

Other scientists and public interest groups have argued that although potentially dangerous projects will be in the minority, there must be a legitimate effort to screen them out. Though 100% safety cannot be guaranteed, a competent regulatory system could reduce the risks considerably and would be worth the cost.

This disagreement over regulation has been exacerbated by the fact that it has proved impossible to draw a clear line that would divide planned projects into those for which risk evaluations will prove to be simple and inexpensive, and projects where data requirements could grow to be complex and expensive.

It is under such pressures from competitive recombinant DNA scientists and industries, under pressures from governments hopeful that their huge investments will pay off, clashing with criticisms from less organized scientists and citizen groups, that risk assessment cultures have been evolving within government agencies and in industry. What sorts of cultures have been developing?

The risks of primary concern have been ecological, yet there has been a tendency within the cultures of risk assessment not to staff with scientists who are educated in modern principles of ecology and evolution. One finds instead many lawyers, chemists, microbiologists, geneticists, agronomists. Government regulators tend not to ask ecologically relevant questions from applicants. They tend not to base broad policy decisions on ecological and evolutionary knowledge and principles. They tend not to sponsor ecological and evolutionary research and education programs that would strengthen the quality of risk assessment. They tend to make important decisions without providing clear scientific explanations.

Yet the defenders of such trends within the cultures of risk assessment claim that they are being 'scientific' and that they are not sacrificing quality. How is this claim defended? How can non-experts claim to be making 'scientific judgments' if they do not gather scientific data and are not ready to detail in print how they evaluate what data there is? Their defense is based primarily on *world view* (or Weltanschauung), that is not recognized to be world view.

At one end of the spectrum of what various types of risk assessors mean by 'risk assessment', when it is said that "we have this situation under control, we are experts in scientific risk assessment", this does not as it might seem necessarily mean that they know how to draw valid scientific conclusions.

Instead there is a genre of risk assessors that speaks in the context of management science. To say that "we are experts in risk assessment" or that "we have sound risk assessment procedures" may mean that they have developed protocols for processing paper work; and "scientific risk assessment" means that the papers are routed past people with scientific degrees, whether their educations have been in appropriate fields or not, or whether their analyses are used in decisions or not. Quality is too often judged in terms of how efficiently paper work can be moved through the system (alternatives to this genre of thinking about risk assessment have been discussed in papers in Krimsky and Golding 1992).

Managerial definitions of quality risk assessment beg us to ask what criteria biotech regulators use for developing the content of the forms to be filled out, for picking scientists to review the forms, and both for specific actions and broad policy decisions. In what ways do ancient philosophical ideas, ideology, and politics enter into 'scientific' decisions? Much of what passes for 'scientific thinking' in biotech risk assessment is world view that is not recognized to contain metaphysical beliefs that have ancient cultural roots, such as essentialism and Platonic or Aristotelian cosmologies. It is called 'scientific thinking' because it follows the perspectives and reasoning of influential personalities in science.

This will be the basic theme of the present essay. What are some examples of ancient philosophy and modern ideology that have been passing as empirical science? What can the history of the development of biotechnology reveal about the ways in which firm scientific knowledge and broader world views have become commonly confused with one another? Why did society wait so long to begin to deal with the potential down-side of biotechnology? What are the implications for whether society can safely continue to promote the use of recombinant DNA techniques?

2. History

2.1 An idealistic beginning for molecular biology and genetic engineering

Recombinant DNA techniques were developed beginning in the 1970s out of the visions, techniques, and discoveries of molecular biology. Molecular biology in turn had been earlier developed in significant part out of the reductionist and deterministic visions of Max Mason and Warren Weaver at the Rockefeller Foundation.

It is now understood, as a result of the research of Pnina Abir-Am, Lily Kay, Robert Kohler, Edward Yoxen, and other historians of science, that in the 1930s Mason and Weaver used the financial and political resources of the Rockefeller Foundation to fashion and promote a new philosophy and practice of biology. The new biology would be based on philosophical reductionism agendas that had been suggested earlier by Hermann Muller and Jacques Loeb. Biology would become 'the chemistry of the gene'.

Thus, from the 1930s to the present there have been two cultures of biological scientists. There have been traditional biological scientists, making investigations into the structure, physiology, evolution, behaviour, adaptations, and ecology of diverse life forms on earth. Their intellectual roots go back to the anatomists, breeders, naturalists, and physiologists of the 18th and 19th centuries who studied organisms in their natural habitats and in the laboratory.

And, there have been the molecular biologists, conducting research into the nature of genetic chemistry and protein synthesis, and promising that one day traditional biology will become obsolete and biology will be rebuilt by them 'from the ground up'. Their intellectual roots trace for the most part back to chemistry and physics. These scientists were mostly chemists and physicists and yet they came to claim that theirs was the 'true' approach to the study of life. Their claim to 'own' biology, a field of knowledge that lay largely beyond their expertise, rested on the reductionistic argument that they were developing knowledge of 'the' supposedly basic chemical substance of life.

Mason and Weaver themselves were refugees from quantum physics. They sought to preserve ancient deterministic and reductionistic dreams against the growth of quantum mechanics, by transplanting the reductionistic/deterministic dreams that they considered to be 'true science' to a new biology. Thus, they not only sponsored new and powerful analytical techniques to find and characterize the hereditary material. They also encouraged the new community to use reductionistic/deterministic and utopian terms of discourse in applying for grants, reporting research findings, making awards, etc. (references in Abir-Am 1987, Kay 1993, Regal 1989).

The dreams of Mason and Weaver were part of a venerable tradition. Theory reductionism or philosophical reductionism has long been tied to the ancient dream that one day all knowledge will be unified and reduced to concepts in the physical sciences, and will be reduced to simple deterministic predictive models that will allow control over physical, organic, and human nature.

The social sciences and humanities will ultimately be reduced ontologically, epistemologically, and discursively to biology with no residue (e.g. Wilson 1975). Biology will in turn be reduced to chemistry, which will reduce to physics, which will reduce to a simple deterministic unity that will allow precise predictions at all levels of life.

The quantum mechanics of the 20th century was only one decisive blow against this vision of the unity of knowledge. But the vision had become so much a part of Western intellectual thought, an ingredient in science policy funding, and so powerful a motivator for scientists, that it did not crumble in the face of mounting evidence against it (Ayala and Dobzhansky 1974; Einstein and Infeld 1966; Fuerst 1982; Koestler and Smythies 1969; Lindley 1993; Mayr 1982; Popper 1982; Regal 1990; Rosenberg 1994).

2.2 Utopianism

The new biology that Mason and Weaver aimed to shape would be not merely abstract scientific knowledge and theory, but would include a social agenda. The promoters and practitioners promised to determine the structure of the gene and to use this information to correct social and moral problems including crime, poverty, hunger, and political instability.

From the perspective of a theory reductionist, it was logical that social problems would reduce to simple biological problems that could be corrected through chemical manipulations of *soils, brains, and genes.* Thus the Rockefeller Foundation made a major commitment to using its connections and resources to promote a philosophy of eugenics.

The Rockefeller Foundation used its funds and considerable social, political, and economic connections to promote the idea that society should wait for scientific inventions to solve its problems, and that tampering with the economic and political systems would not be necessary. Patience, and more investment in reductionist research would bring trouble-free solutions to social and economic problems.

Mason and Weaver helped create a network of what would one day be called molecular biology, that had little traditional knowledge of living organisms and of communities of organisms. It shared a faith in theory reductionism and in determinism. It shared utopian ideals. It learned to use optimistic terms of discourse that brought grants and status. The project was in the general spirit of Bacon's *New Atlantis* and Enlightenment visions of a trouble-free society based on mastery of nature's laws and scientific/technological progress (e.g. Eamon 1994; McKnight 1992).

Historians such as Soraya de Chadarevian and Nicolas Rasmussen are in the process of detailing later phases in the development of molecular biology, during the 1950s, that were also wrapped in enthusiastic social idealism. For example, after the atomic bomb was developed and the atomic age was proclaimed, what is known today as molecular biology was promoted as a part of 'biophysics.' This was to be the peaceful side of physics that would solve untold human problems.

2.3 Philosophy or ideology?

One can argue that the social vision in which molecular biology was imbedded and that was promoted by the Rockefeller Foundation served conservative interests, whatever the politics of individual scientists. It infused society with reasons for resignation to a genetic fatalism. At the same time it raised calming expectations: science and technology would bring grace.

Reductionistic visions had long served the interests of physicists and chemists. They served as blueprints of an intellectual/social hierarchy that mandated a place for them at the top, and that also helped them to obtain research support. These visions came to serve the interests of molecular biologists similarly. In this sense the theoretical simplification of life has been opportunistic. One can argue that the philosophies of theory reductionism and utopianism thus have graded into ideologies as they have become useful to a range of interests, both inside and outside of science, and that they should be called ideologies rather than philosophies.

I do not object to this general argument. Philosophy has often served ideological functions. But I will not make an effort to characterize individual ideas as 'ideological' each time they have been used in self-serving ways, in contrast to detached philosophy. This would distract from the main purpose of this essay which is to begin sketching the ways in which Western philosophical concepts have become confused for 'hard science' and have even become used in regulatory policy.

2.4 Idealists do not prepare for problems

The history of molecular biology helps to explain why its promoters did nothing to prepare their enterprise for the likelihood that there would be grave concerns and serious risks when genetic engineering would one day become possible. It helps to explain why the scientific community today is unprepared to deal with the potential risks and other societal, political, and economic issues raised by biotechnology.

Science and society are becoming aware of the plethora of potential problems only at this late date in the history of molecular biology and biotechnology largely because the unbridled idealism and optimism of the social agenda that gave birth to that research community, and the self-interest that held idealism in place, left little room for doubts.

There was also the contributing fact that so many of the early sponsors and practitioners were physical scientists who had little knowledge of or interest in patterns of evolutionary adaptation, or the tragic history of ecological disturbances by species that were introduced to new areas with idealistic expectations, etc. They were not experts in intricate economic and social issues. If the developing network had been more intellectually open, there might have been balanced discussions, more realistic expectations, and preparation for the future complications that genetic engineering would bring.

2.5 Asilomar: Too little, too late, and no follow-through

Doubts about the Grand Agenda of molecular biology did surface in the 1970s with the famous Asilomar and Gordon conferences. But the network of molecular biologists that had been woven on a loom of idealism was largely unprepared to deal in a few short days with the many doubts that suddenly arose once genetic engineering became a reality.

Observers such as Clifford Grobstein have commented that virtually the only issue that was raised at these conferences that was actually pursued thereafter was the 'biohazard issue' – the concern that a seemingly harmless 'non-wild-type' laboratory GEO might escape and unexpectedly turn out to be able to cause a global catastrophe. Academic ecologists ignored this debate among the molecular biologists. It seemed indeed improbable that organisms that are bred to be highly specialized for life in the laboratory and modified in some arbitrary way might escape and turn out to thrive in nature and even go on to do unprecedented damage.

This biohazard issue was quite different from the 'biosafety issue' that began to concern academic ecologists by 1984. It was fast becoming possible to engineer 'wild-type' GEOs that would be able to thrive in nature. In some cases the traits that were to be added to them would not be arbitrary from an ecological point of view. There would be novel and powerful traits that could increase the competitive abilities of the host species or expand the range of resources that it could exploit. For example, if a new type of resistance to disease were added to a 'wild-type' fish or plant, it could give the transgenic population a great competitive advantage and make it a likely candidate to become a destructive rogue species.

The earlier biohazard issue, though, became a dramatic 'attention-grabber' that unfortunately diverted discussion away from other important concerns that had been raised. Yet it was the most manageable concern, for it was unlikely to begin with, and it could in any event be dealt with by developing containment protocols. And thus the biohazard issue became traumatic for the DNA scientists but, in the end, the focusing of publicity on it allowed genetic engineering research to proceed. There would be no need to freeze or rethink the funding structures, systems of career ladders, and the broad social expectations that had been created. Grobstein wrote,

> Despite the creation of an NIH-led [National Institutes of Health] interagency committee for federal coordination, a forum for concerted deliberation on the excluded Asilomar agenda never came into existence. So the public policy debate and, to some degree, the public impression of recombinant technology remained fixed on worst-case scenarios symbolized by the Andromeda strain (Grobstein 1986).

Concerns over the possible social, economic, and other problems from genetic engineering were reduced to the simple technical matter of containment and to the improbable concern that a biohazard scenario would emerge. Grobstein warned that the result of this 'success' was to fence the issue within the turf of a special interest group within the scientific community and to prevent further effective deliberation by other scientists and the educated public of the complicated and serious social issues that lay ahead.

3. Sociology

The leaders of the genetic engineering community – Grobstein's 'special interest group' within the scientific community – continued to focus on 'containment' as though it were 'the' sole issue of concern, and they did nothing to prepare their science, or society, for the other challenges that lay ahead. The issues that surely lay ahead included the engineering of ecologically competent GEOs that were intended to thrive in nature, food safety, and the enormous institutional and socioeconomic impacts that many expected.

Molecular biology continued to train young scientists narrowly only in chemistry and physics – sometimes also in physiology, microbial genetics, medicine, or agronomy. The biotech community retained its strong taste for theory reductionism, in addition to reductionistic laboratory methods, despite brushing closely with the fact that the entry of GEOs into the world of ecology, the food supply, and the economy would have intricate effects.

Molecular biology continued to consider itself to be a predictive science even as promises were being made that genetic engineering would allow control at higher levels of intricacy and organization, where the emergent properties are not always well understood. Molecular biologists on the whole did little to educate themselves to the discoveries and conceptual developments in ecology and evolutionary biology.

The recombinant DNA community had bad experiences with sensationalistic journalism. These, together with an increasing desire for industrial confidentiality, inspired an atmosphere of defensiveness and even secrecy in their community. Recombinant scientists developed strong ties with the business and financial world and many became entrepreneurial themselves. This alliance created an economically and politically powerful pressure block to oppose effective regulation (Krimsky 1991; Wright 1994). Public desires to regulate biotech for safety reasons were strongly opposed by leaders of the biotech community for economic reasons. Careful regulation of biotech would mean costs in terms of time and money for laboratory workers and industrialists alike. Moreover, the business community, with which recombinant DNA scientists were forging partnerships, had long held strong resentments against all sorts of regulation. The antiregulatory philosophy of the Reagan/Bush administrations in the 1980s, and of neo-conservatives before and after the 1980s, are well known.

One also saw a distinctive strain of 'rugged individualism' take root among some of the more entrepreneurial molecular biologists. It is distinctive in the sense that self-proclaimed 'individualists' of this species have not been adverse to lobbying for enormous public subsidies. This type of rugged individualism had long been popular in the business community. Its devotees had long proclaimed themselves to be scientific 'realists' and 'objectivists' because they felt that they were not swayed by the misguided sentimentalities, communal idealisms, fears, and superstitions of the masses.

Ayn Rand, author of *The Virtue of Selfishness*, and *The New Left: The Anti-industrial Revolution*, is the apostle of so-called 'objectivism'. She argued for a philosophical revolution based on rationality, individualism, anti-collectivism, self-interest, science, progress, and technology. Self-proclaimed 'objectivists', commonly equate 'scientific rationality' with the facts, theories, and reasoning that they use in daily life. 'Irrationality' is the thinking of those who do not think like them.

An egocentric point of view is a common human trait, not restricted categorically to self-proclaimed objectivists (Regal 1990). But objectivists seem especially ready to believe that they are experts on a wide variety of scientific, economic, and philosophical subjects even when they are uninformed. Labeling oneself 'an objectivist', or a 'rationalist', or a 'scientific thinker' seems to give one added confidence in one's particular point of view.

The equation of scientific rationalism with world views by objectivists results in a way of speaking that obscures the distinction between empirical fact and reasoned or absorbed opinion. This way of speaking exists among biotech leaders at least to the degree that it has complicated policy discussions of risks and benefits in which I have participated. For example, some biotech promoters will speak as great scientific authorities about ecological and evolutionary principles (as they imagine these), but they will refuse even to read the professional ecological or evolutionary literature. They will ignore such scientific considerations on the grounds either that ecological principles are self-apparent to them, or that ecologists are not true scientists. [Some biotechnology leaders have not understood that there is a difference between professional ecologists and 'environmentalists' (or understood the differences between mainstream environmentalists and 'deep ecologists'), and so from their point of view it might have been true that (what they thought of as) 'ecologists' were not true scientists.]

Another example of the confusion that one sees among objectivists: The economic dreams and promises of the biotech industry are often spoken of as though they are reliable scientific predictions of things to come. It is, again, as though by making the labels 'objective' and 'predictive science' part of one's self-identity, all of one's strong beliefs must by definition be objective and predictive.

4. Philosophy and Risk Assessment

Given this history, it is no surprise that a great deal of risk assessment in biotechnology has been philosophical beliefs that do not recognize themselves to be philosophy.

Leaders of the biotech community have insisted that their claims that the technology will always be safe and effective have been based on solid science, and that any doubts or concerns have been based on anti-science, rather than on different scientific paradigms.

The fact is that most of the economic promises of the biotech community are years overdue and biotech companies go out of business at a very high rate. Even superficially, their social dreams and their effectiveness claims have not proved to be true scientific predictions in most cases (also, even in this infancy of genetic engineering, there have been accidents and near-accidents – see Doyle et al. 1995; Regal 1994).

There is indeed magnificent solid science in molecular biology, and some biotechnology products are already useful. But there is also confusion over how to use reductionistic scientific findings to make predictions at higher levels of organization. Thus, investment in most biotechnology companies has not paid any returns.

Predictions seemingly 'based on' solid science are not necessarily scientific. A pedestrian example: Suppose one were to claim that they could predict with scientific certainty the time at which a pizza will be delivered, because they base their prediction on the solid science of the chemistry and physics of cooking times and the acceleration characteristics of the delivery vehicle. This would not be a truly reliable scientific prediction, because physics and chemistry are only the elementary terms in a delivery equation. Delivery will also depend on traffic, road conditions, the state of repair of the vehicle, and the ability of the driver to navigate.

Organization at the levels of tissues, organisms, and communities of organisms is many times more intricate than city traffic and sleepless pizza delivery persons. The work-day dream of theory reductionists has been that by specializing one will be able to reliably generalize. This dream can be a great motivator for young scientists who have been persuaded to devote their lives to the study of small bits of nature, but it is not necessarily a realistic expectation.

Spokespersons for the biotech community claim that they will accept safety regulations so long as they are based on 'true science'. But one soon learns that they may have in mind criteria that other scientists would not agree are 'true science'. Thus, the larger question for the sociology and philosophy of science is: who gets to define true science? Should it be the scientific community at large, philosophers of science, experts in appropriate fields, or only those scientists in political/financial control of science policy? What exactly would be the true science on which safety can be based if it is not modern ecological and evolutionary principles?

A cynic may point out that the demands for 'true science' sound suspiciously like arguments from the tobacco industry that there is no scientific proof of negative health effects from tobacco, and that arguments to the contrary are 'non-scientific' and have been made by 'enemies' of the industry. A cynic may point to the recently uncovered strategic campaigns by industry lawyers to control language to control the public image of tobacco, and guard against liability (see for example the special issue of the *Journal of the American Medical Association*, July 19, 1995). Thus the arguments from biotech leaders about what 'true science' is would be merely tactics to distract.

The possibility that there is a strategic campaign of attention-diverting rhetoric at work in the case of biotechnology should not be ruled out. There is an enormous amount of money and political power at stake at university, local, national, and international levels; and power has never confined itself to transparent strategies. Lawyers, lobbyists, and corporate strategists are active at the intellectual/policy leadership level in the biotech community, and they aggressively locate centers of power in national and state capitals to shape a favorable image of biotechnology and to get laws and subsidies that will be favorable to it.

Whatever the political maneuvering may be, idealistic thinking did dominate in the beginnings of molecular biology. True philosophical confusion has taken place and does exist, and these have had at least a significant effect on ways of thinking in the biotech community and on the quality of risk assessment. These are realities that do deserve analysis and future research.

Next, what have been some of the traditional philosophical beliefs that have commonly been mistaken for scientific thinking in risk assessment, and how have they translated into practice?

4.1 Reductionism

Just as physicists once assumed that all things would be understood if the properties of basic atomic particles were understood, molecular biology began as an exercise in imagining that all life can be explained and accounted for by a similar conceptual reductionism of life to the properties of the molecule of heredity and its arrangements. Reductionist enthusiasm went beyond developing methods of analysis to determine chemical structures (methodological and constitutive reductionism). There was a leap in logic to the belief that knowledge from lower levels of organization give one knowledge at all higher levels of organization (theory or philosophical reductionism).

Enthusiasts have assumed that the lens of reductionist simplicity allows them to understand higher levels of organization, when in fact it may sometimes throw intricacy so out of focus that it appears insignificant. To the enthusiast, there is no significant difference between the *Humpty Dumpty* who sat on the wall and the pile of *Humpty Dumpty* pieces that all the king's men could not figure out how to put back together – for it is sufficient to know that both are basically chemicals.

This ambitious claim to knowledge has extended into the policy area. One example of reductionism in policy: The U.S. Food and Drug Administration has accommodated the industry by agreeing that genetic engineering is 'nothing but' an extension of traditional breeding, because it is 'nothing but' moving genes around, and therefore genes and their products which are foreign to a species do not constitute food additives. GEOs will be as safe as organisms modified by traditional breeding techniques, and so screening and food labeling will not be necessary.

Therefore, the addition of genes for scorpion or spider venom to the tissues of corn or soybeans (to protect against insect damage), for example, should not have to go through expensive testing to assure that food from such plants is safe. Genetic engineering is said to simulate a natural process and to be equivalent to traditional breeding which is in turn merely a slight modification of normal sexual reproduction – since they all supposedly reduce to 'mixing genes'.

Yet if one planned to spray the venom or other new pesticide on the crops, expensive testing would be required before the new pesticide could be marketed. The implications of this philosophical gambit mean millions of dollars saved by a biotech company every time it develops a new genetically engineered product to be consumed. This is said to be science-based policy. But public policy in this case is being based on reductionistic philosophy rather than on 'solid science'.

In fact, genetic engineering can raise greater concerns compared to traditional breeding in some applications. Recombinant DNA techniques potentially allow 'phylogenetic leapfrogging' of adaptive traits between totally unrelated species so that truly novel and potent adaptive combinations can be created. They allow genetic modifications without the traditional debilitating effects of the allelic substitutions that have plagued traditional breeding. They will eventually allow a reprogramming of the non-Mendelian portions of genomes that control some of the most profoundly important biological features, but that traditional breeding cannot penetrate and reprogram. They often produce startling 'genetic side-effects' (Regal 1994).

These facts raise especially clear concerns for ecological risks. Recombinant DNA techniques have special potentials to circumvent the inherent limitations of conventional breeding and to be used in powerful ways to modify organisms that could be destructive.

The safety of food and working conditions are separate issues and involve different technical considerations from the question of whether rogue transgenic populations can sometimes be produced. There is evidence that 'genetic side-effects' may be especially profound in the case of GEOs, because an organism's 'buffering' system may not recognize new biochemical processes and moderate their effects. More analysis of the implications of this is urgently needed, but it presently seems that major biochemical side-effects could result and sometimes cause problems for food safety (Regal 1994).

In addition, it is now generally understood that allergenic properties can be passed on from genetic donors to transgenic foods.

4.2 Essentialism

There has been considerable essentialism in the thinking of the biotech community that has been confused with 'scientific thinking'. Policy was being made before 1985 according to the argument that GEOs will be generically safe because they are basically unnatural, overloaded with excess metabolic functions, etc. – as though there would be an 'essence' of GEO and they would all share these characteristics and thus all be safe. (And note, this argument that GEOs are necessarily unnatural contradicts the above argument that transgenic foods do not need to be regulated because they are necessarily natural.)

Scientists who have studied biosafety have mostly backed off from such essentialism, and realize that GEOs must be considered on a case-by-case basis. Some may be safe and others dangerous (Colwell 1989; Regal 1985, 1986, 1988, 1994).

But one still finds significant evidence of essentialism among regulatory officials who have stated that hundreds of (so-called) releases (into confined field plots for testing commercial potential) have shown nothing unexpected, and that because 'nothing bad has happened', it is scientifically demonstrated that GEOs will be categorically safe (references in Regal 1994).

Some biotech leaders have also argued that an ecologically incapacitated plant such as corn or wheat would be an appropriate scientific model for all GEOs, as though all GEOs would all share 'the essence' of transgenic corn.

4.3 Essentialism extended to human motivations and abilities:
  Ramifications for the quality of regulation

Another significant example of essentialist thinking: Biotech promoters too often insist that persons with concerns about biotech form a category and share an essence. When individuals or groups raise economic, safety, ethical, or social questions about specific projects, promoters commonly insist that those who raise these diverse questions are all basically 'enemies' of biotech who are scientifically ignorant, anti-progress, Luddites, and afraid of each and every genetic engineering project. 'Objectivists' see in questions that are put to them, confirmation that the masses are all ignorant and fearful of progress.

Ecology is not a true science in the eyes of biotech leaders. They see ecology as non-reductionistic, non-technological, and anti-progress. The report of the *Ecological Society of America* on the safety of GEOs has been received with suspicion, for example, by leaders of the biotech community (Tiedje et al. 1989).

A cynic might argue that such accusations, made in such a highly political climate, are not reflections of true philosophical confusion about essences, but are merely in the classic tradition of promoting ugly stereotypes and character assassination to marginalize critics (e.g. Keen 1986). Thus, the commonplace essentialism in popular culture allows the opening of a political space in which the stereotype of a 'Luddite' can become constructed and used as a scapegoat to divert attention and rouse emotions. Yet even if the cynic were correct, those who have been persuaded to believe the accusations and act on them, however the accusations were generated, do not recognize that they have fallen into essentialistic or typological thinking. Typological thinking does exist, and it is important to understand this.

Thus one does find lax regulators who take the attitude that regulatory agencies exist to keep an irrational public calm. They do not seem to read or be prepared to discuss the growing scientific literature that outlines genuine scientific reasons to strive for quality in risk assessment. They too often rubber-stamp applications and staff with inappropriately educated employees. Pressures from biotech promoters has led to a culture of government regulators in which it is common to believe that regulation exists primarily to convince an irrational public that the government 'has everything under control.'

Those who have argued that government regulation of biotech is not necessary have also glimpsed this. Henry Miller of Stanford University's Hoover Institute, has accused Terry Medley, a lawyer who heads the United States Department of Agriculture's (USDA) Food Safety and Inspection Service, of seeking to maintain regulations to maintain bureaucratic status. Miller reported that Medley had been telling biotech scientists "that scientific evidence was of secondary significance in policy making; of greater importance were public perceptions of risk (no matter how misguided) and ensuring that U.S. policies conformed to those of our trading partners (no matter how economically regressive)" (Miller 1994).

Miller's accusation that USDA officials will admit that they feel that their risk assessment programs exist primarily for political purposes is consistent with a report by Wrubel et al. (1992). They found, in a study of USDA safety reviews of biotech proposals that there had been scant attention paid to asking useful scientific questions.

The Wrubel et al. report came four years after an extensive report from the General Accounting Office (GAO) of the United States Congress that found that The Department of Agriculture, The Environmental Protection Agency, The Food and Drug Administration, and the National Institutes of Health were making safety determinations without an adequate scientific basis (GAO 1988). The immediate response of USDA officials was that the GAO report was inaccurate. USDA officials then told us privately that they were improving their procedures. But the Wrubel report showed that there had been no detectable progress. As I write, USDA has proposed essentially the deregulation of transgenic crop plants. They have not published any scientific reasons for the proposed policy.

A group of anonymous 'whistle blowers' at the U.S. Environmental Protection Agency (EPA) has published an extensive report that claims that EPA has bent to political pressures and compromised its biosafety oversight role, and has been forcing its employees to keep silent about risks – *Genetic Genie: The Premature Commercial Release of Genetically Engineered Bacteria* (PEER 1995). This report was published through a group that represents the interests of public employees.

I have worked closely with several government agencies for a decade, have served on the Scientific Advisory Board for the EPA, etc., and it has been clear that qualified scientists in the agencies are often shocked and demoralized that political pressures so often combine with scientific ignorance to determine agency policies. Agency heads are acutely aware that since the 'Reagan Revolution' there has been a strong anti-regulatory philosophy and that the promoters of biotechnology have developed close ties to the centers of power.

Thus, efforts to reduce all concerns about biotech to 'irrationality', combined with political pressures, has contributed to the development of a risk assessment culture that is unlikely to be able to make quality risk assessments. They have not been seriously preparing to meet the scientific challenges ahead.

4.4 Platonic cosmology

I have been involved extensively in scientific workshops and policy discussions regarding biotech since 1984. A set of arguments that GEOs should be generically safe to release in nature had been determining U.S. policy and leading toward complete deregulation.

These generic safety arguments turned out to be based on outdated ecological and evolutionary theory, and ecology/evolution in popular thought, that portrayed a perfect balance and organization of nature, the perfection of adaptive features. There was also the idea of plentitude, the notion that every creature that is possible has already lived (Regal 1985, 1986, 1994). Analyses of these ideas by academic ecologists and evolutionary biologists in the 1960s and 1970s had been rejecting them.

The origins of the disproved ideas of balance and perfection of adaptation trace back easily to the origins of ecology and evolution in the natural theology of the 16th through 19th century. Natural theology maintained that God had created a perfectly harmonious universe with perfectly adapted creatures. These ideas trace back even earlier to the revival of Platonic and Aristotelian ideas about nature in 12th and 13th century Christian Europe. Greek cosmology became secularized and the mistaken belief was spread that Darwinian evolution produced a harmoniously balanced nature populated by perfectly adapted creatures (e.g. Bowler 1988).

Thus, the basis of the arguments that biotechnology leaders were using to set United States policy on biosafety were Platonic and Aristotelian cosmologies that assumed that nature is organized in its basic essence in a highly logical and harmonious manner. And thus GEOs could only be less perfect than natural organisms and they could do nothing to upset the supposed balances.

The implications for the quality of ecological risk assessment of the old view in contrast to the modern view are profound. In the Platonic view, nature is in harmonious balance and GEOs can only be imperfect and non-adaptive. They cannot compete with those creatures that the laws of nature have perfected and so they cannot upset that harmonious balance that the laws of nature have produced. Thus, for those who mistook Plato for a modern ecologist, supposedly solid 'science' indicated that no serious risk assessment is necessary. Risk assessment is only necessary as a facade, to keep a scientifically illiterate public calm.

The newer findings in ecology and evolution demolish this comforting ancient view. The new findings indicate that the so-called 'balance of nature' is relative, tenuous, ad hoc, statistical, and organisms are far from perfectly adapted to nature. There is much room for organisms to be made that are competitively superior to those that already exist, and for a prevailing tenuous 'balance of nature' to be destabilized.

This is not to say that every GEO will be ecologically dangerous. Nature will present significant challenges to GEOs, and much genetic engineering is done with ecologically attenuated laboratory organisms and row crops to which have been added non-adaptive traits. I have explained in a number of publications why most GEOs are of types that will fail to thrive naturally (Regal 1985, 1993, 1994).

But there are nevertheless types of GEOs that could cause serious ecological problems, ranging from noxious but tolerable problems, to catastrophic ones. Thus, it is necessary to have risk assessment that is much more than a facade. And there must be serious scientific research and training to provide legitimate foundations for risk assessment (Regal 1987a, 1987b, 1989, 1993).

The older Platonic and Aristotelian ideas are deeply rooted in Western culture and it would not be easy to flag them and mark 'caution' for all time, even if there were not economic and political pressures to pull out the warning flags. These old and misleading balance of nature ideas are an extremely serious problem for the quality of risk assessment. For it will be very difficult to find politicians and regulators who will understand that the old balance of nature ideas are misleading Greek cosmology and who will not mistakenly think that they are logical, scientific 'common sense' because they have a comfortable familiarity.

4.5 Monism and public policy

Philosophers could help to explain that it is not rigorous science or philosophy to believe that there is only one truth or one approach to truth. They could help to explain why balance is needed in science policy. This would include balanced support for diverse approaches to the study of biology, and it would include full consideration of the spectrum of biological knowledge when making policy decisions about biotechnology safety.

Leaders in molecular biology have pressed for funding and staffing in biology to be concentrated in molecular biology. They speak of phasing out the 'old fashioned' life sciences and at some time in the future rebuilding them from the ground up on the foundations of biochemistry. Such policies would result in the elimination of most scientific investigation into nature at its higher levels of organization. Their rationale is again reductionistic. Knowledge of emergent properties is supposedly illusions that will one day be corrected and reduced to chemical theories.

4.6 Utilitarianism and Platonic realism

Policy is still being made according to utilitarianism in combination with idealism or Realism, and this is again mistaken for 'scientific thinking'. The utilitarian premise that rightness or wrongness is determined by consequences quickly leads to the notion that costs and benefits can be scientifically calculated, and by the same standard, so that they can be weighed against each other. Yet academic philosophers understand that it has proved difficult to estimate social costs and social benefits in any truly scientific way. How can one identify the greatest good for the greatest number? Should estimations include future generations?

A common argument in biotechnology has been that the risks are merely hypothetical and this must be weighed against the enormous future benefits. The fact is that it is impossible to be certain about the social benefits, especially in agricultural and environmental applications where the economic, social, and technical issues can be quite intricate. Some will surely get rich, but will society truly benefit in the ways that have been promised?

Yet the teleological purposes of projects, the hoped for ideal outcomes, are treated as though they are scientific Realities, even though the industry is years overdue on most of its promises. Then regulators are asked to weigh these promises heavily against the supposed fact that the risks are merely hypothetical, do not conform to the ideal Reality, and hence have zero mass.

Thus the outcome – determined 'scientifically' – will always be that the risks are negligible compared to the benefits. Regulators have been pressured by biotech proponents inside and outside of government to defining scientific risk assessment as a process of weighing risks against proposed benefits; and yet they argue that detailed socioeconomic analyses of risks and benefits should not be made because risk analysis must be strictly scientific and socioeconomic analyses are not scientific. There is a clear contradiction here, but it is not seen by biotech promoters who have complete faith in the Realism of the proposed benefits.

A further example: When the prices of biotech stocks have plunged because of unkept promises, the idealistic faithful have insisted that it is the market that is unreal, and the science is real. Consider responses to a September 26, 1994 issue of *Business Week* that was critical of industry management and a pattern of unkept biotechnology promises. (The special issue followed other criticisms from business analysts such as those in a special 20 page supplement to the May 20, 1994 *Wall Street Journal*, and Robert Teitelman's *Gene Dreams: Wall Street, Academia, and the Rise of Biotechnology*.) As a reporter summarized the responses,

> To people inside biotech companies, the stock market is what's unreal. ... [In response to the issue of *Business Week*, the insiders argue that:] The reality is the science, and the science is good. "The reality is that this is going to be the technology of the future," says Ed Fritzky, chairman and chief executive officer of Immunex Corp. ... the people in these companies all say the work will go on. Somebody will fund it. Somebody will make money on it, and those who bet otherwise will ultimately lose (Ramsey 1994).

Again, 'science' and 'scientific thinking' in the biotech community are too often defined as that which supposedly true scientists like genetic engineers and molecular biologists happen to be thinking. Many assume that because they are a scientific culture, thus all their beliefs, ecological, social, economic, are 'scientific' rather than a mixture of hard fact and firm theory with sometimes justified, sometimes unjustified extrapolations from these, simple myths, and self-serving ideological beliefs as one might find in any human culture.

5. Policy Implications

This essay illustrates that much of what is supposedly science-based risk assessment is actually Greek metaphysics. Thus, philosophers of science could do a great deal to improve the quality of risk assessment by helping regulators and the public to further identify and understand the differences between judgments based on credible scientific information and theory, and judgments based on world views that include theory reductionism, essentialism, idealism, Greek cosmology, and utilitarianism masking as objective science.

It should be mentioned that some 'environmentalists', especially among the so-called 'deep ecologists', also mistake their personal world views for science. Some of them also mistake Platonic or Aristotelian models of the balance and perfection of nature for hard science. They may strongly oppose any human modifications of nature and may make the false claim that the science of ecology warns that any disturbance of nature is unsafe.

But these idealizations of nature and the excesses of some of the 'deep ecologists' have been discussed for years. Professional ecologists have been engaged for decades in experiments to sort out issues related to idealizations of nature (Botkin 1990; Pimm 1991). What are different models of balance? How natural or unnatural are various types of balance or imbalance? What constitutes truly dangerous ecological damage? The balance issue in this context has not been neglected nearly to the degree that the relationships between philosophy and science have been neglected in the context of biotechnology.

The implications of reductionist and determinist thought for social policy issues with regard to biotechnology, biosafety, and balance in support for the life sciences have scarcely been examined by scholars in the depth that is required, especially considering the profound implications of these matters well beyond the biosafety issue.

The philosopher Karl Popper, in *The Open Society and its Enemies* and *The Poverty of Historicism*, and elsewhere, has analyzed various aspects of reductionism, determinism, and 'scientism' in great detail with regard to political ideology, democratic freedoms, and academic standards and conventions in the social sciences and humanities. Thus, the interface between philosophy and social policy has not been strictly speaking neglected. Yet, treatments such as Popper's are so broad that they can seem remote from daily policy battles and Popper's analyses have too often been forgotten.

The present example stresses that if historians, philosophers, and sociologists of science and technology will do their homework, they can have something important to contribute to a range of policy deliberations that are in progress as society enters the era of biotechnology – an era that many have argued will surpass the Industrial Revolution in its impact on human institutions, economic patterns, life-styles, and values.

There is much need for careful analyses of the rhetoric that is being used not only in risk issues but in debates and decisions related to the reshaping of economic patterns, redistributions of economic and political power, the reshaping of the relationships between citizens and institutions, the structure and nature of scientific research, teaching, and beliefs, relationships between scientists and the public. Questions about the quality of risk assessment programs for the safety and effectiveness of GEOs are very important. But there is also an important need to more deeply analyze the relationships of reductionistic and idealistic world views to science policy and funding, to the rhetoric of persuasion, and the relationships of science policy and techniques of persuasion to social, economic, and political dynamics and trends.

References

Abir-Am, Pnina 1987. 'The biotheoretical gathering, transdisciplinary authority and the incipient legitimation of molecular biology in the 1930s: New perspectives on the historical sociology of science.' *History of Science* 25, pp.1-70.

Ayala, Francisco and Dobzhansky, Theodosius 1974. *Studies in the Philosophy of Biology: Reductionism and Related Problems.* Berkeley: University of California Press.

Botkin, Daniel B. 1990. *Discordant Harmonies: A New Ecology for the 21st Century.* New York: Oxford University Press.

Bowler, Peter J. 1988. *The Non-Darwinian Revolution.* Baltimore: The Johns Hopkins University Press.

Doyle, Jack D., Stotzky, Guenther, McClung, Gwendolyn and Hendricks, Charles 1995. 'Effects of genetically engineered organisms on microbial populations and processes in natural habitats.' *Advances in Applied Microbiology* 40, pp.237-287.

Eamon, William 1994. *Science and the Secrets of Nature: Books of Secrets in Medieval and Early Modern Culture.* Princeton, New Jersey: Princeton University Press.

Einstein, Albert and Infeld, Leopold 1966. *The Evolution of Physics.* New York: Simon and Schuster.

Fuerst, John A. 1982. 'The role of reductionism in the development of molecular biology: Peripheral or central?' *Social Studies of Science* 12 (2), pp.241-278.

[GAO] U.S. General Accounting Office 1988. *Biotechnology: Managing Risks of Genetically Engineered Organisms.* Washington D.C.: Government Printing Office (GAO/RCED-88-27, June).

Grobstein, Clifford 1986. 'Asilomar and the formation of public policy.' In: Raymond A. Zilinskas and Burke K. Zimmerman (eds.), *The Gene-Splicing Wars: Reflections on the Recombinant DNA Controversy.* New York: Macmillan, pp.3-10.

Kay, Lily 1993. *The Molecular Vision of Life.* New York: Oxford University Press.

Keen, Sam 1986. *Faces of the Enemy: Reflections of the Hostile Imagination.* San Francisco: Harper & Row.

Koestler, Arthur and Smythies, J.R. 1969. *Beyond Reductionism: New Perspectives in the Life Sciences.* Boston: Beacon Press.

Krimsky, Sheldon 1991. *Biotechnics and Society: The Rise of Industrial Genetics.* New York: Praeger.

Krimsky, Sheldon and Golding, Dominic (eds.) 1992. *Social Theories of Risk.* Westport Connecticut: Praeger.

Lindley, David 1993. *The End of Physics: The Myth of a Unified Theory.* New York: Harper Collins.

Mayr, Ernst 1982. *The Growth of Biological Thought.* Cambridge: Harvard University Press.

McKnight, Stephen A. (ed.) 1992. *Science, Pseudo-science, and Utopianism in Early Modern Thought.* Columbia, Miss.: University of Missouri Press.

Miller, Henry 1994. 'The brainless wonder of U.S. biotech regulations.' *Washington Times* (26

August), p.A21.

[PEER] Public Employees for Environmental Responsibility 1995. *Genetic Genie: The Premature Commercial Release of Genetically Engineered Bacteria*. (810 First St. NE, Suite 680, Washington D.C. 20002. Tel. (202)408-0041, E-mail: 76554.133@compuserve.com).

Pimm, Stuart L. 1991. *The Balance of Nature? Ecological Issues in the Conservation of Species and Communities*. Chicago: University of Chicago Press.

Popper, Karl R. 1982. *The Open Universe: An Argument for Indeterminism*. Tolowa, N.J.: Rowman and Littlefield.

Ramsey, Bruce 1994. 'Biotech Blues: Industry confident about future, but financial community is getting nervous.' *Star Tribune* (28 December), p.1D (reprinted from Seattle Post-Intelligencer).

Regal, P.J. 1985. 'The Ecology of Evolution: Implications of the Individualistic Paradigm.' In: H.O. Halverson, D. Pramer, and M. Rogul (eds.), *Engineered Organisms in the Environment: Scientific Issues*. Washington, D.C.: American Society for Microbiology, pp.11-19.

————. 1986. 'Models of Genetically-Engineered Organisms and Their Ecological Impact.' In: Harold Mooney (ed.), *Ecology of Biological Invasions of North America and Hawaii*. New York: Springer-Verlag. (Reprinted in *Recombinant DNA Technical Bull*. Sept. 1987).

————. 1987a. 'Safe and Effective Biotechnology: Mobilizing Scientific Expertise.' In: John Fowle, III (ed.), *Application of Biotechnology: Environmental and Policy Issues* (AAAS Symposium #106). Boulder, CO: Westview Press, pp.145-164.

————. 1987b. 'Meeting Legitimate Public Concerns Over Biotechnology: The Need for a Special Infrastructure.' *Minnesota Acad. Sci.* **53** (1), pp.18-32.

————. 1988. 'The adaptive potential of genetically engineered organisms in nature.' Special Combined Issue of *Trends in Ecology and Evolution* **3** (no.4, April), and *Trends in Biotechnology* **6** (no.4, April), pp.36-38.

————. 1989. 'Biotechnology jitters: Will they blow over?' *Biotechnology Education* **1** (2), pp.51-55.

————. 1993. 'The true meaning of 'exotic species' as a model for genetically engineered organisms.' *Experientia* **49**, pp.225-234.

————. 1994. 'Scientific principles for ecologically based risk assessment of transgenic organisms.' *Molecular Ecology* **3**, pp.5-13.

Rosenberg, Alexander 1994. *Instrumental Biology, or the Disunity of Science*. Chicago: University of Chicago Press.

Teitelman, Robert 1989. *Gene Dreams: Wall Street, Academia, and the Rise of Biotechnology*. New York: Basic Books.

Tiedje, James, Colwell, Robert K., Grossman, Yaffa L., Hodson, Robert E., Lenski, Richard E., Mack, Richard N. and Regal, Philip J. 1989. 'The planned introduction of genetically engineered organisms: Ecological considerations and recommendations.' *Ecology* **70** (2), pp.298-315.

Wilson, Edward 1975. *Sociobiology: The New Synthesis*. Cambridge: Harvard University Press.

Wright, Susan 1994. *Molecular Politics: Developing American and British Regulatory Policy for Genetic Engineering, 1972-1982*. Chicago: University of Chicago Press.

Wrubel, R.P., Krimsky, S. and Wetzler, R.E. 1992. 'Field testing transgenic plants: An analysis of the US Department of Agriculture's environmental assessments.' *BioScience* **42**, pp.280-289.

Risk Assessment of Genetically Engineered Microorganisms: From Genetic Reductionism to Ecological Modeling

Sheldon Krimsky

1. Introduction

Rapid developments in agricultural biotechnology in the 1980s have given rise to the first field tests of genetically modified plants and microorganisms. Public concerns over the unintended effects of releasing genetically engineered organisms (GEOs) have highlighted the importance of ecological risk assessment as a means of anticipating and managing possible untoward consequences.

Two modes of thinking have framed the discussion of risks associated with the release of GEOs into the environment. The genetic reductionist framework places greatest weight on understanding the foreign genes and the phenotypic characteristics of the host organism. The ecological framework is site specific and requires field testing of the GEO under the conditions of application. The former assumes a predictive theory between the genetic sphere and the ecological sphere, while the latter offers little credence to predictive risk assessment of GEOs and must accept the dismal conclusion that every ecological assessment experiment places the environment at risk.

The use of microcosms to test GEOs prior to release has been proposed as a bridge between the extreme positions of the genetic reductionists who defer to genetic knowledge for insuring the safety of released organisms and advocates of a radical empiricism who argue that risk analysis begins and ends in the field. An intermediate step of *microcosm analysis* has been proposed that could provide reliable and useful information about the survival, competitiveness and dispersal of genetically modified microorganisms released in the soil. This chapter examines the possibilities and limitations of microcosms, tradeoffs in microcosm structure between modeling actual conditions and gaining replicable and dependable results, and the problems of standardization.

2. Prospective versus Explanatory Risk Assessment

Two kinds of risk assessment can be distinguished which we can call retrospective and prospective. In retrospective risk assessment, an adverse event takes place and the role of the risk assessor is to ascertain what the cause was. Typically, industrial accidents are followed by investigations into the cause or causes of the event. Deciphering the cause of an accident like the chemical release in Bhopal, India is not an end in itself (with the exception of tort litigation). Rather the knowledge gained is expected to make the technological system safer. The term "fault tree" analysis applied to technological risks describes a method of identifying all possible events leading to the hazard event. Fault tree analysis can be used to estimate the probabilities or explain the cause of an outcome (Krimsky and Golding 1991: 100). Retrospective risk assessment is about the past but is almost always directed toward the future.

Prospective risk assessment exclusively seeks to predict possible hazardous outcomes before they occur. Three major streams of prospective risk assessment are natural hazards research, studies of nuclear power plant safety, and chemical toxicology. The term "event tree" analysis describes a method used to estimate the probability of systems failure. In toxicology, the goal is to predict the health effects on humans, animals or plants of the consumption of or exposure to chemical agents. The fundamental problem of prospective risk assessment is the problem of induction, namely, how can we predict the future from our knowledge of the past. The prediction of natural hazards from actuarial data is a form of atheoretical inductivism where future probabilities are inferred strictly from past frequencies. Whereas the development of predictive risk assessment for technological systems and toxicological effects of chemicals on humans employs a combination of theory and empirical information (Krimsky and Golding 1992: 3-22).

Prospective risk assessment is induction with high stakes. The wrong estimate could mean thousands of birth defects, as in the use of thalidomide, to unacceptable deaths, such as those resulting from swine flu vaccine, or transplacental carcinogenesis that accompanied the administration of diethylstilbestrol (DES) to tens of thousands of pregnant women. Each system of prospective risk assessment is layered with methodological obstacles. Predicting birth defects, cancer risks or drug side effects usually involves one or more of the following methods: animal to human extrapolation; inferences from a small sample of humans to a large population; inferences from *in vitro* to *in vivo* conditions; extrapolating the effects of using large doses of a substance over a short period of time on a small number of animals to estimate the effects of small doses on large numbers of people over a long period of time. Despite fifty years of toxicological studies and assay development, the uncertainties of predicting human effects of drugs and chemicals on the basis of animal studies have not been solved. On the contrary, recent experiments have raised new questions about the use of toxicological testing methods on animals or cells to predict health effects on humans (Ames and Gold 1990).

3. Ecological Risk and Bioengineered Organisms

Since the early 1980s, the role of risk assessment for predicting changes in ecological systems began receiving special attention as the prospect of releasing genetically engineered organisms (plants, animals and microorganisms) into the environment seemed close at hand (Gillett 1986). The ecologists and molecular geneticists had, by and large, viewed the problem of predicting adverse outcomes of environmental releases from quite different perspectives. I have argued elsewhere that molecular biologists, by discipline, seemed more confident in the predictability of genotype to phenotype than ecologists and evolutionary biologists (Krimsky 1991).[1] Those trained in ecology and field studies generally believed that predicting the fate of GEOs on the basis of genetic information and *in vitro* experiments was based on false confidence, perhaps even a myth about the predictive power of genetic knowledge.

Predictive knowledge of GEOs became a central part of the debate over environmental release. The policy issues of immediate concern began to draw attention to the conflicting viewpoints of scientists schooled in different disciplines. First, there were disagreements over the need for risk assessment for GEOs. Since we create all sorts of hybrid plants in which unknown numbers of genes are exchanged across species and taxa, why all the tumult when we transfer a single known genetic locus.

Second, there are disagreements over the relevance and significance of historical ecological data for predicting the fate of GEOs. For example, some biologists were predisposed to use the accumulated knowledge of exotic introductions as a baseline for understanding what could happen when GEOs were introduced. Others argued that exotic introductions cannot inform the risk of GEOs since the latter are most frequently indigenous plants that have been modified in some small way, by virtue of the genome changes. Exotics, on the other hand, are significantly alien to the environment in which they have been released and so may face no counterbalancing or stabilizing mechanisms against untoward growth, competition or dispersal. Often cited examples of exotic introductions that have resulted in severe damage are the grasses of Eurasian origin introduced into the American west and kudzu introduced into the Southeastern United States.

A third area of disagreement centered on the dialectics of quantity and quality. According to one view, minor adjustments of the genome of plants and microorganisms are not likely to produce major ecological shifts between the organism and its environment. Writing in *Science*, Winston Brill, comparing microbes to chemicals argued that small changes to the latter may result in unexpected toxicological properties whereas, "by comparison, minor modifications obtained by breeding safe plants or mutating safe microbes do not yield progeny that become serious problems"[2] (Brill 1985a: 383). With respect to the ice minus example, one scientist compared the organism to a set of piano keys. Imagine one key removed. The piano will not sound like another instrument; it will simply be unable to play certain tunes well. The piano analogy breaks down when we consider that a key removed offers nothing positive to the player or composer while ice minus was expected to offer a practical benefit to farmers and its purpose included its ability to survive and function in the environment.

The notion that significant phenotypic changes would not result from single gene or several gene changes is not persuasive to some biologists who draw their examples from our knowledge of the natural history of microorganisms. Harvard biologist Fakhri Bazzaz counts himself among those who do not accept the view that the quantity of change is related to the quality of change: "It is conceivable that a small change in genetics will actually lead to a fairly large change in the behaviour, the ecological behaviour, of an organism, and in some cases that could have a detrimental effect on the ecosystems into which these organisms are introduced" (Bazzaz 1985: 55).

A fourth area of disagreement concerns the possible outcomes of transferring a foreign gene to an organism or moving a gene to a new locus in the same organism. The extreme reductionist argues that the gene would either do what it was designed to do or do nothing at all. Others cite pleiotropy as a realistic possibility, namely that single gene products can affect more than one trait, or epistasis, the capacity of one gene to modify the expression of another gene that is not an allele of the first. Looming behind these debates is the historical issue of emergence versus determinism and the conflict between mechanistic and interactionist paradigms of genetics (Lewontin et al. 1984). These alternative viewpoints about the role of genes is reflected in the uncertainties over risk assessment.

Each of the three categories of GEOs, namely, plants, animals, and microorganisms, offer some unique challenges for risk assessment. Of the three, however, microorganisms are least likely to be recalled or destroyed once released. For this reason, they are perceived by some to represent a heightened area of concern for intentional release.

4. Applications of Bioengineered Microorganisms

The most promising areas of application of genetically engineered microorganisms (GEMs) in the environment include: the use of genetically engineered microbes in mining or crude oil recovery operations; bioremediation of toxic materials in contaminated soils such as dioxin or PCBs; bacterial or viral insecticides; nitrogen fixing bacteria; the release of microorganisms as biosensors; and bacteria designed to reduce frost damage.

Given this broad range of application, is there a way to minimize the ecological risks of certain releases? Is there useful information that can be gained about risks prior to releasing organisms in the field? Will this information be of such a nature as to preclude catastrophic releases? Will it prevent or reduce releases of GEMs that may be ecologically harmful and costly but not catastrophic? Microbial ecologists have suggested that microcosm and greenhouse tests can serve this function as a means of screening out hazardous products.

How realistic is this process? These recommendations were advanced during the period "ice minus", a frost inhibiting microorganism, was approved for field testing. Since there is little chance that a released genetically modified microorganism can be recalled or destroyed once it enters the environment, the function of the greenhouse or microcosm test is to identify a potentially hazardous GEM that is not likely to show up in an analysis based exclusively on the foreign DNA, the host organism, and the history of its use.

There are plenty of skeptics around who argue that such laboratory or quasi-laboratory experiments cannot guarantee safety. An organism might pass the microcosm test while still exhibiting adverse effects. Since that is true of any screening assay or risk assessment, should the likelihood of false negatives serve as a reason to prohibit all releases of GEMs? This question is answered differently by different stakeholders. Hard line environmentalists who oppose the release of any GEOs argue that (1) there is a real possibility of a catastrophic effect and (2) the potential benefits of the organism cannot justify those risks however remote. Similar arguments were used during the early developments of recombinant DNA research to effect a permanent moratorium on genetic engineering.

There may in fact be circumstances in which the risk of a catastrophic consequence from a released transgenic organism is more than idle speculation. Were that to be the case, then any risk assessment is a devil's gamble. A reasonable "precautionary principle" that avoids high consequence events even at low probability when there is no social imperative, is a prudent course of action. While ecologists and environmentalists considered the possibility of adverse outcomes, few, if any, mainstream scientists elevated those potentially adverse outcomes to the level of catastrophic consequences.

The first field test of a genetically engineered microorganism in the United States involved a strain of *Pseudomonas syringae* called ice minus because it was associated with protecting crops from ice damage from subfreezing temperatures. It took five years of regulatory and legal maneuvers before the tests were carried out in California (Krimsky and Plough 1988). The most extreme risk scenario raised about the test postulated that the ice minus bacteria might be wafted to the atmosphere in sufficient quantity to affect weather patterns, e.g., ice crystallization in the atmosphere. The U.S. Environmental Protection Agency (EPA) solicited consultation from atmospheric scientists who, based on theoretical calculations, dismissed the concern that field tests could induce an atmospheric perturbation. This left open the question of massive spraying of ice minus on thousands or tens of thousands of acres. In anticipation of large scale testing, the EPA collected data on the upward flux of bacteria sprayed on a field.

Radical shifts in weather patterns from anthropogenic causes could certainly be considered catastrophic. Nevertheless, global warming, while offering such a grim prospect, has not resulted in the mass mobilization against fossil fuels. Many of the examples cited of adverse consequences resulting from the release of non-native species (exotic introductions) while surely problematic or a nuisance, don't conjure up apocalyptic consequences. Insects like fire ants and plants like kudzu are popular examples of the unintended effects of exotic introductions. Fire ants were introduced accidentally while kudzu was brought to the United States intentionally. It is possible that the human and ecological effects they brought about could have been identified prior to their introduction by the appropriate risk analysis. In contrast, multitudes of new crops were introduced into agriculture without incident. Moreover, even the foreign introductions that have caused problems are not viewed as catastrophes, although no one questions the severity of problems like the introduction of brown snakes into Guam, rabbits into Australia or gypsy moths and kudzu in the United States (U.S. Congress 1993). Proponents of releasing GEOs argue that many of the most widely cited examples, kudzu notwithstanding, were unintended introductions.

5. Risk Assessment of GEMs

The release of GEMs into the environment offers a unique challenge to risk assessment because: the effects of microorganisms are not as obvious as those of plants or animals; GEMs reproduce quickly and are impossible to recall; unlike nutrients, toxins and pollutants, microorganisms can reproduce and move about the environment on their own; and microorganisms exchange their DNA with other species quite readily adding to the complexity of risk assessment. Moreover, extrapolating from one microbial species to another or from tests conducted under one set of environmental conditions to another is often unreliable.

Two approaches have been suggested for assessing the risks of GEMs into the environment. The first approach would focus primarily on the source materials, that is the host organism and the foreign DNA. Based on what is known about the soil ecology of the host organism and the foreign protein transferred, it is presumed that one can make sound judgments about the phenotype of the recombinant organism and its relationship with its environment. For example, Miller (1991) maintained that genetically engineered microorganisms are not new because the transfer of DNA from unrelated organisms has been occurring since the origins of life. As a result, microorganisms have seen all possible combinations. Brill (1985b: 117) commented in a letter to *Science* that "a tremendous amount of gene transfer occurs naturally, not only among related genera, but also between unrelated microorganisms and even between kingdoms... What scientists create through genetic engineering is minuscule and ecologically insignificant compared to what occurs continually and randomly in nature." He also argued (Brill 1985a: 383) that indigenous microorganisms saturate natural habitats to which they are highly adaptive and that "the extra burden to the organism carrying new genes should decrease its ability to compete and persist." Campbell (1991) concurs that newly introduced GEMs are not likely to displace or outcompete the natural microbes. Also, since the genetic modifications on microbes are well characterized single gene additions or deletions, it is argued that the phenotypic changes can be accomplished with a high degree of safety.

In general, those people tied to the development of biotechnology are inclined to use the paradigm of crop breeding to evaluate the products of biotechnology while ecologists and environmentalists are drawn to the paradigm of exotic introductions.

Another line of argument, critical of selecting out GEMs as a special case, holds that we should not regulate an organism by the methods of its production but rather only by its properties per se (Miller 1994).[3] This issue arose during the debate over ice minus. One variant of ice minus was found in nature, while a second version, with virtually the same gene deletion, was produced in the laboratory by recombinant DNA techniques. There were no regulations on releasing large quantities of the ice minus strain cultured from the natural environment, while there were strict regulations for releasing the rDNA strain.

Ideally, one should only have to study the phenotype of an organism to assess risk. An organism with the same phenotype produced by different processes should be subject to the same risk estimate. A 1989 report of the Ecological Society of America, a group that has traditionally expressed caution over the release of genetically engineered organisms, stated: "We contend that transgenic organisms should be evaluated and regulated according to their biological properties (phenotypes) rather than according to the genetic techniques used to produce them" (Tiedje et al. 1989: 302). This idea certainly holds true for chemicals whose properties are independent of how the chemical is manufactured. However, in chemical risk assessment we have seen the evolution of canonical toxicological tests. This has not been the case for the products of biotechnology; not only are microorganisms not as precisely defined as chemicals but they mutate in unpredictable ways. Until we have effective means for evaluating the phenotypes of transgenic organisms for human and ecological risk, regulators may have pragmatic grounds for screening organisms according to the methods by which genetic changes have been made (Krimsky 1995).

Ecologists and evolutionary biologists are dubious of *a priori* assumptions about the safe releases of genetically modified microbes such as the addition of foreign genes to an organism necessarily reduces its fitness. According to Sharples, evolutionary theory teaches us that "at least some genetic alterations improve the abilities of organisms to survive, reproduce, compete for resources, or invade new habitats" (Sharples 1987: 1330).

A second approach to risk assessment of GEMs seeks ecological data from simulated environments designed to model the complexity of the actual environment. These are generally referred to as microcosm or greenhouse experiments. Since these experiments are contained, there are no risks to the environment. The question is: Can these experiments really tell us anything about how a GEM will behave under natural conditions or do these tests offer a false sense of security. For example, will it be possible to use microcosm data to determine whether a genetically engineered microbe will outcompete its parental strain or spread to other niches beyond the desired agro-ecosystem, or in the case of microbial biodegradators, beyond the target site? How well does the microcosm replicate field conditions? What properties of GEMs can be measured in microcosms that are relevant to field releases? How can one be confident that the microcosm will yield consistent and reproducible results? How can we improve the reliability of the microcosm to predict the behaviour of GEMs in the field?

One recent experiment suggests that the answer may be clearly in the affirmative. Holmes and Ingham used microcosms containing the indigenous soil biota and plants to test the effects of releasing a genetically modified strain of *Klebsiella planticola*. The organism was modified with the gene to synthesize ethanol from organic waste. The engineered bacterium was introduced to enclosed soil chambers in which wheat plants were growing. The plants in the chamber with the genetically modified *Klebsiella* were killed while those in the control chamber remained healthy. The mechanism postulated to explain this effect is that the introduced microbe reduced the colonization of plant roots by mycorrhizae which makes the plants less competitive with weeds and more susceptible to disease. Also, in certain types of soil, plants died from ethanol produced by the GEM in the root system (Holmes and Ingham 1994).

This result refutes the conclusion that no significant ecological effects will result from the addition of a GEM to the soil. Moreover, the results may not be predictable from information about the foreign DNA and the host organism. Ecologists have argued that knowing the change in phenotype is not sufficient to predict the outcome of a release since it is the interaction of that phenotype with the environment that matters and that result usually requires a field test.

6. Microcosms and their Critics

Microcosms came into use in the 1970s for examining the fate and transport of chemicals introduced in the soil, such as pesticides or industrial toxic wastes (Draggon and Van Voris 1979). These early microcosms used standardized soil mixtures, often sterile soil, soil with no plants and no microorganisms. These systems were useful in examining the physical and chemical changes taking place and enabled researchers to standardize and replicate certain measurements (Metcalf 1975). They could use radio-labeling to trace the movement of chemicals without releasing radioactive materials in the environment (Cole et al. 1976; Gillett and Gile 1976).

When microcosms came into use for studying the fate of organisms in biological systems, the issue of their size, shape, composition and treatment became more salient. The notion of a microcosm offered by the U.S. National Research Council as "an intact, minimally disturbed piece of an ecosystem brought into the laboratory for study... that behaves ecologically like its counterpart in the actual field", establishes a standard of simulation that far exceeds the synthetic microcosms applied to chemical mobility which seek to control a few variables. Fredrickson et al. (1990) claim that microcosms can be useful to predict field effects even if they do not fully replicate the field; the key is in calibrating the microcosm with the field.

The lack of standardization of microcosms for risk assessment in biotechnology has presented some problems. The research literature reveals that the term microcosm applies to many sizes and shapes of experimental systems including test tubes containing 2 grams of soil, plastic trays (.05 x .3 x .5 m) and soil cores (.4 diam x .6 m).[4] The one exception is that the American Society for Testing and Materials (ASTM) developed a standard microcosm in 1987 for testing the fate and effects of xenobiotics. Without the standardization of microcosms for the assessment of microbial behaviour it is near impossible to compare risk assessment tests, to replicate experiments, and to build a body of dependable knowledge.

There are several things to consider in the development of microcosms for risk assessment of genetically engineered microorganisms. Do the microcosms reflect the native flora and fauna? Is the soil composition and physical structure comparable to the natural conditions in the field? Will the treatment of the microcosm during the test period replicate the conditions facing a GEM in the natural environment? The key to standardization is to establish uniform parameters of measurement, size, watering regimes, and assay methods for detecting organisms, while allowing sufficient flexibility in constructing the microcosm so that it comes as close as it can to replicating real field conditions.

The microcosm must be initialized to its natural environment. The most common way to accomplish this is to extract the soil from the location where GEMs will be released. A soil core microcosm (a cylindrical core) extracted from the site of interest is then brought into the laboratory for inoculation of genetically modified organisms (Gile et al. 1979).

There are still many problems with this methodology. By extracting the soil one can change its physical structure, for example, by compacting it. In removing the soil from its natural setting one changes the environmental parameters. Temperatures, water flow through the soil, plant roots, and insect population are likely to differ between the soil core and its habitat of origin. The size of the core may also be a problem in cases where edge effects could be important in the growth or dispersal of microorganisms. The microcosms have high surface to volume ratios and surface boundaries which do not exist in the field may distort the results of microbial experiments.

Microcosms cannot address the effects of GEMs on large invertebrates, or the effects of vectored transport across large boundaries compared to the scale of the microcosm, or toxicity to certain large plants. Microcosms cannot replicate the results of air currents that may transport organisms or the use of large aerosol delivery systems. Cavalieri (1991: 571) notes: "Questions such as the persistence of the genetically engineered microorganisms in the field, its effects on non-target species, alteration in its host range, and its performance under different climatic conditions cannot be fully addressed in microcosm studies or small-scale controlled field tests."

The most serious criticism of microcosms comes from a critic of regulation, Winston Brill (1985a: 384) who claims they are irrelevant to field conditions "because different soils, soil treatments, and weather conditions can dramatically alter the growth rate, population, and persistence of a microbe, greenhouse or growth chamber experiments have little relevance to field results." The consequence of this argument is that releasing modified microorganisms in the field is the only viable screening method.

Several research efforts have responded to the challenge to improve the effectiveness of microcosm risk assessment. First, soil-core microcosms are allowed to equilibrate in the field, sometimes for as long as two months. This is to allow the soil in the microcosm to take on more of the qualities of the field soil before measurements are taken on the survival and dispersal of the organisms. Equilibration is limited to certain seasons. A second approach is to establish standards of reliability for the microcosm. Since water is an important factor in the dispersal of microorganisms, watering regimes that simulate actual field patterns will give a more accurate picture of microbial activity.

Another contribution to the role of microcosms in risk assessment is the development of a calibration standard. What confidence can scientists have that the microcosm results are replicable? How do we know that the introduced GEM is behaving oddly because of something peculiar to the microcosm rather than the GEM itself? According to Fredrickson et al. (1990: 194), "the majority of microcosm studies have made little or no attempt to field-calibrate the microcosm or relate findings to the field." Levy et al. (in Krimsky et al. 1995) have proposed a calibration method based on an internal standard. This involves using a mutant strain that provides a characteristic pattern of survival and spread in a given microcosm. Once the GEM is introduced, one can always refer back to the mutant strain and its pattern of behaviour to determine whether the microcosm is behaving in its expected fashion. In addition, the GEM can be introduced paired with the organism used as part of the internal standard. One can then compare the behaviour of the mutant strain with that of the GEM. In this sense, the microcosm can be calibrated with a mutant strain that has a characteristic pattern of behaviour.

6. Conclusion: The Expectation of Predictive Ecology

There is no way to demonstrate that an organism is safe. All one can expect to do from a methodological standpoint is to demonstrate either that (a) an organism is hazardous or (b) when tested against various hazard scenarios, the results falsify the conjectures that a hazard exists. The powerful legacy of Popperian philosophy (Popper 1965) has important implications for risk assessment in biotechnology, especially when we are a long way from canonical testing protocols.

If microcosms are to be useful as a screening mechanism for selecting our potentially hazardous microorganisms, we must be capable of using them to model falsifiable hypotheses of realistic risk scenarios. We must also accept, perhaps on faith, the notion that an organism which tests favourably against a series of risk scenarios deemed most probable by ecologists is less likely to turn up as a hazard than, ceteris paribus, an organism that is not subject to such tests.

We should not be trying to prove that an organism is safe. We should be trying to demonstrate it is hazardous. Once the hazard hypotheses are falsified, our confidence level in the safety of the organism will be heightened. Since there are practical limitations on the number of tests we can demand from companies, the selection of those tests is critical for risk assessment. Worst case scenarios with a remote probability may not be as useful as moderate risk scenarios with a higher expected probability for observing an effect. One might also use microcosms to test a variety of suggested principles such as: "microorganisms with added genes will be less competitive," or "a few genes will not transform a non-pathogen into a pathogen."

Predictive ecology is still in its infancy. The effort to standardize microcosms as screening assays for genetically engineered microorganisms with regard to hypotheses about survival, competitiveness, dispersal, and pathogenicity might advance the broader agenda in which prospective risk assessment can be applied to the ecological sciences (Krimsky et al. 1995).

It is useful to consider the theoretical limitations for using microcosms to predict the behaviour of GEMs in the natural environment. Does small scale provide a limiting factor and if so for what properties and what reasons? Is the issue complexity? Are small samples (intact soil cores) inadequate to represent the complexity of the actual ecological system? There are obvious limitations of microcosms in that we cannot put trees or animals in the microcosm. But what if we are trying to understand microbe to microbe interactions in a soil type? Are there system complexity issues that preclude the use of microcosms for predicting effects in the environment? Assuming the soil microenvironment is a random subset of the soil macroenvironment minus the large elements, will the absence of the larger elements affect the microbial behaviour?

Let us assume our soil core microcosm represents a random sample of the field area. However, the random sample may not reflect the heterogeneity of the soil ecology. We would need to know something about the variance of the parameter under consideration to determine how many intact soil cores are necessary for achieving results that reflect the heterogeneity of the field.

The fact that one system is used to model a larger system of higher degrees of complexity is not in itself a limitation provided we understand the role of complexity in predicting the parameter of interest. Thus, while standardization of microcosms will be helpful in comparing and contrasting risk assessment data for GEMs, theoretical work is also needed that allows us to understand when microbial experiments in earth samples enable us to make inferences about similar experiments under actual field conditions.

The social response to the problem of managing the ecological risks of GEMs may be likened to the proverbial query about whether the glass is half full or half empty – it has an optimistic and pessimistic dimension. From the optimistic perspective, there has been a noticeable increase in the application of anticipatory ecological risk assessment in the form of greenhouse and microcosm studies. The field of ecotoxicology has embraced the issues of bioengineered organisms. There have been methodological advances in the use of microcosms for predicting ecological effects of field experiments.

Notwithstanding this progress in ecological modeling, a pessimistic perspective cannot be avoided as we observe a global retreat from the social commitment to anticipatory regulation. Nowhere is this more evident than in the United States. The U.S. Congress has abolished the 23 year old Office of Technology Assessment, which has produced many studies on bioengineered organisms and the environment. The U.S. system of regulation has moved toward a cost-benefit approach that places low priority on the protection of natural habitats per se and is moving rapidly toward a clear and present danger standard to justify regulatory intervention. Thus, at a time when a new biotechnology industry is advancing and scores of bioengineered organisms are being released, a new ideology is sweeping the dominant political culture of the governments of major industrial societies that sees little value in the investment of ecological risk assessment. If history is any guide, this could change dramatically if an untoward event were to take place from the release of a bioengineered organism.

Acknowledgements

I wish to thank Roger P. Wrubel for his helpful comments and collaboration on related work. The research for this chapter was supported in grant from the *Center for Environmental Management* at Tufts University titled "Improving the Assessment of Transgenic Microorganisms Released into the Environment: An Integrative Approach" under assistance agreements CR813481 and CR820301 with the U.S. Environmental Protection Agency. The information and opinions in this chapter do not necessarily reflect the views of the agency or the center, and no official endorsement should be inferred.

Notes

1.   See especially Chapter 8, 'Debates over deliberate release: Disciplinary fault lines.' In: S. Krimsky, *Biotechnics and Society*, 1991.

2.   Brill (1985a: 384) argued: "A program that aims to utilize, in agriculture, a plant, bacterium, or fungus considered to be safe but with several foreign genes will have essentially no chance of accidentally producing an organism that would create an out-of-control problem."
3.   Miller (1994) highlighted the distinction between product and process regulation emphasizing the former: "We contend that transgenic organisms should be evaluated and regulated according to their biological properties (phenotypes) rather than according to the genetic techniques used to produce them."
4.   In describing the types of microcosms Metcalf (1975: 243) states: "Laboratory model ecosystems or microcosms are potentially almost as diversified as the natural environment whose components are being modeled. Such systems range in complexity from petri dishes containing soil microflora and flasks containing microorganisms in water or nutrient medium to elaborately constructed and instrumented terrestrial chambers ... and model streams."

References

Ames, Bruce N. and Swirsky Gold, Lois 1990. 'Too many rodent carcinogens: Mitogenesis increases mutagenesis.' *Science* **249** (August 31), pp.970-971.

American Society for Testing Materials 1988. 'Standard guide for conducting a terrestrial soil-core microcosm test, ASTM Designation E:1197-87.' *Annual Book of ASTM Standards* 11.04, pp.801-803.

Bazzaz, Fakhri 1985. Quoted in: H.O. Halvorson, D. Pramer and M. Rogul (eds.), *Engineered Organisms in the Environment: Scientific Issues*. Washington, D.C.: American Society for Microbiology, p.55.

Berry, D.F. and Hagedorn, C. 1991. 'Soil and groundwater transport of microorganisms.' In: L.R. Ginzburg (ed.), *Assessing Ecological Risks of Biotechnology*. Boston: Butterworth-Heinemann.

Brill, Winston J. 1985a. 'Safety concerns and genetic engineering in agriculture.' *Science* **227** (January 25), pp.381-384.

————. 1985b. 'Genetic engineering in agriculture [letter].' *Science* **229** (July 12), p.117.

Campbell, A.M. 1991. 'Microbes: The laboratory and the field.' In: B.D. Davis (ed.), *The Genetic Revolution*. Baltimore, MD: Johns Hopkins Univ. Press, pp.28-44.

Cavalieri, Liebe F. 1991. 'Scaling-up field testing of modified microorganisms.' *BioScience* **41** (no.8, September), pp.568-574.

Cole, L.K., Metcalf, R.I. and Sandborn, J.R. 1976. 'Environmental fate of insecticides in terrestrial model ecosystems.' *International Journal of Environmental Studies* **10**, pp.7-14.

Fredrickson, J.K., Van Voris, Peter, Bentjen, S.A. and Bolton, H. Jr. 1990. 'Terrestrial microcosms for evaluating the environmental fate and risks associated with the release of chemicals or genetically engineered microorganisms to the environment.' *Hazard Assessment of Chemicals* **7**, pp.159.

Gile, J.D., Collins, J.C. and Gillett, J.W. 1979. *The Soil Core Microcosm – A Potential Screening Tool* (EPA-600/3-79-089, August). Corvallis, Oregon: USEPA Corvallis Environmental Research Laboratory.

Gillett, James W. 1986. 'Risk assessment methodologies for biotechnology impact assessment.' *Environmental Management* **10**, pp.515-532.

Gillett, J.W. and Gile, J.D. 1976. 'Pesticide Fate in Terrestrial Laboratory Ecosystems.' *International Journal of Environmental Studies* **10**, pp.15-22.

Holmes, T.M. and Ingham, E.R. 1994. 'The effects of genetically engineered microorganisms on soil food webs.' Supplement to the *Bulletin of the Ecological Society of America* **75** (2). Abstracts of the 79th Annual ESA Meeting: Science and Public Policy. Knoxville, TN, August 7-11, 1994.

Krimsky, Sheldon. 1991. *Biotechnics and Society: The Rise of Industrial Genetics.* New York: Praeger.

————. 1995. 'Biotechnology regulation [letter].' *Science* **267** (February 17), p.945.

Krimsky, Sheldon and Golding, Dominic 1991. 'Factoring Risk into Environmental Decision Making.' In: R.A. Chechile and S. Carlisle (eds.), *Environmental Decision Making: A Multidisciplinary Perspective.* New York: Van Nostrand Reinhold.

Krimsky, Sheldon and Golding, Dominic (eds.) 1992. *Social Theories of Risk.* New York: Praeger.

Krimsky, Sheldon and Plough, Alonzo 1988. Ch.3: 'The release of a genetically engineered organism into the environment: The case of ice minus.' In: *Environmental Hazards: Communicating Risk as a Social Process.* Dover, MA: Auburn House Press.

Krimsky, Sheldon, Wrubel, Roger P., Naess, Inger G., Levy, Stuart, Wetzler, Richard E. and Marshall, Bonnie. 1995. 'Standardized microcosms in microbial risk assessment.' *BioScience* **45** (no.9, October), pp.590-599.

Lacy G.H. and V.K. Stromberg. 1990. 'Pre-release microcosm tests with a genetically engineered plant pathogen.' In: D.R. MacKenzie and S.C. Henry (eds.), *Biological Monitoring of Genetically Engineered Plants and Microbes.* Bethesda, MD: Agricultural Research Institute, pp.81-98.

Lewontin, R.C., Rose, Steven and Kamin, Leon J. 1984. *Not in Our Genes.* New York: Pantheon.

Metcalf, Robert L. 1975. *Evaluation of a Laboratory Microcosm for Study of Toxic Substances in the Environment.* Washington, D.C.: National Science Foundation.

————. 1977. 'Model ecosystem approach to insecticide degradation: A critique.' *Annual Review of Entomology* **22**, pp.241-261.

Miller, H.I. 1991. 'Regulation.' In: B.D. Davis (ed.), *The Genetic Revolution.* Baltimore, MD: Johns Hopkins Univ. Press, pp.196-211.

————. 1994. 'A need to reinvent biotechnology regulation at the EPA.' *Science* **266** (December 6), pp.1815-1818.

National Research Council 1989. *Field Testing Genetically Modified Organisms: Framework for Decisions.* Washington, D.C.: National Academy Press, p.117.

Popper, Karl. 1965. *The Logic of Scientific Discovery.* New York: Harper & Row.

Sharples, Frances E. 1987. 'Regulation of products from biotechnology.' *Science* **235** (March 13), p.1332.

Tiedje, J.M., Colwell, Robert K., Yaffa, L., Hodson, Robert E., Lenski, Richard E., Mack, Richard N. and Regal, Philip J. 1989. 'The planned introduction of genetically engineered organisms: Ecological considerations and recommendations.' *Ecology* **70** (April), pp.297-315.

U.S. Congress, Office of Technology Assessment 1993. *Harmful Non-indigenous Species in the United States* (September). Washington, D.C.: OTA.

3

The Impact of Background Models on the Quality of Risk Assessment as Exemplified by the Discussion on Genetically Modified Organisms

Ad van Dommelen

1. Introduction

Given the high status of natural sciences, one may be tempted to think that 'scientific knowledge' is some sort of general currency that may be applied as a matter of course to any particular situation. That would be a misguided conception of the products of science. The application and interpretation of theories calls for critical reflection aided by *general methodology* (cf. van der Steen 1993). The tools of general methodology go beyond experimental methodology; they aim to safeguard conceptual and logical hygiene of definitions and inferences in general.

In my view, what is sorely missing in the connection between theory and practice is an adequate perspective on how to *deal* with our theories in practical contexts. This is an art in itself and we will not be able to do justice to the complexities of applying theories before we master this art. 'Scientific knowledge' is largely an abstraction. To make my analysis more concrete, I will focus on scientific *models*, in which our knowledge becomes practical. I argue that uncovering the theoretical models underlying risk assessment will help us deal more adequately with its practical challenges. Whereas risk assessment debates often centre around calls for more "data" and "evidence", I think it is paramount that we assess the models upon which our risk assessments are erected in the first place. It is difficult to evaluate arguments in risk assessment since they rely on implicit, complex background assumptions. I argue here that we must limit assessments to specific contexts, since the validity of background assumptions is context-dependent. In this chapter I apply this perspective to ongoing debates about adequate risk assessment of releasing genetically engineered or modified organisms (GMOs) into the environment.

2. Conceptual Clarity

To introduce my approach I give a preliminary example. The risks of modern biotechnology have been claimed by opponents of strict regulation on the deliberate release of GMOs to be "the same in kind" as the risks of more traditional breeding techniques (cf. NAS 1989; Miller 1994). Since acceptance or rejection of this claim affects the performance and interpretation of risk assessments, we should know if it is adequate. Before we can decide on the adequacy of any claim, we must be clear about its meaning. The expression "the same in kind" is anything but clear. Obscurity of terms is a serious obstacle in risk assessment. It generates spurious controversies that persist since conceptual clarity is seldom an explicit theme in risk assessment.

With respect to the appropriate regulation, it is quite clear what "the same in kind" implies: no new framework of regulation is required as compared to the framework that already exists for conventional techniques. In relation to the actual risks that are involved, however, it is not so clear what this credo signifies. The only way to clarify the expression "the same in kind", is to go back to the models that underlie the assessment of traditional and modern practices. These models are in fact very different. The general model for the assessment of conventional risks is largely *empirical*; we have experienced for centuries that certain activities bear certain risks. The general model that we might utilize for the interpretation of possible risks of applying rDNA techniques, on the other hand, is largely *theoretical*. Empirical evidence bearing on these techniques is now too fragmented to go by and doubts exist about its adequate interpretation.

Thus, the statement that the two types of risk are "the same in kind" is vague. It is unclear what empirical results could corroborate this analogue, which is essentially a comparison of models: a model for assessing the risks of applying traditional breeding techniques compared to a model for assessing the risks of applying modern recombinant DNA techniques. No proper standard of comparison is available, since the two models are not well articulated.

If the outcomes of the two models are qualified as "the same in *kind*", then this does not tell us much about the relative severity of risks. Two models may give outcomes in the same *dimensions*, whilst generating very different *magnitudes* within the corresponding dimensions. A fire-cracker and a hydrogen-bomb bear risks in the same *dimension* of explosive danger, but their diverging *magnitudes* in this dimension justify diverse ways of dealing with them. Should rDNA techniques produce risks in the same dimensions (= 'the same in *kind*') but with larger magnitudes than more traditional techniques, then risk assessors should treat them as a new problem. 'New' magnitudes in 'old' dimensions may call for a customized regulatory framework.

The debate on deliberate release is riddled with concepts and inferences that are as ambiguous as 'the same in kind'. Another example is the concept of 'familiarity' that has been put forward as a criterion to judge the need for risk assessment of GMOs. Familiarity as such is a meaningless notion. The alleged 'familiarity' of the behaviour of a 'new' organism again presupposes a comparison of two models: one that we already have experience with and one that we are trying to come to grips with. The label of 'familiarity' expresses the idea that we can understand the new model as essentially corresponding to the old model. We should specify *in what respects* the features of GMOs are familiar. This should invite a comparison between models for the behaviour of GMOs and other organisms serving as a standard of comparison, in the environments we wish to consider. The results of comparisons will depend on the context. Thus, general claims about risks based on 'familiarity' without qualification are grossly inadequate.

Much-cited unclear phrases like "same in kind" and "familiarity" have the net effect that the problems at hand are wrongly lumped together in a 'black box' of presumed understanding, their complexities hidden from view. They invoke an improper, rhetorical type of reasoning by careless analogy, which covertly compares unarticulated underlying models. We should make these models explicit, and try to 'open' these black boxes so as to arrive at more sophisticated assessments.

Right now there is no consensus about the quality of risk assessments in the context of genetic engineering. Optimistic observers claim that a scientifically based agreement about proper risk assessments already exists. More sceptical observers have claimed that the assessments represent "plausible speculation" rather than reliable science (Alexander 1985: 58). If we opt for the latter qualification, as I would, our problem is: how to judge the adequacy of 'plausible speculation'? Contrary to more skeptic views, I think we can do quite a lot about this.

Not all arguments in the debate have an equally valid claim to plausibility. Giving due attention to principles of general methodology can help us to expose implausible assumptions. To appreciate this we must try to be *explicit* about our claims. Many participants in the risk assessment debate manage to keep track of the context-dependent character of their scientific claims. However, few of them make this effort *explicit* in their arguments. Being explicit about the limits of our risk assessment claims is probably our best chance to advance the larger debate and to prevent that the same old 'plausible' claims are repeated over and over again, without any progress.

3. The Quality of Science: Models as Critical Tools

To fully appreciate how studying underlying models can help us assess scientific claims in a policy context, we must reflect upon our picture of science. In recent years many science researchers have elaborated sociological perspectives on science. While I think this general approach has produced many useful insights into the nature of scientific knowledge, it cannot claim primacy in our evaluation of science. Let me give an example. David Collingridge and Colin Reeve (1986) have studied several policy controversies in which opposing parties strongly rely on scientific knowledge. Their conclusion was that the appearance of political relevance (which increases the 'error cost') on the scene of scientific research, puts "science under stress". According to Collingridge and Reeve, this leads to a loss of scientific quality and ultimately to the impossibility of solving controversies. The very relevance of scientific knowledge thereby finally turns it into a useless product. Collingridge and Reeve call this an "ironical role" that is necessarily played by science in the context of policy: "Consensus on scientific questions which are more than marginally relevant to policy is (..) impossible. Science under these conditions leads not to agreement, but to endless technical bickering about an evergrowing number of issues" (Collingridge and Reeve 1986: ix). In the end, the ongoing scientific controversies primarily provide the room for policy makers to let their political preferences prevail.

A somewhat similar perspective on the structure of scientific knowledge that becomes relevant to policy has been given by René von Schomberg. He has argued his case for controversies about the deliberate release of GMOs. In his view, in the relation between science and politics, "the necessary is impossible and the impossible is necessary" (von Schomberg 1995a: 17). In the view of Von Schomberg also, science has a rather ironical function: "Instead of serving to disencumber the political discourse, science contributes to burdening it down further by spreading dissent and sparking conflicts within the political arena" (von Schomberg 1995a: 17).

Although I agree that this is often the actual situation, I disagree with the suggestion that it is *necessarily* the case. It seems to me that the traditional one-sidedness of the internalistic point of view towards science, has in some cases been replaced by an equally one-sided externalistic understanding of science. I would argue that methodological analysis can help us redress the paradoxes and the loss of quality in science which Collingridge and Reeve, and Von Schomberg usefully uncover.

The following may illustrate this. Von Schomberg characterizes certain scientific controversies as 'epistemic debates', which have the same practical effects as what Collingridge and Reeve call 'endless technical debates'. Von Schomberg argues that, "in the case of epistemic discussions in science, we cannot reasonably expect a consensus among disputing experts from different scientific disciplines, since their arguments cannot substantiate the truth of claims but, rather, do state their incompatible plausibility" (von Schomberg 1993: 1). In my view this is an altogether too pessimistic picture of science. My claim would not be that all controversies are in fact decidable (cf. van Dommelen 1995), but I do think that "truth" is not the only relevant standard, nor the most important one, by which to judge the relevance of claims in a practical context (see section 4). The example below illustrates how my assessment of scientific controversies in this debate differs from more sociological accounts.

One of the arguments that keeps cropping up in the controversy about the risk assessment of deliberate release centres on general effects that genetic modification would have on 'fitness'. Broadly speaking, the opponents of strict regulation on deliberate release hold that GMOs are burdened with an 'excess baggage' of DNA synthesis, which requires extra energy from the organism, thereby decreasing its fitness compared to the original host organism. This selective disadvantage will make it perish eventually. Proponents of strict regulation, on the other hand, argue that the extra genetic load may occasionally lead to traits that give the GMO a selective advantage, even though it requires more energy to realize the traits.

In the analysis of Von Schomberg (1995b: 122-125), the antagonists in this debate cannot do better, for the time being, than give 'plausibility claims' to support their positions. In his view, the debate is what he calls an 'epistemic debate', which makes decisive conclusions impossible. I disagree. Underlying these so-called 'plausibility claims' are theoretical models that describe the system of which a GMO becomes a part upon release. Methodologically, opposing models fostering the controversy are not equally adequate.

Although the argument of 'excess baggage' in itself is relevant, it is interpreted by opponents of regulation against the background of a very limited theoretical model. In the underlying model the concept of fitness is implicitly interpreted as a one-place predicate, which it is not. It is simply impossible to assess 'the' fitness of an isolated organism, whether it has been genetically modified or not. The concept of 'fitness' is at least a two-place predicate, characterizing a *relationship* between an organism and its environment. A model for the viability of an organism that deletes the role of the environment, cannot be the basis of a plausible claim in this context. Straightforward methodological analysis shows that this general model cannot adequately represent the larger system a GMO becomes part of. The model is a poor basis for a risk assessment, and it leads to unwarranted general claims.

A better, admittedly more complex, way to consider the viability of a modified or unmodified organism is by way of a model that expresses complexity in terms of so-called *'norms of reaction'*. In the words of Suzuki et al., we must recognize that: "For a particular genotype, we could prepare a table showing the phenotype that would result from that genotype for development in each possible environment. Such a tabulation of environment-phenotype relationships for a given genotype is called the norm of reaction of the genotype" (Suzuki et al. 1986: 6). This model implies that we cannot legitimately 'delete' the environment from consideration.

Taking this complexity into account is not just a matter of adding another expert opinion in a pluralistic intellectual setting. It completely changes the terms of the debate. Ignoring this is not the same as taking a specific 'plausible' position or standpoint in the debate. It means that one decides (knowingly or not) to conceptually distort the problem originally addressed. This is indeed a sure recipe for endless controversy, giving politicians and policy makers the opportunity to proceed as they see fit. It is clear that more data cannot end such a conceptual misunderstanding. The only adequate way to deal with it is to uncover methodological flaws in the underlying models.

The opposing claims in this example are thus not equally plausible. Methodological analysis in this case yields a clear-cut solution of the controversy. We should take sides and opt against the model supporting the 'excess baggage'-argument, which Philip Regal has analyzed and dismissed as the 'pregnant pole vaulter'-model (Regal 1986). This generic model is simply not sophisticated enough to be useful.

If we treat the discussion in this example as an 'epistemic debate' or an 'endless technical debate', we approach it too much as a 'black box'. Sociological charac-terizations of scientific controversies tend to disregard the possibility that we can open up the 'black boxes' under dispute. Articulating and clarifying the claims in a debate and analysing the underlying models and their implications, sometimes allows us to assess the quality of the arguments based on them. That may help to dissolve controversy.

4. Usefulness Instead of Truth

Models come in diverse kinds. My focus is on theoretical models. A theoretical model is a list of assumptions that describe a system. The purpose of a model determines what items should be in the list, that is, what aspects of the system will be included or disregarded. The assumptions are subject to methodological restrictions. For example, contradictory assumptions are not allowed.

A more complex restriction is that the 'system' as modelled must fit the problem that the model was designed for. Thus, in evaluating a model, we must attend to the important criterium that a model must be 'useful' in relation to its purpose (cf. Kooijman 1993: 8). This criterion does not coincide with the demand that a scientific insight should be 'true' or 'realistic'. In most practical situations the 'truth' of a theory or model cannot fully be assessed. The criterion of 'truth' is not very informative and it easily leads to frustration and relativism. The more important issue in practical situations is: does the model work, does it do what we expect from it?

Philosophers of science have mostly disregarded the practical importance and the special character of theoretical models in applications of scientific knowledge. Models function as interpretative 'crossroads' between theory and practice. *Theory* underlies a model as backing for model-assumptions and *practice* is reflected in the 'system' that is characterized by these assumptions.

One can relevantly ask about the truth of one's assumptions, but the *relevance* of (selectively chosen) assumptions is not a matter of truth alone. The rather practical approach to truth that model-builders tend to foster can be illustrated by Richard Levins' characterization of model-building: "Truth is in the intersection of independent lies" (Levins 1966). To evaluate a model, its 'adequacy' or 'usefulness' must enter the picture, because our choice of assumptions depends on *external purposes*. An important question to be answered is whether the theoretical system described by a model fits well with the complex of factors that affect the problems with which the model is intended to deal. If this is not arguably the case, then the model at hand is not a serious candidate to apply to the problem.

The primacy of 'usefulness' in our assessment of models can be illustrated by the famous wave-particle dichotomy that features in theoretical physics. Philosophers of science who have been trying to find out which of the two models could be 'true', came out frustrated. A much more fruitful way to look at this dichotomy is to see the two models as offering us alternative approaches which are *useful* for different purposes. This pragmatic way of appreciating models need not lead to philosophical relativism. Depending on the specific *purpose* we have, some models will be more useful than others. This perspective is compatible with pluralism: in different cases different models may be useful with respect to a specific purpose.

To illustrate the fruitfulness of this approach, consider the following example of an erroneous risk assessment practice. Wrubel, Krimsky and Wetzler (1992) assessed the quality of 30 environmental assessments that were executed by the Animal and Plant Health Protection Service (APHIS), which oversees the field testing of transgenic plants as a part of the United States Department of Agriculture (USDA). One of the findings was that for 27 of the 30 investigated cases: "No data or discussion [were] provided or cited for any of the conclusions on competitive ability .." (Wrubel et al. 1992: 286). Interviews with the responsible risk assessors showed that they assumed the competitive ability of engineered plants could not pose problems because their additional metabolic load would always decrease their fitness. A general recommendation that Wrubel et al. give as a result of their study is that: "APHIS should be more explicit about justifications for its assessment conclusions" (Wrubel et al. 1992: 288).

The assumption concerning competitive ability is deeply problematic because ecological phenomena such as competition cannot be assessed on the basis of single features of organisms. When we try to situate competitive ability in a larger ecological model, we will almost immediately find that it expresses a *relationship* and not a *unitary feature*. More technically, 'competitive ability' is not a one-place predicate (as in 'organism X *has competitive ability A*' – the way it was interpreted by APHIS), but at least a two-place predicate (as in 'organism X has competitive ability A *in relation to* organism Y'). Indeed, since the environment plays a role in relations among organisms, *competitive ability* is at least a three-place predicate.

Therefore, any generalizing conception that GMOs are by their nature competitively disabled, cannot pass as a viable 'position' or a useful assumption, because it is conceptually flawed *for methodological reasons.*

Speculation about risks of GMO releases always relies on (implicit or explicit) background models. We should aim to make the models explicit and criticize and improve them by scrutinizing the relevance, coherence and validity of their assumptions. When, for example, participants in the biosafety debate are drawing analogies to *traditional breeding* practices or, alternatively, to our experiences with *introduced species*, we can think of them as 'playing' with models. Their 'play' should be subject to the rules of the underlying model-building game. To assess the relevance and validity of generalized analogies such as those of *traditional breeding* or *introduced species*, we need to investigate the more complex models supposedly supporting those analogies. That way we can expose the *positive, negative* and *neutral* analogies lurking beneath the surface of generalized comparisons (cf. Hesse 1966). As Albert Einstein remarked: "Everything should be as simple as possible, but not one bit simpler". Thinking in terms of the underlying models, their possibilities and their limits, will allow us to observe this methodological imperative and to come to grips with the suggestive rhetorics that permeate arguments in policy debates.

Methodological criteria of model-building can help us to discover context-dependent limitations of models. Thus, we can regain control over socio-political considerations which affect the choice of particular models. In this way we may turn models into critical tools of scientific reasoning, which may help us improve its social embedding. My approach aims to re-vitalize the potential of self-critique that has historically been the *raison d'être* of scientific research. Analysing the methodological status of the scientific models by which we attempt to bridge the relationship between theory and practice, is probably our best hope to make science serve society.

5. Models Precede Data

The importance of theoretical models is not to be underestimated. Indeed, our thinking can be seen as a constant play of applying and revising our, mostly implicit, models of the world. It is a mistake to think that we can dismiss our models as soon as we have empirical findings at our disposal. Data can only be interpreted against the background of the model which guided data-gathering in the first place. Without this they become useless. Besides, in the context of risk assessments, data are typically scarce. In most cases we have little more than theoretical models to navigate by. The 'same in kind' claim discussed above, for instance, cannot be evaluated on the basis of empirical facts. It expresses an analogy, which can guide our expectations, but is beyond the possibility of an empirical test. The 'facts' that risk assessors hope to base their judgement on are always a reflection of the models used.

If the models are inadequate, we easily get 'self-fulfilling prophecies' in the outcome of a risk assessment. Margaret Mellon and Jane Rissler claim that risk assessments can often be characterized as situations of "don't look, don't find" (Mellon and Rissler 1995). I would add that such unfortunate situations reflect a lack of explicit attention for the underlying models of risk assessment. Risk assessments are not based then on adequate models.

The mere accumulation of facts seldom suffices to dissolve controversies, because we need models to interpret facts. Relationships among system components are not 'given'. They result from modelling. Therefore, when we give a certain value to an aspect of the system (when we produce a fact), we still need the rest of the model (of the system) to assess the significance of that 'fact' for the risk assessment. That is why we should never take models for granted. This has not been given sufficient attention in the literature on risk assessment.

The limited value of isolated 'empirical evidence' can be illustrated by the following example. More and more evidence is being accumulated that lateral genetic transfer in nature is widespread (cf. Beijersbergen 1992, 1993). The 'facts' uncovered can be interpreted in opposing ways in risk assessment. Some observers have taken the existence of lateral transfer in nature as a reassurance with regard to possible risks: 'If recombination already occurs in nature, why worry about some more that humans can make'. Winston Brill, for example, states: "Without man's intervention microbes are continually mutating, sharing, and rearranging genes through such agents as transposons, viruses, and plasmids" (Brill 1985a: 382). In his view there is no reason to worry about the consequences of deliberate release, because: "What scientists create through genetic engineering is minuscule and ecologically insignificant compared to what occurs continually and randomly in nature" (Brill 1985b: 116).

Whereas the natural occurrence of genetic transfer is a reason for some to infer that recombinant DNA technology cannot cause unwanted surprises, it makes others cautious about deliberate release. In the view of Frances Sharples, for instance, artificial transfer may create new risks: "The ease with which new genes can be inserted into bacteria via plasmid vectors in recombinant technology is thus a two-edged sword. It may be very difficult to keep inserted genes isolated in single bacterial strains" (Sharples 1983: 55). The consequences of introducing a genetically modified organism may be difficult to assess, since the genetic material involved may spread in uncontrollable directions. Thus Tiedje et al. argue: "If lateral transfer occurs, an engineered gene may persist in the natural environment even after the genetically engineered organism itself is no longer present" (Tiedje et al. 1989: 299). This example illustrates that the same 'evidence' (of lateral gene transfer) can give rise to completely opposite conclusions. The only way to assess the quality of those conclusions is by studying the quality of the underlying models that are used to interpret the evidence.

Risk assessors must face an almost paralysing interpretative circle: to produce empirical evidence, they need theoretical insights, which must draw in turn on empirical findings. The following may serve to illustrate this. One possible ecological risk scenario that could follow the introduction of a genetically modified plant in the field is that the expression of the transgene may cause the plant to expand its ecological range and invade a new plant community. Since this can have severe ecological and economic consequences, we want to estimate the risk before going ahead with such a release. But how can we know whether such a thing might happen? How well equipped are we from a theoretical point of view to make such an assessment? Do we have the theoretical sophistication that is needed to conduct an adequate risk assessment?

Let me cite just some of the factors that can affect this particular risk. They include, "the availability of resources, pathogens, herbivores, seed predators, competition with other plant species, the availability of symbionts such as mycorrhizal fungi, or the availability of open sites for germination and seedling establishment" (Schmitt and Linder 1994: 71). When it comes to interpreting the relative importance of these factors, however, we are almost in the dark. Schmitt and Linder (1994) conclude that "surprisingly little is known about ecological limits on the distribution and abundance of plant species" (Schmitt and Linder 1994: 72).

In other words, we have no reliable model to assess the risks of plants invading new plant communities. There is no easy way to compensate for this lack of insight. For the present this impedes our objective of making reliable risk assessments. The value of any experiment or field test with 'no observed effect' as a result has to be judged against the background of the underlying model that was used to conduct the test. Going ahead without an adequate model may easily lead to the production of what Regal has called "nondata on nonreleases" (Regal 1994: 11).

Against this complex methodological background it is amazing that quite general claims are being made about the possible risks of intentional release of GMOs. We should distrust such claims, which can hardly be supported by proper scientific inference. Taking adequate care of the models with which we interpret the world is a prerequisite for drawing sound conclusions. Too often, models and their assumptions are left *implicit* in arguments and controversies. This diminishes possibilities for criticism and improvement of our reasoning and confuses the risk assessment of planned introductions of GMOs. Careful analysis of underlying models can help us improve the assessments. Theoretical models have a 'grammar' of their own and reflecting upon its implications will help us make rational choices between competing models in specific situations and may thereby help us dissolve seemingly endless controversies.

6. Spurious Controversies

Below I give additional examples of arguments in the debate on the risks of deliberate release, which cannot be sensibly evaluated without explicit reference to the underlying models. Since the models underlying these arguments have been disregarded, there is room here for improvement of the debate.

In a recent publication in *Science*, Henry Miller and Douglas Gunary take sides on what they think is an appropriate basis for a regulatory framework. They favour an approach that is based on what they call "established scientific principles" and criticize any approaches that incorporate "a fallacy based on scanning across experiments whose only common element is the use of the same genetic modification technique" (Miller and Gunary 1993: 1500). The former basis would support opponents of strict regulations; proponents of strict regulation would establish their arguments on the latter basis. Miller and Gunary choose to largely ignore the underlying controversy and to focus on what they call a "broad scientific consensus" about the basis of risk assessment, citing several reports and leaving out critical positions.

An element of this self-styled 'consensus' is the idea that the *product* and not the *process* of genetic modification should be the subject of regulation. In fairness to Miller and Gunary, this is indeed claimed in many publications about the risk assessment of deliberate release. To Miller and Gunary, reviewing the product instead of the process of genetic engineering is an important prerequisite of what they call a 'science-based' regulatory framework. Innocent as their claim may seem, it in fact takes away our attention from more important matters. On a simple interpretation this statement is true in the sense of tautological: 'The only thing that should be subject to regulation is the thing that can cause harm. The process will only cause harm through a product, so it is the product that should be regulated'.

True, the *mere* fact that organisms are produced by a particular process has no implications whatsoever for risks. But, the point of those who criticize this claim is obviously that genetic engineering may pose special risks because, *as a new process*, it may lead to new products – with possibly unexpected results. Whatever stance one takes in matters of regulation, this is surely an issue that must be addressed; so processes are not entirely irrelevant. Modern techniques of recombination might be more dangerous than traditional ones, for instance, since they allow organisms to get past 'adaptive valleys' of low fitness that would be crossed neither in nature nor in traditional breeding.

The opposing views may be characterized as follows. Proponents of strict regulation hold that old and new processes of genetic modification, in some respects, result in different products and, possibly, different risks. The critics opposing strict regulation argue that old and new processes yield essentially similar products and risks. In either case we are dealing with a view of process-product *relationships*. The critics themselves characterize their own approach as product-based, and the alternative view as process-based. This characterization is confused. Both parties need assumptions about processes. The issue is not *whether* we need assumptions. We need to know *which* assumptions are reasonable.

A parallel analysis holds for another argument of Henry Miller in his campaign against existing regulation. He claims that we should strive for more generic forms of regulation in contrast to case-by-case review (Miller 1987, 1994a, 1994b, 1995). Here again, Miller argues that his claim is based on "scientific principles". Let me try to analyse this controversy and the misunderstanding that causes it.

An important challenge to reasonable risk assessments is to find relevant *categories* that enable us to deal with cases of deliberate release. An evaluation of every individual case without the use of generic categories is not a rational option. In that respect the controversy over case-by-case *or* generic review is spurious and the consequence of conceptual confusion. The real problem is that no system of relevant categories is now firmly in place, as yet. Potential risks attach to many different features of modified organisms, so we have categories along all sorts of dimensions. Few individual cases will belong to the same categories, and in practice this could now lead to an assessment of every case individually. Our aim should be to arrive at generalizations about salient dimensions that permit us to disregard others. For example, *if* we would know that organisms with a low fitness cannot have undesirable features such as pathogenicity or weediness, we could exempt a major category (organisms with a low fitness) from regulation. Unfortunately, proper generalizations are hard to come by. The one about fitness, for example, is problematic since fitness is not a unitary feature; fitnesses depend on the environment. Also, organisms with a low fitness may get involved in lateral gene transfer.

The dispute over the case-by-case approach is in fact a dispute about *candidate-generalities* or models that are needed to justify exemption from regulation for particular categories of organisms. Justification will have to rely on biological theory. Therefore, we must know what levels of generality can be attained in biological theorizing. In fact highly general theories or models are possible only to a limited extent in biology (cf. van der Steen and Kamminga 1991).

An important reason for this is the prevalence of *natural history* and the role of evolution in biological science. We may distinguish differences in research styles between molecular biology and genetics on the one hand and evolutionary biology and ecology on the other, but in relation to risk assessments we cannot interpret this as merely a form of pluralism. Consideration of evolutionary and ecological aspects should always be elementary in questions of risk assessment. Giving due attention to the underlying models covering these aspects, enables us to make adequate methodological analyses and may help us keep track of the relevance of different considerations in both theoretical and practical problems.

Molecular biology and ecology are highly similar in one respect at least. Both have to deal with a certain 'invisibility' of effects. Molecular biology in so far as it can only relate to the molecular level of life in indirect, experimental ways; ecology in so far as the historical natural processes it is studying often exceed the life time of individual researchers. Both obstacles are dealt with in a similar vein: by constructing models of the systems under study. This similarity may turn out to be more important for our purpose of improving risk assessment than the much debated 'style differences'.

The models of molecular biologists and ecologists are different in that their *explicit* assumptions concern *different* levels of organization. *Implicitly*, however, both the models constructed for the molecular level and those constructed for the ecological level, encompass assumptions about the relevance or irrelevance of different levels of conceptual and empirical 'resolution'. This is a consequence of the *purpose* we have in mind when building a model. These purposes are reflected in the 'trade-offs' that must be made to make a model possibly useful to encounter the complexity of real situations. The balance of explicit and implicit assumptions reflects choices made in view of the purposes that models are intended to serve. Models with the purpose of studying life at the molecular level versus models aiming to cover ecosystems will naturally strike different balances.

7. Modelling Pathogenicity

The controversy over the implications of pathogenicity in the risk assessment debate can also be more usefully interpreted in terms of the underlying models than in terms of the limited empirical evidence. In 1987 the National Academy of Sciences (NAS) issued a report of its Committee on the Introduction of Genetically Engineered Organisms into the Environment. The Committee concluded that knowledge of scientific principles and experience with rDNA-engineered organisms allow for the safe and prudent use of such organisms outside research laboratories. It does not give an extensive justification for its judgement. I will focus on one specific assessment from the report to show that it would be hard to provide an adequate justification.

One of the arguments in the report (NAS 1987: 15) concerns the possibility that engineered organisms might inadvertently cause disease:

> Among the dangers envisioned in R-DNA genetic engineering of microorganisms is the inadvertent conversion of a nonpathogen into a new, virulent pathogen. How valid is this concept? It is important to recognize that virulent pathogens of humans, animals, and plants possess a large number of varied characteristics that in total constitute their pathogenic potential. The traits contributing to pathogenicity include the ability to attach to specific host cells, to resist a wide range of host defense systems, to form toxic chemicals that kill cells, to produce enzymes that degrade cell components, to disseminate readily and invade new hosts, and to survive under adverse environmental conditions outside the host. Together with the need to compete effectively with many other microorganisms for survival, these traits form an impressive array of requirements for pathogenicity. *The possibility that minor genetic modifications with R-DNA techniques will inadvertently convert a nonpathogen to a pathogen is therefore quite remote...* . [italics added]

In risk assessment of deliberate release, this is an oft-cited and important generic safety argument. The NAS report suggests that nonpathogens pose no inadvertent risks. The consequences of this assessment for regulation can be serious. Bernard Davis, for instance, has concluded along this line of reasoning: "Instead of insisting, as a number of ecologists have done, that we require extensive tests of every genetic novelty, on a case by case basis, for possible spread and harm, we know enough to justify exempting recombinant products of nonpathogenic bacteria" (Davis 1989: 865). Thinking in terms of the underlying models raises doubts for several reasons. In the first place, hazards are not limited to disease, and causes of infectious disease are not limited to pathogens. The latter point is obvious from the following, common definition of "pathogen".

> [A pathogen is] any microorganism which, by direct interaction with (infection of) another organism (by convention, a multicellular organism), causes disease in that organism. A pathogen is not, therefore, any microorganism which is causally connected with disease: for example, a microbe which produces a toxin that causes disease in the absence of the microbe itself would not be regarded a pathogen.

A case in point is insect control through pest-resistant plants. Plants can be made resistant to insects, for example, by taking the genes that produce delta-endotoxin in *Bacillus thuringiensis*, inserting them in strains of *Pseudomonas fluorescens* and releasing the latter in the rhizosphere of plants (Atlas 1985: 223). According to the definition, *Bacillus thuringiensis* is not a pathogen; it is already widely used for biological control of pest-insects and is considered safe for many agricultural applications. Delta-endotoxin can cause disease in insects, but since it is not an organism it cannot be considered pathogenic. Also, the engineered strains of *Pseudomonas fluorescens* can cause disease in insects, but, since they can only do so indirectly (through the activity of delta-endotoxin) they are not considered to be pathogenic. Although the original strains of *Pseudomonas fluorescens* cannot cause disease in insects and the engineered strains can, this cannot be considered as the conversion of a nonpathogen into a pathogen. Also, should the ability to produce delta-endotoxin inadvertently be conferred to another micro-organism, which thereby becomes capable of causing disease in insects, this would not be considered as an inadvertent conversion of a nonpathogen into a pathogen.

The point of risk assessments that focus on possible pathogenicity in engineered organisms is that we don't want the organisms to cause undesirable diseases. The emphasis in the passage quoted from the NAS report on pathogenicity narrowly defined is therefore misleading. Non-pathogens can potentially cause disease in many different ways.

Generic safety arguments envisaging nonpathogenic organisms are also problematic because it is hard to draw the line between pathogens and nonpathogens. A full-fledged definition of 'pathogenicity' would show that we are dealing with a context-dependent feature. Organisms are not pathogens or nonpathogens simpliciter. An organism X is a pathogen with respect to organism Y in conditions C if X has certain effects Z on Y in C. 'Pathogenicity' is therefore a *four-place* predicate covering a complex relationship, not a simple one-place predicate representing a non-relational feature. Hence organisms known to be nonpathogens in circumstances we have investigated may well turn out to be pathogens in different circumstances.

For example, the pathogenicity of a micro-organism can depend on the condition of a host. A so-called 'opportunist pathogen' will not be pathogenic to a specific host when the latter is in a 'normal' condition. The opportunist may become pathogenic, however, as soon as the host becomes weakened for some reason. This is a serious complication in the assessment of pathogenicity. Since an 'opportunist pathogen' is not pathogenic under normal circumstances and becomes pathogenic when the host is weakened, we can say in that case that a nonpathogen changes into a pathogen. Since it is conceivable that one engineered trait in an opportunist pathogen might give it the ability to weaken its host (by producing a toxin, for instance) and thereby to become pathogenic to that host, the statement that "minor genetic modifications" will not convert a nonpathogen into a pathogen is misleading.

"Minor genetic modifications" may also lead to pathogenicity through increased virulence, and they may cause a broadened host range (Adelberg 1985), such that a pathogen may come to cause disease in new species.

Let's move on to another element in the larger assessment of the NAS Committee. Remember that the Committee remarks that pathogenicity results from an "impressive array" of required traits: the ability (1) to attach to specific host cells, (2) to resist a wide range of host defense systems, (3) to form toxic chemicals that kill cells, (4) to produce enzymes that degrade cell components, (5) to disseminate readily and invade new hosts, and (6) to survive under adverse environmental conditions outside the host, together with (7) the need to compete effectively with many other microorganisms for survival.

The NAS report argues that minor genetic modifications will not transform a nonpathogen into a pathogen because pathogenicity involves so many different traits. As it stands, the argument is unsatisfactory for the following reasons.

First, if a micro-organism is artificially given one of the traits, say the ability to attach to specific host cells, this may well be the starting point for the organism to acquire the other traits through natural selection.

Second, the argument assumes that nonpathogens do not possess *any* of these traits. This assumption is entirely unfounded. Why could not some nonpathogens miss only one trait, a trait which is easily introduced in artificial modification, by design or by oversight? If the only trait missing is the ability to "resist a wide range of host defense systems", then a mutation introducing this ability would convert a nonpathogen into a pathogen. Indeed examples of this are known. Strains of *Agrobacterium tumefaciens* differ in their host ranges due to slight genetic differences. The wide host range (WHR) strain cannot infect some plants that the limited host range (LHR) strain can infect; WHR bacteria provoke a hypersensitive response which confers resistance on the plant (Nester et al. 1985). As Robert Colwell (1985: 231) notes, a mutation deleting the ability to provoke the response would make the WHR strain pathogenic to previously resistant plants.

Third, the argument assumes that the changes in traits needed for pathogenicity to arise require *genetic* changes. This assumption is obviously false. For example, changes in the environment may well affect competitive ability in an organism (cf. trait 7).

These observations may suffice to demonstrate that the concept of 'pathogenicity' and its biological reality are so complex that they do not allow of general claims about risk assessment. Methodological constraints call for limited, context-dependent views of pathogenicity.

8. Conclusion

The analytic approach exemplified in this chapter can be applied to any argument in the risk assessment debate on the deliberate environmental release of GMOs. Doing so will help us evaluate the 'plausible speculations' which are so common in this debate. Delving beneath the surface of scientific controversies to the level of models that underlie the claims and arguments of opposing parties can foster a science that serves society. Translating abstract science to practical contexts in appropriate ways is a skill that is vital to trustworthy scientific expertise.

The reason for this is not confined to the functional demand that scientific knowledge be applied in logical ways. Adequate application of scientific knowledge also implies a social and moral obligation for experts to understand and explore the limits of their authority. Ulrich Beck has called scientific knowledge the "sensory organs" of our modern "risk society". The science and technology community has a responsibility to keep those "sensory organs" sensitive and open to critique. Methodological analysis is an indispensable ally in our attempt to achieve this goal.

The alleged value-freedom of scientific knowledge has been much debated. I would argue that taking care of methodological hygiene in producing scientific knowledge and in applying science to practical contexts has strong moral implications. Uncritical interpretations of scientific claims may have consequences that affect people's lives. Therefore, being critical about one's own claims and making an effort to dismantle misguided arguments are a *conditio sine qua non* for scientific expertise. Failing to live up to this obligation is not just methodologically, but also morally disreputable.

Acknowledgements

This work was supported by the Netherlands Organization for Scientific Research (NWO). I thank Michael Altmann, Philip Regal, Wim van der Steen and Cor van der Weele for helpful comments on earlier versions of this chapter.

References

Alexander, M. 1985. 'Ecological Consequences: Reducing the Uncertainties.' *Issues in Science and Technology* **1** (3), pp.57-68.

Atlas, R.M. 1985. 'State of the Art: Case Histories of Engineered Organisms for Environmental Release.' In: H.O. Halvorson, D. Pramer and M. Rogul (eds.), *Engineered Organisms in the Environment: Scientific Issues*. Washington, DC: American Society for Microbiology, pp.223-225.

Beijersbergen, A. 1993. *Trans-Kingdom Promiscuity – Similarities between T-DNA Transfer by Agrobacterium Tumefaciens and Bacterial Conjugation*. Leiden.

Beijersbergen, A., Dulk-Ras, A.D., Schilperoort, R.A. and Hooykaas, P.J.J. 1992. 'Conjugative Transfer by the Virulence System of *Agrobacterium tumefaciens*.' *Science* **256**, pp.1324-1327.

Brill, W.J. 1985a. 'Safety concerns and genetic engineering in agriculture.' *Science* **227** (25 January), pp.381-384.

————. 1985b. 'Genetic engineering in agriculture [letter].' *Science* **229** (12 July), p.117.

Collingridge, D. and Reeve, C. 1986. *Science Speaks to Power – The Role of Experts in Policy Making*. London: Frances Pinter.

Colwell, R.K. 1985. 'Biological Responses to Perturbation: Genome to Ecosystem.' In: H.O. Halvorson, D. Pramer and M. Rogul (eds.), *Engineered Organisms in the Environment: Scientific Issues*. Washington, DC: American Society for Microbiology, pp.230-232.

Davis, B.D. 1989. 'Evolutionary Principles and the Regulation of Engineered Bacteria.' *Genome* **31**, pp.864-869.

Dommelen, A.M. van 1995. 'Quality of Risk-Assessment: Artificial and Fundamental Controversies.' In: R. von Schomberg (ed.), *Contested Technology - Ethics, Risk and Public Debate*, Tilburg: International Centre for Human and Public Affairs, pp.193-207.

Hesse, M.B. 1966 (1970). *Models and Analogies in Science*. Notre Dame, IN: University of Notre Dame Press.

Kooijman, S.A.L.M. 1993. *Dynamic Energy Budgets in Biological Systems – Theory and Applications in Ecotoxicology*. Cambridge, UK: Cambridge University Press.

Levins, R. 1966. 'The Strategy of Model Building in Population Biology.' *American Scientist* **54**, pp.421-431.

Mellon, M. and Rissler, J. 1995. 'Transgenic Crops: USDA Data on Small-Scale Tests Contribute Little to Commercial Risk Assessment.' *Bio/Technology* **13** (January), pp.96.

Miller, H.I. 1987. 'The Case for Qualifying "Case by Case".' *Science* **236**, pp.133.

————. 1994. 'Risk-Assessment Experiments and the New Biotechnology.' *Trends in Biotechnology* **12**, pp.292-295.

————. 1994. 'A Need to Reinvent Biotechnology Regulation at the EPA.' *Science* **266** (5192 – 16 december), pp.1815-1818.

————. 1995. 'Unscientific Regulation of Agricultural Biotechnology: Time to Hold the Policymakers Accountable?' *Trends in Biotechnology* **13**, pp.123-125.

Miller, H.I. and Gunary, D. 1993. 'Serious Flaws in the Horizontal Approach to Biotechnology Risk.' *Science* **262** (3 December), pp.1500-1501.

[NAS] National Academy of Sciences, Committee on the Introduction of Genetically Engineered Organisms into the Environment 1987. *Introduction of Recombinant DNA-engineered*

Organisms in the Environment: Key Issues. Washington, DC: National Academy Press.

[NAS] National Academy of Sciences 1989. *Field Testing Genetically Modified Organisms: Framework for Decisions*. Washington, DC: National Academy Press.

Nester, E.W., Yanofsky, M.F. and Gordon, M.P. 1985. 'Molecular Analysis of Host Range of *Agrobacterium tumefaciens.*' In: H.O. Halvorson, D. Pramer and M. Rogul (eds.), *Engineered Organisms in the Environment: Scientific Issues*. Washington, DC: American Society for Microbiology, pp.191-196.

Regal, P.J. 1986. 'Models of Genetically Engineered Organisms and Their Ecological Impact.' In: H.A. Mooney and J.A. Drake (eds.), *Ecology of Biological Invasions of North America and Hawaii*. New York, NY: Springer-Verlag, pp.111-129.

————. 1994. 'Scientific Principles for Ecologically Based Risk Assessment of Transgenic Organisms.' *Molecular Ecology* 3, pp.5-13.

Schmitt, J. and Linder, C.R. 1994. 'Will Escaped Transgenes Lead to Ecological Release?' *Molecular Ecology* 3 (1), pp.71-74.

Schomberg, R. von 1993. 'Introduction.' In: R. von Schomberg (ed.), *Science, Politics and Morality; Scientific Uncertainty and Decision Making*. Dordrecht: Kluwer Academic Publishers, pp.1-4.

————. 1995a. 'The Erosion of our Valuespheres: The Ways in which Society Copes with Scientific, Moral and Ethical Uncertainty.' In: R. von Schomberg (ed.), *Contested Technology – Ethics, Risk and Public Debate*. Tilburg: International Centre for Human and Public Affairs, pp.13-28.

————. 1995b. *Der rationale Umgang mit Unsicherheit – Die Bewältigung von Dissens und Gefahren in Wissenschaft, Wissenschaftspolitik und Gesellschaft*. Frankfurt am Main: Europäischer Verlag der Wissenschaften.

Sharples, F.E. 1983. 'Spread of Organisms with Novel Genotypes: Thoughts from an Ecological Perspective.' *Recombinant DNA Technology Bulletin* 6 (June), pp.43-56.

Steen, W.J. van der 1993. *A Practical Philosophy for the Life Sciences*. New York: SUNY.

Steen, W.J. van der and Kamminga, H. 1991. 'Laws and natural history in biology.' *British Journal for the Philosophy of Science* 42, pp.445-467.

Suzuki, D.T., Griffiths, A.J.F., Miller, J.H. and Lewontin, R.C. 1986. *An Introduction to Genetic Analysis*. New York: W.H. Freeman and Company.

Tiedje, J.M., Colwell, R.K., Grossman, Y.L., Hodson, R.E., Lenski, R.E., Mack, R.N. and Regal, P.J. 1989. 'The planned introduction of genetically engineered organisms: Ecological considerations and recommendations.' *Ecology* 70 (2), pp.298-315.

Wrubel, R.P., Krimsky, S. and Wetzler, R.E. 1992. 'Field Testing Transgenic Plants. An Analysis of the US Department of Agriculture's Environmental Assessments.' *BioScience* 42 (4), pp.280-289.

4

Politics and Science in Risk Assessment

Manuela J. Jäger and Beatrix Tappeser

1. Introduction

At the beginning of the seventies when the feasibility of genetic engineering was first demonstrated, the scientists themselves were frightened to a certain degree by the risks associated with these techniques and called for a moratorium on certain types of experiments (Berg et al. 1974). But after they realized the extent of possible applications, they quite soon considered the limitations and strict regulations to be obstacles to rapid development. Special conferences were organized to find the best way to avoid a debate on the risks in the public and to elaborate those arguments which paved the way for deregulation and unlimited research. Since then "molecular politics" has become an important task of the scientific community all over the world. Molecular politics, as Susan Wright uses this phrase, means the use of technical arguments and assumptions for political means and goals (Wright 1986, 1994).

Today, twenty years later, scientists and others complain about public mistrust and do not understand why citizens are not more willing to impart overall credibility to researchers and their interpretation of the risks associated with genetically engineered organisms (GMOs).

Important parts of the scientific community do not want to acknowledge that there are serious contradictions between the database of risk research, the evaluation of this database and the political interpretations deduced from this evaluation.

When Paul Berg and others published their letter about 'Potential Biohazards of Recombinant DNA Molecules' in *Science* (1974), the main areas of concern were the possibilities of survival and spread of GMOs and the dissemination of the new recombinant gene sequences to bacterial hosts throughout the different bacterial communities via horizontal gene transfer.

To meet the concerns and comply with their own recommendations, general assessments were made about the survival and spread of GMOs and the stability of isolated DNA. However, these assessments were often based on plausible assumptions rather than experimental results.

When GMO applications achieved a more sophisticated state at a later stage, the general view was that microorganisms adapted to a perfect laboratory environment could never survive in natural environments for longer periods of time due to their reduced fitness. Especially GMOs carrying genetically engineered plasmids would not survive, due to their extraordinary burden of genetic information (Heitkamp et al. 1990).

Consequently, if GMOs were released into natural environments by chance (through lack of physical containment), the perception at that time was that the "biological containment" of cloning bacteria would be sufficient and their survival would have no negative impacts. The same belief was held concerning the persistence of isolated nucleic acids; they would be degraded by nucleases rapidly, no matter whether they were introduced in terrestrial or aquatic ecosystems or the mammalian digestive tract.

Given these conditions, evaluating the impacts caused by possible future survival of these organisms seemed to be unnecessary. Additionally, genetic engineering could be carried out without taking extensive safety measures. Those were exactly the arguments used to promote deregulation.

There are two lessons we can learn from this line of argument. First: because there was no possibility to predict the exact development of organisms with new traits and because of the lack of knowledge, survival and spread of genetically engineered organisms and their recombinant DNA was perceived as a risk at least at the beginning of the debate. This holds true especially for microbial communities in different environments (water, soil, etc.). Second: to shape the public discussion assumptions were made about the probability of survival and the persistence of DNA. These assumptions served as appeasement, but were not based on 'hard' facts. They are part of the "molecular politics".

In the following, we will present some selected data on the survival and spread of GMOs, the persistence of isolated DNA in different environments and the possibilities of uptake, integration and expression of recombinant DNA in different organisms. Additionally, we will provide a short overview of an analysis of the existing knowledge about the ecological impact of transgenic plants with different traits. We are doing this to underline that molecular politics are still being practiced, and that there is a big gap between the existing databases and the evaluation of their data.

2. Survival and Spread of GMOs

2.1 Survival in the laboratory

After testing under various laboratory conditions, it was ascertained that *E.coli* K12 (a typical laboratory strain thought not to be able to survive outside special nutrition media) do not show reduced fitness in numerous cases. For example, Cremers and Groot succeeded in reisolating *E.coli* K12 from laboratory coats: the dried bacteria survived 20 days in clothes. Survival may even be longer, because wild-type *E.coli* are able to stand lengthy starvation periods and to act dynamically on changes of the environment, especially in stationary growth (Zambrano et al. 1993).

2.2 Survival in waste water and sludge

Dott et al. (1991) inoculated 6 different strains of GMOs into drinking water, surface water, waste water and soils. Upon introduction into sewage water under aerobic conditions, the genetically manipulated strains died off quickly, but there was no difference in die-off rates under anaerobic conditions. Only one of the genetically engineered strains did not survive the test period of 31 days. But it turned out that the same GMO which did not survive very well in any kind of water demonstrated the longest life-span when inoculated into sandy or nutrient rich garden soils (Dott et al. 1991).

Competitors pose the most important factor influencing bacterial survival in waste water. Because the predator populations are subject to seasonal changes, season is an important factor in risk evaluation of the survival of GMOs (Inamori et al. 1992). Viable cell counts in supernatant decrease quickly after the introduction of recombinant *E.coli* K12 into the aeration basin of a model waste-water treatment plant, but this reflects only a partial account of the events. After inoculation, a considerable amount of the bacteria deposit in sediment and attach to sludge particles escaping grazing and other competitive mechanisms in this way.

2.3 Survival in aquatic ecosystems

To calculate the survival of microorganisms in aquatic ecosystems, consideration has to be given not only to free-standing water but also to additional habitats such as sediments and stone surfaces. Sludge particles at the bottom of lakes provide especially favorable niches for survival.

Additionally, laboratory bacteria may adapt to poor media (as occurs in actual environmental conditions). For example, the *Pseudomonas putida* species will gradually adapt to the lake water microcosms and hence be able to survive for longer periods of time without being genetically different from the non-adapted populations (Sobecky et al. 1992). Mieschendahl et al. (1993) demonstrated survival of *E.coli* K12 in river water up to 62 days.

2.4 Survival in soil

It is estimated that only 1% of the bacteria inhabiting soil is known (Torsvik et al. 1990). Only few of them are cultivable using current techniques. Wellington and coworkers (Wellington et al. 1993) reviewed the data of survival in soils with reference to environmental influences and/or cloned sequences. The data show that recombinant bacteria are less fit than their parental strain in 30% of the cases investigated, are more fit in 20% and no differences can be measured in 50%. Even if the GMOs do not survive in the long term, Wellington and his coworkers assume that gene transfer to indigenous microorganisms can occur. This would most probably not be detected, as it may occur below detection limits (Wellington et al. 1993).

2.5 Further points to consider

The distinction between cultivable and dormant cells is an important one in every environment (Zambrano et al. 1993). The dormancy problem is receiving increasing attention, since results differ tremendously according to whether there is direct counting or counting only of cultivable cells. Dormancy does not lead to the loss of plasmids. Non-cultivable bacteria stay viable for years and may be retrieved later (Atlas et al. 1992). GMOs can become dormant.

This short summary of selected data shows that GMOs find ways to survive in natural environments, directly contradicting the early assumptions about the possibilities of survival of laboratory-adopted GMOs. Additionally we have to admit that our knowledge is very limited and reliable statements on the outcome of the surviving organisms are not possible

2.6 Spread of cloned sequences

There is another main area of concern first pointed out by Berg and others in 1974: the possibilities of horizontal gene transfer. Twenty years later, there is a great deal of knowledge about the very different mechanisms that are employed to achieve horizontal gene transfer. Scientists use this knowledge to overcome all the different restriction systems nature has developed to maintain the genetic make-up of bacterial strains or plant varieties, for example.

Therefore, risk assessment cannot end with the assumption that a given GMO will not survive. Rather it should be extended to the fate of its DNA, which may be stably integrated, eventually expressed and by chance may provide advantages to indigenous microorganisms (Schmidt et al. 1994).

3. Persistence of "Naked" DNA

3.1 Persistence in the laboratory

Laboratory experiments and the application of PCR (polymerase chain reaction) usually reveal that DNA is more stable than ever imagined and clings to many different surfaces.

3.2 Persistence in waste-water treatment plants (water/sludge)

Nucleic acids released in waste-water treatment plants – dissolved in the supernatant - will be rapidly and efficiently (> 99%) degraded by chemical (e.g., acidic hydro-lysis), enzymatic (e.g., nucleases) and biological (e.g., "eating up") means. Nevertheless, adsorption to particles mainly in the sludge will stabilize isolated DNA (Gross et al. 1994). This happens quite fast and withdraws a considerable amount of released nucleic acid from the rapid turn-over in the supernatant. Moreover, quite a lot of the nucleic acids will be transferred to subsequent containers in the treatment plant and to rivers.

3.3 Persistence in aquatic systems

Although dissolved nucleic acids are also rapidly degraded when released into water systems, binding to organic or inorganic particles immensely prolongs their per-sistence. Dissolved as well as adsorbed DNA can efficiently transform bacterial cells (Romanowski et al. 1993).

Transformation by bound DNA is not restricted to plasmids, but also occurs with chromosomal DNA (Romanowski et al. 1993) and is stimulated by defined conditions of poor nutrients.

3.4 Persistence in soils

Isolated DNA in non-sterile soils will persist quite a long time depending on various factors. Analogous to aquatic systems, particle adsorbed nucleic acids introduced into non-sterile soils are protected against degradation by nucleases (Khanna and Stotzky 1992). Choice of the right method is essential for monitoring (Recorbet et al. 1993). Adsorbed nucleic acids do not loose their capacity to transform. Bacteria living in soil may especially cling to the particles loaded with DNA in order to take it up. Recent experiments with transgenic herbicide-resistant maize revealed that it is possible that the recombinant pat-gene which gives resistance to Basta (phosphinotricin) has a longer half-life in soil than the genomic DNA of the maize itself. Persistence of the pat-gene was shown for more than six months (Sandermann 1995, personal communication). This difference could be due to the synthetic nature of the used gene, because it was resynthesized in the laboratory to adapt it to the codon-use in plants, although other reasons are possible. In each case, it is necessary to conduct additional experiments.

3.5 Persistence in the digestive system

Earlier studies supported the assumption that DNA is cut into small fragments by the acid milieu of the stomach and subsequently is further degraded to mono-nucleotides by the nucleases of the digestive system. Applying PCR technology, Schubbert and his coworkers were able to detect M13-phage plasmid DNA in the faeces of mice, which had received the plasmid hours earlier. Moreover, they succeeded in detection of M13 sequences of up to 976 base-pairs in the blood stream and within white blood cells. This number of base-pairs surely applies to gene or exon length, and the highly recombinogenic fragments may even be complemented further as the authors pointed out.

Again these data prove that the early assumptions about a rapid degradation of isolated DNA-sequences were wrong.

4. Integration and Activation of Trans-Genes in Eukaryotic Cells

Bearing in mind the data on survival of GMOs and persistence of DNA in several environments, questions arise as to whether the GMOs themselves or their nucleic acids are able to penetrate eukaryotic cell barriers and whether a chance of integration and expression of foreign DNA is provided inside the cells. This should be an area of concern, because cloning of oncogenes in bacteria with self-replication units opens new ways of exchanging these genes, for example. If cloned bacteria can survive (as has been proven) and its DNA is quite stable (as has be shown), these genes could possibly access human cells and constitute a new type of cancer risk. Human and animal oncogenes have never been part of bacteria until now and therefore this represents a type of risk which is created for the first time by genetic engineering.

4.1 Uptake of nucleic acids via bacteria or aerosols

Since 1980 it has been known that various cultured mammalian cells are capable of taking up bacterial cells containing plasmids when mixed together. In 1993, Heitmann and Lopez-Pila repeated similar experiments and demonstrated expression of viral genes from prokaryotic plasmid DNA. They indicated that phagocytosis (active intake) of complete recombinant *E.coli* took place. If intracellular lysis of the bacteria ingested occurs, this will not necessarily destroy their plasmids in every cell.

4.2 Integration into the genome/stability

Foreign DNA reaching the nucleus may be stabilized there by integration into the chromosome, mediated through recombination. Inactivation through methylation is a major problem for genetic engineers and may contribute to the cells' defense to avoid unintended expression of foreign sequences. These defense mechanisms have to be surrounded in order to achieve stable trans-gene expression. Increased emphasis is put on the exploitation of the underlying structural elements to combine these elements with trans-genes for stable expression. This increases the possibilities that foreign DNA can be expressed even in mammalian cells.

Gene therapy protocols show the possibilities for taking up isolated or liposome-coated DNA into eukaryotic cells with subsequent expression. Successful DNA delivery via aerosols has been achieved (Stribling et al. 1992).

If we consider the numerous data presented until now, we must conclude that the early assumptions on the survival of GMOs and the persistence of DNA have been proven to be incorrect. Additionally, there is evidence that there are new avenues of gene transfer between different organisms, especially when gene constructs are used which combine different recognition and replication components useful in different cell systems.

5. Database on Ecologically Relevant Points to Consider in Release Experiments

Margaret Mellon and Jane Rissler of the Union of Concerned Scientists did a thorough analysis of American deliberate release experiments (Mellon and Rissler 1995). They focused on evaluating the data collected by the US Department of Agriculture (USDA), which are meant to support the conclusion that transgenic crops are environmentally safe.

According to their analysis, the USDA has approved 850 applications allowing over 2000 field tests since 1987. Until May 1994, the USDA had received 269 reports on the field tests, but only 139 were available to the public. The 85 most recent reports were analyzed by them.

Weediness: None of the 85 reports referred to experiments. Most (86%) contained only general observations, and fourteen percent did not mention weediness.

Gene flow: Of 24 reports which concerned crops with wild relatives in the United States, 23 did not address the impacts of gene flow on wild relatives.

New viruses: Of the 19 reports concerning virus resistance, none contained experiments attempting to measure the production of new virus strains. Two addressed the risks in preliminary experiments, and 17 did not even mention this special problem.

Non-target effects: Fifteen reports concerned insect-resistant crops expressing a bacterial insecticide protein normally found in *Bacillus thuringiensis*. None of the reports even mentioned the likelihood of adverse impacts on non-target organisms, which will come in contact with this insecticide protein for the first time.

A similar evaluation of the European field release experiments has not been conducted until now. One reason among others is that it would be much more difficult to get the reports, because they are still not available in the public domain. Since 1994 a European Community directive has been in effect that is somewhat similar to the Freedom of Information Act in the USA. However, German authorities are very restrictive in releasing any information, for example.

In the German application approval, where it is stipulated how the monitoring of release experiments is to be done and which are available, the points addressed by Mellon and Rissler are not mentioned. The applicant has to visually inspect his fields, but the method for doing this is left to his/her own discretion. This means that the normal release experiments are not combined with experimental procedures or monitoring, which would produce data on the possible environmental impact of transgenic crops. The only exceptions are the specially designed release experiments which are being conducted at the universities of Munich and Aachen.

Commercialization of transgenic crops has begun in the United States and Europe. It is said that the safety of transgenic crops can be deduced from the data collected during experimental field releases.

Experiments in natural science should provide reliable data, but the analysis of Mellon and Rissler shows that the data are insufficient in this field. Consequently, the conclusion that transgenic crops are safe cannot be supported.

6. Discussion

Whereas there are now a lot of data which underline the possibilities for survival and spread in the field of contained use, the situation is just the other way round in the field of deliberate release. Only few data are available concerning the ecological development of GMOs. The database is almost non-existent that would enable a decision about if and what the ecological impacts will be. Nevertheless, the conclusions drawn from the accumulated knowledge in the one field and the lack of knowledge in the other field are the same: there is no need of stringent regulation and deregulation can continue.

How can this happen?

The present analysis shows that the original assumptions (see introduction) about the survival of GMOs and the persistence of DNA were wrong. Additionally, plasmid design raises the probabilities of horizontal gene transfer in microbial communities and between eukaryotic and prokaryotic cells.

Bearing in mind our ignorance of soil communities (for example, the relationships between organisms of different bacterial classes and eukaryotic taxa), there is an urgent reason to reconsider the possible ecological and health impacts that would be produced by any kind of release of GMOs. This applies to both those GMOs that are not meant to be released into the environment but where release is tolerated, and to those GMOs whose release into the environment is planned.

In most cases, contained use means use in a fermentation plant and the release of GMOs with waste water, sludge, solid waste and used air. These GMOs contain nucleic acid constructs carrying sequences which contribute to effective replication in different cellular backgrounds, stability and integration via recombination, transfer and extraordinary high expression rates. They are – and this is the essence of the art - especially designed to fulfill these jobs. These vectors can be used without special safeguards when the cloned transgenes are thought to be non-hazardous. Vector constructs specially designed for safe use of genes with potential hazardous impact do not live up to the expectations. Work with isolated recombinant DNA-sequences does not qualify as genetic engineering, and consequently is not subject to legal regulations and safety measurements.

Laboratory or *in situ* model based studies on survival, DNA-persistence and gene transfer are no perfect scale for measuring what happens in complex terrestrial and aquatic environments and digestive systems. Our knowledge about the "avenues and barriers for genetic transmission" (Istock 1991) which exist in natural environments is limited. There is recent evidence that apparently harmless GMOs – circumstances permitting – will have tremendous effects on essential natural functions if they are released into the environment. Genetically-engineered bacteria (*Klebsiella planticola*) – designed for degrading of organic waste while producing ethanol – cut quite a lot of the mycorrhizal fungi, which support plant growth at critical early states (Holmes et al. 1994). This has a lethal impact on wheat plants. The release of these bacteria would have resulted in serious problems in agriculture, not only from an ecological perspective.

There are some other lessons we can learn from this and other examples. First, microorganisms do not have to be pathogenic to have environmental effects. But pathogenicity is now nearly the only criterion left for implementing stringent safety measurements for contained use. And second, when bacteria designed for contained use – often with special demands for nutrients not easily or not at all available in the environment – manage to survive and compete with the indigenous microorganisms, we can nearly be sure that those GMOs designed for survival in the environment will have surprises in store.

Molecular politics do not help to engender public trust and good faith. Only good science and proper risk assessment procedures can provide reliable knowledge. Democratic and responsible decisions can be founded only on the background of such knowledge.

Acknowledgment

This work was partly supported by *Kontrollstelle für Chemiesicherheit, Gift und Umwelt* (Kantonales Laboratorium Basel-Stadt), Switzerland.

References

Atlas, M., Bennett, A.M., Colwell, R., Van Elsas, J., Kjelleberg, S., Pedersen, J. and Wackernagel, W. 1992. 'Persistence and survival of genetically-modified microorganisms released into the environment.' In: Stewart-Tull, D.E.S., Sussmann, M. (eds.), *The Release of Genetically Modified Microorganisms*. New York: Plenum Press, p.117.

Awong, J., Bitton, G. and Chaudhry, G.R. 1990. 'Microcosm for assessing survival of genetically engineered microorganisms in aquatic environments.' *Applied and Environmental Microbiology* 56, pp.977-983.

Berg, P., Baltimore, D., Boyer, H.W., Cohen, S.N., Davis, R.W., Hogness, D.S., Nathans, D., Roblin, R., Watson, J.D., Weissman, S., Zinder, N.D. 1974. 'Potential Biohazards of Recombinant DNA Molecules.' *Science* 185, p.303.

Chao, W.L. and Feng, R.L. 1990. 'Survival of genetically engineered *Escherichia coli* in natural soil and river water.' *Journal of Applied Bacteriology* 68, pp.319-325.

Cremers, H.C.J. and Groot, H.F. 1991. *Survival of E.coli K12 on laboratory coats made of 100% cotton*. Bilthoven: Rijksinstituut voor Volksgezondheid en Milieuhygiëne. Report No. 719102009.

Davies, J. 1994. 'Inactivation of antibiotics and the dissemination of resistance genes.' *Science* 264, pp.375-382.

Dott, W., Khoury, N., Ankel-Fuchs, D., Henninger, W., Kämpfer, P. 1991. 'Überlebensfähigkeit von genetisch veränderten *Escherichia coli*-Stämmen. 2. Mitteilung: Überleben von Reinkulturen in verschiedenen Wasser- und Bodenmatrices.' *Zentralblatt Hygiene* 192, pp.1-13.

Gross, A., Wurz, A. and Willmund, R. 1994. *Untersuchungen zum Verbleib rekombinanter Plasmid-DNA in einer Modellkläranlage*. Korrespondenz Abwasser (in press).

Heitkamp, M.A., Kane, J.F., Morris, P.J.L., Bianchini, M., Hale, M.D., Bogosian, G. 1993. 'Fate in sewage of a recombinant *Escherichia coli* K-12 strain used in the commercial production of bovine somatotropin.' *Journal of Industrial Microbiology* 11, pp.243-252.

Heitmann, D. and Lopez-Pila, J.M. 1993. 'Frequency and conditions of spontaneous plasmid transfer from *E.coli* to cultured mammalian cells.' *BioSystems* 29, pp.37-48.

Holmes, T.M. and Ingham, E.R. 1994. 'The effects of genetically engineered microorganisms on soil foodwebs.' Supplement to the *Bulletin of the Ecological Society of America* 75 (2). Abstracts of the 79th Annual ESA Meeting: Science and Public Policy. Knoxville, TN, August 7-11, 1994.

Inamori, Y., Murakami, K., Sudo, R., Kurihara, Y. and Tanaka, N. 1992. 'Environmental assessment method for field release of genetically engineered microorganisms using microcosm systems.' *Water Science and Technology* 26, pp.2161-2164.

Istock, C.A. 1991. 'Genetic exchange and genetic stability in bacterial populations.' In: R. Ginzburg (ed.), *Assessing Ecological Risks of Biotechnology*. Stoneham, MA: Butterworth-Heinemann, pp.123-150.

Khanna, M. and Stotzky, G. 1992. 'Transformation of *Bacillus subtilis* by DNA bound on montmorillonite and effect of Dnase on the transforming ability of bound DNA.' *Applied and Environmental Microbiology* 58, pp.1930-1939.

Mazodier, P. and Davies, J. 1991. 'Gene transfer between distantly related bacteria.' *Annual Reviews on Genetics* 25, pp.147-171.

Mellon, M. and Rissler, J. 1995. 'Transgenic crops: USDA data on small-scale tests contribute little to commercial risk assessment.' *Bio/Technology* 13, p.96.

Mieschendahl, M. 1993. 'Konstruktion von Phagemiden zum Nachweis von gentechnisch veränderten Mikroorganismen – ein Methodenvergleich.' In: *Nachweisverfahren für Mikroorganismen, Viren und Gene in der Umwelt*. Fachtagung des Umweltbundesamts, Berlin, 25./26.03.1993.

Recorbet, G., Picard, C., Normand, P. and Simonet, P. 1993. 'Kinetics of the persistence of chromosomal DNA from genetically engineered *Escherichia coli* introduced into soil.' *Applied and Environmental Microbiology* 59, pp.4289-4294.

Romanowski, G., Lorenz, M.G. and Wackernagel, W. 1993. 'Plasmid DNA in a groundwater aquifer microcosm – adsorption, Dnase resistance and natural genetic transformation of *Bacillus subtilis*.' *Molecular Ecology* **2**, pp.171-181.

Schmidt, F., Brokamp, A., Henschke, R., Henschke, E. and Happe, B. 1994. 'Möglichkeiten und Risiken der landwirtschaftlichen Nutzung gentechnologisch veränderter Mikroorganismen.' In: BMFT Germany (ed.), *Biologische Sicherheit/Forschung Biotechnologie*. Vol. 3, pp.985-1008

Schubbert, R., Lettmann, C.M., Doerfler, W. 1994. 'Ingested foreign DNA persists in the gastrointestinal tract and enters the bloodstream of mice.' *Molecular and General Genetics* **242**, pp.495-504.

Sobecky, P.A., Schell, M.A., Moran, M.A. and Hodson, R.E. 1992. 'Adaption of model genetically engineered microorganisms to lake water: Growth rate enhancements and plasmid loss.' *Applied and Environmental Microbiology* **58**, pp.3630-3637.

Stribling, R., Brunette, E., Liggitt, D., Gaensler, K. and Debs, R. 1992. 'Aerosol gene delivery *in vivo*.' *Proceedings of the National Academy of Science USA* **89**, pp.11277-11281.

Torsvik, V., Goksoyr, J., Daal, F.L. 1990. 'High diversity in DNA of soil bacteria.' *Applied and Environmental Microbiology* **56**, pp.603-619.

Trieu-Cuot, P., Carlier, C., Martin, P. and Courvalin, P. 1987. 'Plasmid transfer by conjugation from *Escherichia coli* to gram-positive bacteria.' *FEMS Microbiology Letters* **48**, pp.289-294.

Wellington, E.M.H., Herron, P.R., Cresswell, N. 1993. 'Gene transfer in terrestrial environments and the survival of bacterial inoculants in soil.' In: C. Edwards (ed.), *Monitoring Genetically Manipulated Microorganisms in the Environment*. New York: John Wiley & Sons Ltd, pp.137-170.

Wright, S. 1986. 'Die Sozialgeschichte der Kontroverse um die rekombinante DNS in den USA.' In: Kollek, R., Tappeser, B., Altner, G. (eds.), *Die ungeklärten Gefahrenpotentiale der Gentechnologie*. München: J. Schweitzer Verlag, pp.177-187.

Wright, S. 1994. *Molecular Politics – Developing American and British Regulatory Policy for Genetic Engineering, 1972-1982*. Chicago and London: The University of Chicago Press.

Zambrano, M.M., Siegele, D.A., Almiron, M., Tormo, A. and Kolter, R. 1993. 'Microbial competition: *Escherichia coli* mutants that take over stationary phase cultures.' *Science* **259**, pp.1757-1760.

5

Species as Natural Kinds that Express Distinctive Natures: The Case for a Moratorium on Deliberate Release

Brian Goodwin

1. Introduction

This paper arises out of a meeting held in Penang, Malaysia, in July 1994, where a group of scientists met to discuss health and safety issues connected with the use of genetically modified organisms (GMOs) in medicine and agriculture. The meeting was sponsored by the Third World Network, a non-governmental organisation (NGO) that came to prominence after the Earth Summit in Rio de Janeiro, Brazil. It has wide membership throughout the countries of the South and is particularly concerned to safeguard countries from potential dangers arising from implementation of the Uruguay round of GATT agreements, TRIPS (trade related intellectual property rights), and biotechnology transfer. The meeting was prompted by the perception that there is a new biology emerging which is critical of the conceptual foundations of Neo-Darwinism and its views on the nature of organisms and species. The altered perspective that arises from this new biology is relevant to the ethical debate on the use of organisms for strictly functional purposes, as will be discussed below. It also emphasizes the nature of organisms as highly complex, nonlinear dynamic systems whose response to perturbation is intrinsically unpredictable.

This unpredictability and our lack of understanding of the behaviour of complex systems such as organisms and ecosystems is what gives rise to the issues of biosafety in relation to biotechnology and the case for a moratorium on the release of transgenic varieties into the environment, pending the establishment of an internationally binding safety protocol.

2. Species as Natural Kinds

In Darwinism, species are given the status of historical individuals that have evolved by random genetic variation and selection of the fitter variants. They therefore are purely functional entities that have arisen by historical contingency. They have no necessary natures, and the biological realm is therefore not rationally intelligible; it is a collection of species that have the ability to survive in particular habitats. If evolution occurred again, a quite different collection of species would be expected, within this perspective. A dominant view in contemporary biology is that organisms are essentially gene machines; that is, the genome of an organism contains all the information required to make the organism, starting from a fertilized egg (Dawkins 1976, 1986). The result is that organisms as irreducible entities in biology have disappeared, replaced by genes and their molecular products.

However, as argued elsewhere (Webster and Goodwin 1982, 1996; Goodwin 1994), this genetic and molecular reduction of organisms is unable to account for morphogenesis, the process whereby the distinctive morphology of a species is generated through the epigenetic transformations of the egg into the adult form. To develop an adequate theory of this process it is necessary to understand organisms as systems embodying principles of organisation that underlie the coherent spatial order that we see in the relationships of their parts (limbs, trunk, head, eyes, nose, etc; or stem, leaves and flowers). These organising principles are traditionally associated with what are called *morphogenetic fields*, which combine physical, chemical, and biological properties in ways that are distinctive to living organisms. Just as in physics the spatial forms that are expressed in crystals, liquids, and gases are understood in terms of fields that describe relationships between constituent parts, so in an organism the spatial patterns observed as morphology, and the temporal patterns seen as behaviour, need to be understood as a consequence of the action of fields defined by ordering relationships between parts such as molecules, cells, tissues and organs. This simultaneously re-establishes organisms as irreducible entities or coherent wholes in biology and locates gene activities as constituent processes within these fields, which involve spatial organising principles together with temporal dynamics.

Morphogenetic fields also express a different principle of causation from that which is used in mechanical descriptions of natural processes, such as the billiard ball model of collisions between gas molecules or the description of falling bodies as inert objects acted upon by an external force called gravity. An alternative theory of causation has been proposed by Harré and Madden (1972) and by Bhaskar (1978) in which entities are themselves endowed with causal powers which express themselves in distinctive ways in specific circumstances, such as the power of a liquid (a hydrodynamic field) to flow with spiral motion down a drain or to express a wave pattern when acted upon by wind passing over its surface. Understood within this causal perspective, morphogenetic fields embody causal powers that are the basis of an organism's capacity to generate a distinctive adult morphology from an egg or a bud. For example, the morphological features that distinguish the tetrapods (4-legged animals) through the forms of their limbs arise from the powerful particulars distinctive to the limb field. These are described in a mathematical model (Oster et al. 1988) capable of generating the range of tetrapod limbs under variation in parameters and initial conditions on the limb field (Shubin and Alberch 1986). Identification of the equivalence classes of form generated by such a model allows one to identify similarities and differences of morphology between organisms and their parts, thus constructing a rational taxonomy on the basis of biological forms as natural kinds (Webster and Goodwin 1996). Species are not, then, historical accidents shaped by functional necessity, but expressions of particular types of order distinctive to the living state.

The significance of this approach to biological form is that species acquire a status that they do not have in Darwinism. *Species as natural kinds that express distinctive natures* invites, though it does not require, a relationship to organisms that recognises their intrinsic qualities, so that they are valued for their beings rather than simply for their utility. A conceptual basis for this significant shift of understanding can be found in Kant's philosophical view that we experience the coherent wholeness of organisms as something of value in itself, the worth of organisms then residing in their being rather than in their results or their functions (cf. Cassirer 1981: 309-311). Organisms cease to be gene machines and become self-causing agents, implying the existence of a self that is expressed dynamically by an inner coherence that perpetuates an individual identity through the transformations of a life-cycle and a life history. This creates the space for some type of subjective experience on the part of the organism, which in the context of animal welfare entails recognition of the rights of organisms to conditions that allow for the full expression of their natures.

The transition from a third person, external, or 'objective' description of organisms and their generative causal origins to the view that they are agents that express qualities and can be perceived to have subjective experience is not a logical deduction. It is a recognition that a theory of organisms as self-generating agents is consistent with the view that they have subjective experience, without any suggestion that either subjective or objective descriptions can be reduced to the other. These represent complementary and mutually irreducible perspectives (Wemelsfelder 1993), which may eventually be unified within an extended scientific context which I have called a *science of qualities* (Goodwin 1994).

The new biology that is emerging is part of the general movement currently known as the sciences of complexity (Lewin 1992; Waldrop 1992; Kauffman 1993). The perception of some of those engaged in this movement is that complex dynamic systems, which are now being used to model phenomena in physics and economics as well as biology, involve processes of self-organisation and emergence that require new principles of how order arises out of complexity (including chaos). The shift of focus from certainty, prediction, and control, which characterise positivist science, to uncertainty, unpredictability, and cooperative interaction challenges a number of assumptions that have underlain applied science, and is naturally meeting resistance both from within science and from those who set priorities on research funding.

The problems addressed within this new science and its philosophical and ethical extensions are clearly relevant to the issues of how organisms are used in biotechnology, where they are treated as functional commodities which humans may redesign and use in any way that suits their purposes. The view of species as natural kinds and organisms as self-generating entities with intrinsic values opens the door to a discussion of their rights, extending to species and organisms the status of subjects in law. The implications of this new perspective within biology, which in fact shares many features with the attitudes of many indigenous cultures towards nature, are now under active exploration in many different areas including animal welfare and biotechnology. They are shifting the discussion from a purely functional perspective on the use of organisms to one that is based on new scientific as well as bioethical principles. Let me now turn to the biological basis for a biosafety protocol for biotechnology.

3. Genome Dynamics and Unpredictability

There is a basic discrepancy between the rhetoric used to promote biotechnology and the reality of the genetic processes on which it is based (Ho 1995). The rhetoric claims that genes are stable units of hereditary information that code for particular characters such as insecticide resistance or increased growth rate (via growth hormone, for example). When these genes are transferred from one species to another, the transgenics simply acquire the character coded by the genes. This is described as a process that is basically akin to those that have occurred during evolution in the production of new varieties and species, so that biotechnology is natural and safe. However, the very basis of biotechnology involves molecular mechanisms that reveal a very different nature for the genetic material and hereditary processes (Ho 1995). Genomes are not stable collections of hereditary information, but highly dynamic systems whose stability depends upon complex patterns of interaction between component parts.

Genomes are networks whose stable states result from the interplay of an extensive range of molecular processes. The molecular mechanisms that make it possible to pick up a gene from one organism and transfer it to the genome of another, the basis of biotechnology, are precisely those that render the genome dynamic and labile, warranting the now accepted term of 'the fluid genome'. Enzymes cut and splice sections of DNA; transposons and 'jumping genes' are mobile genetic elements that move about the genome and result in phenotypic changes that depend upon the position into which they are inserted in a chromosome; viruses and plasmids ('vectors') can pick up bits of DNA and transfer them from one organism to another, within or between species. All of these processes occur naturally and result in the high mobility and fluidity of the genetic material, as observed in the rapid spread of antibiotic resistance among different species of bacteria, rendering problematic the use of antibiotics.

So in a consideration of biotechnology we need to start from the recognition that genomes are fluid and that phenotypic characters are the result of stable patterns of interaction within genetic networks, not stable units of DNA as the carriers of hereditary information. Why, then, is biotechnology potentially dangerous, since it is simply using molecular mechanisms that occur naturally to move genes about in ecosystems? The reason is two-fold.

1.   The results of gene transfer are intrinsically unpredictable because of genome fluidity and the destabilising effect of gene transfers from one species to another. Hence new and unexpected characters can arise in transgenics, not simply the ones expected from the transferred gene.
2.   Rate of genetic change is dramatically increased by biotechnology, because genes are transferred from one species to another, jumping the species barriers arising from isolating mechanisms that normally prevent interbreeding. Thus the dynamically stable states that have emerged in plant and animal ecosystems over thousands of years can be destabilised and undergo cascades of change.

Biotechnology has been likened to nuclear technology in that natural processes are accelerated so that runaway reactions become potentially unstable and need stringent controls to avoid melt-down. We face the equivalent of nuclear meltdown in ecosystems by the destabilisation of genetic processes that are fluid but have many checks and balances in the natural world due to the isolating mechanisms that prevent most species from interbreeding. Those checks and balances remain in place with traditional breeding methods, but they have now been removed by the techniques of direct gene transfer between any species. Some gene transfers will be benign and possibly beneficial while others will have severe ecological consequences.

The characteristic response times of ecosystems can be very long. It is known from studies in Germany that the time lag for the spreading of non-native trees and shrubs can vary between 8 and 388 years, with an average of 147 years, while that for perennials and biennial plants is 68 and 32 years, respectively. Testing for the genetic stability of transgenic crops for periods of 1-3 years before release is therefore grossly inadequate. Minimum observation periods of transgenic stability and gene spread under ecologically realistic field conditions should be of the order of 20 years. This would begin to satisfy the requirements of responsible management of the technology, comparable to the development time of new pharmaceuticals which is often 10 years or more in order to meet safety requirements.

It is known that herbicide tolerance has already spread in Europe by spontaneous hybridisation between genetically engineered oilseed rape and a weedy natural relative, *Brassica campestris*, after two generations. Wild relatives of this weed are distributed world-wide, so a global contamination is possible. Whereas herbicide resistance is not likely to result in extensive ecological disturbance, as far as we currently know, insecticide resistance is being field tested in various countries of the South, and this is likely to be highly destabilising ecologically, when the transferred genes move to weedy relatives. The initial promise that the 'gene revolution' would provide chemical free agriculture, unlike the 'green revolution' that was chemical-based, is not being honoured so that the environmental problems of the latter are now added to the ecological problems of the former.

4. The Need for a Biosafety Protocol

These considerations all demonstrate the urgent need for an internationally binding safety protocol governing the production, distribution, and use of genetically modified organisms. The elements of such a protocol should cover such aspects as the demonstration of need for the transgenic that cannot be satisfied by safe, conventional methods; compulsory certification of production and distribution of GMOs; risk assessment with adequate testing procedures and periods prior to any release of GMOs; a case by case assessment because of the unpredictability of consequences; use of the precautionary principle; and public participation in decision-making regarding GMO use. Achieving agreement on such a protocol is likely to take several years. The proposal from the Penang meeting organised by the Third World Network is that there be a five year moratorium on the release of GMOs into the environment pending the establishment of a biosafety protocol (see 'The Need for Greater Regulation and Control of Genetic Engineering', Third World Network 1995). This is required for the protection of ecosystems and human health.

When we add to this the ethical dimension that comes from the recognition of species as natural kinds that express distinctive natures, so that we recognise their intrinsic qualities and value them for their beings rather than simply for their functions, we arrive at a context of discussion which has been clearly described by Gunther Altner (1991): "Human history and the history of nature are part of a comprehensive process. The rapid dynamic of human history is threatening to tear apart the indispensable ties which bind us to the history of nature, which runs more slowly. For this reason, moratoria (pauses for thought) are indispensable, so that we can examine the unforeseeable consequences of science, technology and progress. For such moratoria to be regulated there is a need for a democratically legitimated process of institution and control with the participation of the critical public. There must be an end to the undervaluation of nature in theoretical and practical calculations which regard it as a resource that is available more or less freely. The rights of nature must be shaped in such a way that nature is taken seriously as a 'third partner' in business alongside labour and capital."

The call by the Third World Network for a moratorium to establish a biosafety protocol on GMOs is a step in this process of protecting the health of humans and ecosystems and granting natural rights to organisms as natural kinds.

References

Altner, G. 1991. *Natur-Vergessenheit*. Darmstadt: Wissenschaftliche Buchgesellschaft.

Bhaskar, R. 1978. *A Realist Theory of Science*. Brighton: Harvester.

Dawkins, R. 1976. *The Selfish Gene*. Oxford University Press

———. 1986. *The Blind Watchmaker*. London: Longmans.

Goodwin, B.C. 1994. *How the Leopard Changed its Spots*. London: Weidenfeld and Nicolson.

Harré, R. and Madden, E.H. 1972. *Causal Powers. A Theory of Natural Necessity*. Oxford: Basil Blackwell.

Ho, M-W. 1995. *Unravelling Gene Biotechnology*. Soundings (in press).

Kauffman, S.A. 1993. *The Origins of Order: Self Organization and Selection in Evolution*. Oxford: Oxford University Press.

Lewin, R. 1992. *Complexity: Life at the Edge of Chaos*. New York: Macmillan.

Oster, G.F., Shubin, N., Murray, J.D. and Alberch, P. 1988. 'Evolution and morphogenetic rules: The shape of the vertebrate limb in ontogeny and phylogeny.' *Evolution* **42**, pp.862-884.

Shubin, N., and Alberch, P. 1986. 'A morphogenetic approach to the origin and basic organisation of the tetrapod limb.' *Evolutionary Biology* **20**, pp.373-397.

Third World Network 1995. *The Need for Greater Regulation and Control of genetic Engineering: A Statement by Scientists Concerned about Current Trends in the New Biotechnology*. Jutaprint: Penang.

Waldrop, M. M. 1992. *Complexity: The Emerging Science at the Edge of Order and Chaos*. New York: Simon and Schuster.

Webster, G.C. and Goodwin. B.C. 1982. 'The Origin of Species: A Structuralist Approach.' *Journal of Social and Biological Structure* **5**, pp.15-47.

———. 1996. *Form and Transformation. Generative and Relational Principles in Biology*. Cambridge University Press (in press).

Part II

Limits of Risk Assessment: Regulatory Practice

6

Bounding the Risk Assessment of a Herbicide-Tolerant Crop

Les Levidow, Susan Carr, René von Schomberg and David Wield

1. Introduction

For the hazards of releasing genetically modified organisms (GMOs), what kind of 'risk assessment' is possible? What are its limits? How do such limits arise? In other words, how is the risk assessment bounded?

To explore such questions, this essay analyses how the European Union handled a proposal for market approval of a herbicide-tolerant crop. The proposal encountered significant dissent from EU member states as well as environmentalist groups. In effect, this decision tested environmental 'precaution', the safety criteria, and their scientific basis. It became a test case for the regulatory capacity to accommodate the wider debate on herbicide-tolerant crops. For this case study, we analyse the limits of risk assessment and its institutional context.

Our analysis is structured as follows: theoretical perspectives on boundaries of risk assessment (section 2); how the EU established a precautionary framework for regulating GMO releases (section 3); how UK regulators interpreted the safety legislation for a herbicide-tolerant crop (section 4); how the EU procedure fragmented the risk issues into separate administrative responsibilities (section 5); how, in effect, EU member states promoted different concepts of environmental protection (section 6); and, in conclusion, how this case illustrates limits of risk assessment (section 7). For its research materials, this essay draws upon risk assessments, policy documents, NGOs' statements, journalistic accounts, and interviews with key participants.

2. Theoretical Perspectives

Social science perspectives have analysed how public debate serves as both an impetus and awkward referent for safety regulation. Often a regulatory procedure leads to further controversy – e.g., over 'risk acceptability', as if the degree of risk were scientifically known. The GMOs debate has centred upon 'hazard identification', amidst scientific disagreements over how to identify cause-effect pathways of potential harm. Early US regulation deepened the original controversy, as regards whether all GMOs warrant 'additional regulation', and with what expertise. This conflictual outcome should 'not be viewed as an exceptional case' where the experts have failed to settle the issues; rather, it illustrates how safety regulation implicitly becomes 'a social assessment of a new technology', involving diverse social actors (Limoges et al. 1990: 171).

In accommodating public controversy, safety regulation encounters difficulties which are often attributed to public ignorance or fear. However, such difficulties may also derive from internal assumptions or limits of risk assessment. This case study explores four such boundaries – of responsibility, causality, acceptability and expertise – which have been theorized as follows.

Bounds of administrative responsibility

Modern technological systems involve complex chains of potential harm which elude scientific disciplines, and which span the administrative division of labour: "Risks lie ... across specialized competences and institutional responsibilities, across the distinction between value and fact ..." (Beck 1992: 70). For GMO releases, new regulations had the potential to bridge those gaps.

Bounds of causality

Often technological controversy concerns the scope of the risk-generating system. For example, an official risk assessment limited itself to investigating the safety of a nuclear reprocessing plant; it excluded implications for the wider nuclear industry, such as the fuel cycle, as if these ultimate effects were not an issue (Wynne 1982). Yet harmful effects may lie beyond risk assessment, i.e. beyond the cause-effect pathways of engineering or epidemiology models. Moreover, even if a decision formally concerns a single case, e.g. a technological apparatus or product, it may effectively set a precedent for further developments and so meet resistance for that reason.

Bounds of acceptable effects and control

Risk controversy may derive from the control measures needed to prevent harm, as much as from the potential for measurable harm. Risk assessment generally makes assumptions about human behaviour, on which the 'safety' of a technological system may depend; for example, a chemical is declared safe 'if used as directed'. In this way, the technology implies a model of the social order. Such models can serve as prescriptions for human behaviour; these are often challenged as unreliable, or as unacceptable (Wynne 1992).

Bounds of expertise and plausibility

For GMO releases, risk controversy has concerned the range of scientific knowledge necessary for predicting the environmental effects. Contending approaches arise from 'the diversity of disciplinary taken-for-granted notions and practices', which literally construct the risk object; scientific disciplines conflict in the very development of risk assessment (Limoges et al. 1990: 167). In general, molecular biologists emphasize the genetic precision of GMOs, agronomists emphasize their past experience with the agricultural crops being genetically modified, while ecologists suggest an analogy to non-indigenous organisms which have unexpectedly gained a selective advantage in a new environment.

Thus regulators face competing claims for the relevance of scientific disciplines. At stake are 'prospective plausibility claims' – claims not simply about risk, but about the epistemic basis of predictability, and thus about the appropriate resources and expertise (von Schomberg 1993: 9, 15).

Contested boundaries

All those boundaries became contested when EU member states considered market approval for a herbicide-tolerant crop. For each boundary, the following questions can be posed (and later discussed in the concluding section):

1. How have administrative responsibilities been extended, linked or fragmented?
2. What potential effects of the product are not officially 'caused' by it? How has safety regulation set the conceptual bounds of causality?
3. What has risk assessment presumed about acceptable control methods and acceptable effects?
4. How has risk assessment set the bounds of adequate expertise? How have 'plausibility claims' been adjudicated or reconciled?

3. Statutory Framework: Precautionary Potential

When the European Community established a statutory framework for regulating GMO releases, this responded to the risk debate of the 1980s, when environmentalists succeeded in stigmatizing GMOs as an abnormal danger (Gottweis 1995; Levidow 1994: 274-76). They criticized herbicide-tolerant crops in particular, for perpetuating farmers' dependence upon herbicides, for aggravating weed problems, and for eventually imposing a 'genetic treadmill', by analogy to the 'pesticides treadmill'.

Herbicide-tolerant crops highlighted disputes over how to conceptualize GMOs, e.g. as self-reproducing pollutants or as environment-friendly products (Levidow and Tait 1991). To some extent, GMOs served as a proxy for contending models of sustainable agriculture, in Europe and the USA (e.g. MacDonald 1989; BWG 1990; Levidow 1991). Biotechnology R&D faced a legitimacy problem, as well as diverse national approaches to safety regulation.

3.1 Ambiguous precaution

In response to these political obstacles, the European Community enacted new legislation: the Deliberate Release Directive 90/220. This sought to 'establish harmonized procedures and criteria' for assessing GMO releases. Described as a 'preventive' measure, it noted that completion of the internal market must be based on 'a high level of [environmental] protection' – an aim set by its legal base, Treaty Article 100a (EEC 1990: 15). According to the Environment Directorate, DGXI, Directive 90/220 extended 'a preventive approach that the Community is taking on environmental and other issues' (CBC 1990: 18).

In substance the Directive is more than merely 'preventive', because it is designed to prevent hazards not yet documented for GMOs (Tait and Levidow 1992). Its precautionary features included the following (see Figure 1, top):

*   Its Preamble warns that living organisms may reproduce, cross national frontiers, and cause 'irreversible' effects; this rationale drew an implicit analogy between GMOs and non-indigenous organisms.
*   The regulatory scope is process-based: it imposes statutory controls upon all

organisms which are created through the genetic modification process.
- Prior to each GMO release, the applicant must submit an environmental risk assessment, e.g., as regards the potential for 'ecological interactions'; this requirement places the burden of evidence upon the applicant.
- Member states must undertake all appropriate measures 'to avoid adverse effects on human health and the environment' from GMO releases (Article 4). For each R&D release, the applicant must obtain a prior consent from the designated 'competent authority' of the country in which it takes place.
- For market approval of a GMO product, the application must be filed in the member state where marketing is expected to begin. If it recommends approval, then an EU-wide procedure allows for objections, to be resolved by voting if necessary. Final approval would then apply to all member states.

Environmentalists generally welcomed the Directive, though its precautionary content was left open-ended, in at least two respects:
- 'Step-by-step' principle: Regulators had devised voluntary guidelines on 'progressively decreasing physical containment', thus allowing 'a logical, incremental step-wise process whereby safety and performance data are collected' (OECD 1986: 29). The Directive provided statutory backing for that 'step-by-step' principle. However, it did not define a 'step', nor 'evidence for safety', nor 'environmental harm'; rather, the Directive established procedures for defining these terms in practice.
- 'Product' effects: An early report, commissioned by DGXI (Directorate-General for Environment, European Commission), provided a scientific argument for new GMO legislation, by attributing ecological uncertainties to the novel genetic combinations which are facilitated by the recombinant DNA process. The report described 'agriculture and other human-created systems' as particularly vulnerable to disruption. This vulnerability was conceptualized in two ways: by analogy to introduced non-indigenous organisms; and by analogy to agricultural products whose usage had caused problems, e.g. reduced biodiversity, pathogen invasions, pest resistance, herbicide resistance (Mantegazzini 1986: 76-80). Relative to these wide-ranging problems, the Directive left ambiguous the breadth of the risk assessment for genetically modified products at the commercial stage.

3.2 Precaution under pressure

Soon after its enactment, the Directive was publicly attacked as 'irrational' by some industry lobbyists and was similarly criticized from within the European Commission. Process-based regulation was unfairly caricatured for assuming that GMOs are inherently dangerous. There were political disputes over the need to change or supersede the Directive, even before its basic requirements were implemented in most EC member states.

Figure 1: Deliberate Release Directive 90/220: Interpreting Precaution

Precautionary features of the Directive

• requires a prior risk assessment and written consent for every release;
• assigns to releasers (notifiers) the burden of evidence for safety;
• sets procedures and criteria for 'preventive action' (precaution);
• does not set standards, nor defines environmental harm;
• allows member states to oppose market approval, but final decision applies EC-wide.

Policy language recasts the state's role

> Preamble of 90/220 (EEC 1990):
> > complete the internal market – provide high level of (environmental) protection

> Bangemann report (CEC 1991):
> > promote competitiveness – assess safety (of products)

> 'Research after Maastricht' (CEC 1992):
> > respect free competition – create an overall economic 'environment'

Homogenizing the environment: Disharmony over PGS' herbicide-tolerant OSR

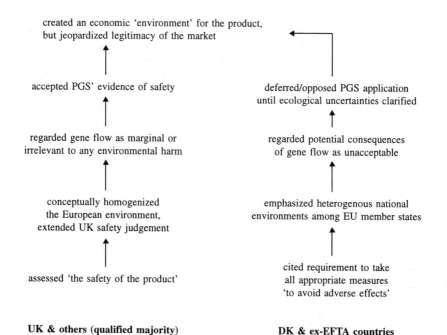

created an economic 'environment' for the product, but jeopardized legitimacy of the market

accepted PGS' evidence of safety

deferred/opposed PGS application until ecological uncertainties clarified

regarded gene flow as marginal or irrelevant to any environmental harm

regarded potential consequences of gene flow as unacceptable

conceptually homogenized the European environment, extended UK safety judgement

emphasized heterogenous national environments among EU member states

assessed 'the safety of the product'

cited requirement to take all appropriate measures 'to avoid adverse effects'

UK & others (qualified majority)   **DK & ex-EFTA countries**

Such political pressures set the context for implementing the Directive (see Figure 1, middle). According to the Preamble, the Directive aimed to complete the European internal market, while providing a uniformly 'high degree of protection' for the environment and human health (EEC 1990: 15). Subsequently the policy emphasis was altered by the European Commission, which sought to 'enhance industrial competitiveness', while assessing the 'safety' of products (CEC 1991). In a general policy statement, both the environment and the state were redefined in market terms:

> It is these [public authorities] which must bring about the creation and maintenance of an overall economic 'environment' and a respect for free competition, which is necessary so that firms can effectively develop supply policies. And this is very much the Community's task. The Treaty [of Rome] clearly confirms this, especially in the version adopted at Maastricht (CEC, 1992: 16).

A further statement on biotechnology regulation emphasized that the current process-based approach 'is unfavourably perceived by scientists and industry'. It implied that those perceptions must be accommodated in order to encourage biotechnology investment and economic competitiveness. The Commission sought to ensure that 'advances in scientific knowledge are constantly taken into account and that regulatory control is based on potential risks' (CEC 1993: 100-103). Thus industry and Commission officials sought relaxed controls, e.g., as if new knowledge would readily clarify risks. The precautionary potential of Directive 90/220 was coming under pressure.

4. UK Clarifies 'Product Safety'

All the above issues were put to a difficult test when Plant Genetic Systems (PGS) submitted its marketing application for herbicide-tolerant oilseed rape to the UK's Department of the Environment (DoE) in February 1994. The application was considered by the Advisory Committee on Releases to the Environment (ACRE), which recommended UK approval in April. The DoE in turn recommended EU-wide approval in May (see Figure 2, Chronology). In reaching their judgement, UK regulators had to resolve long-standing uncertainties about predicting and defining environmental harm.

The UK had incorporated Directive 90/220 into national law via the Environmental Protection Act 1990, Part VI. This prohibited any GMO release which poses 'a risk' of harm to 'the environment', which was defined to encompass 'land, air and water' – all the natural resources which support living organisms (EPA 1990; Levidow and Tait 1992). As a rationale for regulating all GMO releases, the DoE cited the genetic novelty of GMOs as a source of unpredictability, as regards risks of an ecological imbalance or selective advantage. The DoE conceptualized GMOs as 'novel organisms' by analogy to non-indigenous organisms, some of which had unpredictably caused environmental harm (Levidow and Tait 1993: 200).

In the early 1990s, ACRE hardly discussed how to interpret their regulatory framework for assessing herbicide-tolerant crops. Meanwhile, ACRE's Chairman anticipated political difficulty in approving such products, because they offered no obvious public benefit and were being criticized mainly for their herbicide implications: "There is little chance that the regulatory process will help to overcome public resistance to the development of such plants because the environmental issues are not significant ..." (Beringer 1993: 251). That is, their direct ecological effects would not warrant blocking market approval.

Figure 2: **EU Disputes over Herbicide-Tolerant Crops: Chronology**

(A year in brackets denotes an item in the References section.)

January 94:	When UK announces its Fast-Track procedure for 'low-risk releases' and 'low-hazard GMOs', it defers herbicide-tolerant oilseed rape for later consideration (DoE/ACRE 1994).
January 94:	When the CAs' 8th meeting considers a marketing application for herbicide-tolerant tobacco, they discuss how to handle the herbicide implications of herbicide-tolerant crops.
February 94:	PGS (1994) submits marketing application for herbicide-tolerant oilseed rape to the UK's DoE.
April 94:	Greenpeace UK sends ACRE a detailed letter opposing market approval of the PGS oilseed rape application; ACRE (1994) meeting recommends that the UK grant approval.
May 94:	UK sends PGS dossier to DGXI with recommendation for EU-wide approval under Part C of Directive 90/220.
June 94:	When the Council of Environment Ministers grant market approval to the herbicide-tolerant tobacco, their Preamble asserts that Directive 90/220 excludes the herbicide implications (EEC 1994).
July 94:	Denmark objects to PGS application at CAs' 10th meeting; DGXI co-ordinates conciliation procedure in Article 21 committee.
August 94:	PGS application is criticized in letters from three CAs – Denmark, Austria and Norway – which regard the herbicide implications as integral to Directive 90/220.
November 94:	Norway's referendum votes against joining EU.
December 94:	CAs still had reached no consensus on the PGS application, so DGXI initiates a voting procedure under Directive 90/220, Article 21.
February 95:	PGS application gains a qualified majority in the voting procedure (which follows Treaty of Rome rules). Nevertheless approval is further delayed: the European Commission does not send a proposal to the Council of Ministers. The semi-official explanation for delay is a backlog of documents which require translation into all EU languages; an unofficial reason is disagreement among Commissioners on the PGS market approval.
July 95:	At its 27 July meeting, the European Commission is finally expected to adopt a decision granting market approval for PGS crop – but a decision is again delayed.

4.1 Claiming a 'negligible risk'

When the DoE formally implemented the EPA 1990 in early 1993, it began to define environmental harm. New guidelines classified environmental effects of GMOs on an ordinal scale of 'hazard' levels, ranging from negligible to severe. For example, 'a change in population densities' would be 'low harm'; a change in their genetic composition, though not mentioned, was implicitly 'negligible harm' (DoE/ACRE 1993: 61-65). The DoE subsequently announced a Fast-Track procedure, for accelerating approval of 'low-hazard GMOs' and 'low-risk releases' (DoE/ACRE 1994). Its criterion for 'low hazard' was 'GMOs that do not possess inherent characteristics that pose a risk of damage to the environment'. For 'low-risk releases', the realization of any hazard could be prevented by management measures, e.g. physical or biological confinement. In effect, 'low risk' meant preventing uncertain effects which may be considered harmful.

At that time, in January 1994, the DoE did not categorize any herbicide-resistant oilseed rape (OSR) as a 'low-risk release', much less as a 'low-hazard GMO'.

> ACRE's *ad hoc* group felt that herbicide-resistant OSR was not appropriate for the fast track, i.e. that ACRE should still be consulted on a case-by-case basis. The Fast Track was based upon generic advice for particular crops with particular traits (interview, DoE official, 27 Jan 95).

In early 1994, herbicide-tolerant crops still warranted confinement measures and careful scrutiny, according to UK regulators.

> There was uncertainty about a possible change or increase in survival of the genetically modified crop, and about the effects of gene transfer. Our main concern had been the herbicide-tolerance gene (interview, DoE official, 12 July 1995).

> OSR wasn't included in the Fast Track because *Brassica napus* seeds are persistent and can become volunteers in following crops. The problem of volunteer OSR is controlled by herbicides, e.g. glyphosate [Roundup], so we needed to think more about it before approving a crop which would eliminate a herbicide which is used to control volunteers (interview, ACRE member, 5 June 1995).

Nevertheless, only three months later, ACRE recommended market approval for the PGS crop. How could this judgement be consistent with the earlier uncertainty?

> There is no inconsistency here, because we lacked confidence about the safety of herbicide-resistant OSR as a whole; we did not necessarily regard it as high risk. The PGS application was for a specific herbicide-resistance gene in spring OSR, for which ACRE felt greater confidence (interview, ACRE member, 20 Jan 1995).

How did their confidence about the PGS crop depend upon its specific characteristics? Apparently this case was less difficult because the inserted gene made the crop tolerant to glufosinate/Basta, rather than to glyphosate/Roundup, which was more widely used to control volunteer OSR in other crops. PGS had inserted the gene in order to ensure 100% hybrids in seed production – not in order to sell Basta-tolerant seeds as such.

In another respect, however, the PGS marketing application posed a special difficulty because it was for a 'new hybridization system', whose products could include a range of OSR varieties and chromosomal positions for the inserted gene. These new varieties could eventually comprise most of Europe's OSR crop. With the prospect of such large-scale use, the safety judgement became even more difficult (according to interviews with various ACRE members). Moreover, "ACRE members felt that there was a major political uncertainty because this was the first marketing application [to start from the UK]; perhaps the system was jumping too fast" (ACRE member, interview, 25 Jan 95).

In the PGS marketing application, the company followed government guidelines by distinguishing between hazards and the risk of their realization (as in DoE/ACRE 1993). The PGS risk assessment identified five 'hazard factors', while claiming that these posed no risk of harm. (See Figure 3, points 3 and 5 in particular.) As regards the prospect that the genetic modification would confer a selective advantage upon the crop, PGS noted that there was no intention – nor any evidence – that the crop would become more invasive. "If, in contrast to the expectations, adverse effects would be identified, it may be decided to remove plants either mechanically or by chemical control" (PGS 1994: 20-21, 27).

Figure 3: Plant Genetic Systems: February 1994 risk assessment for marketing oilseed rape, genetically modified for tolerance to Basta (glufosinate)

Summary: *The following table summarizes the assessment of the general hazard factors as determined for the hybrid system in oilseed rape.*

Hazards		Likelihood	Consequence	Risk for Harm
1.	The activity of the vector agent *(Agrobacterium)* is not limited to the initial transformation procedure	None	–	None
2.	The newly introduced traits are unstable	Negligible	Negligible	None
3.	The genetically modified plant has become more invasive	Extremely Low	Negligible	None
4.	Due to the genetic modification, there is a change in existing and/or a new interaction between the modified and an environmental element/function	Extremely Low	Extremely Low	None
5.	The traits will be transferred to related wild species	Extremely Low	Negligible	None

Conclusion: *At present, as there is no indication on specific impacts associated with the introduction and the expression of the hybrid system in oilseed rape, it is concluded that the impact of the genetically modified lines will be equivalent to that of the oilseed rape cultivars grown commercially today.*

The company did not claim to resolve uncertainty about gene transfer, much less about the prospect of herbicide-tolerant weeds. For this scenario, PGS claimed that the likelihood of viable hybrids was 'extremely low' and, more importantly, that any harmful consequences would be 'negligible' (PGS 1994).

PGS acknowledged some implications for herbicide usage. Given that the crop is tolerant to the herbicide Basta, the tolerance 'could enable farmers to use such products for weed control'. Also, the spread of the herbicide-tolerance gene 'may exclude certain uses of such products [glufosinates] for broad weed management'; however, given that they 'are not used today for the control of volunteer oilseed rape in subsequent cropping, no particular problems are anticipated' (ibid.; cf. Rüdelsheim 1993). In other words, the predominant use of glyphosate would not be affected.

4.2 Defining environmental harm

In considering the PGS application, UK regulators had to judge which hypothetical effects are relevant, plausible and/or acceptable (see Figure 4). As a baseline for their overall judgement, they felt that herbicide-tolerance genes would confer no selective advantage on OSR or weedy relatives in the 'non-agricultural environment'. This judgement had diverse rationales among UK regulators and advisors. For example, small-scale field trials had made this crop more 'familiar' and had provided evidence of 'no problems'. From an ecological perspective, "Herbicide-tolerance genes are found in low frequencies in natural populations around the world; this suggests that the gene is costing their hosts, in metabolic terms" (interview, ACRE member, 2 Feb 1995); that is, such genes apparently confer a selective disadvantage. Yet regulators had difficulty in acquiring new scientific knowledge which could back up their safety intuition.

As a politically more difficult task, regulators evaluated potential effects in 'the agricultural environment'. Civil servants reached agreement that 'environmental harm' meant only third-party harm, i.e., any agricultural problems caused to a farm by crops from another farm. (That is, statutory regulation encompassed the scenario in Figure 4, middle column, but not the right-hand column.)

> Even before the ACRE meeting of April 1994, MAFF [Agriculture Ministry] had already agreed with the DoE that 'harm' in this case should be defined as essentially harm to third parties. They also accepted that gene flow to third-party farms would not be significant, that 'Basta is not used to control OSR (volunteer weeds)', that the probability of converting any weed to a herbicide-tolerant form was remote, and that herbicide-resistance genes would be [selectively] neutral in the natural environment. This stance, coupled with their definition of harm, formed the basis of the majority judgement at the ACRE meeting (interview, ACRE member, 27 Oct 94).

ACRE members accepted the DoE-MAFF definition of harm, though they did not adopt a formal rationale for their safety judgement. Later on, members clarified that environmental harm to agriculture would be 'an intractable weed problem', whereby herbicide-tolerant weeds spread uncontrollably from farm to farm, or whereby such weeds become unmanageable (according to our interviews). "It would be environmental harm if a farmer finds weeds affecting his crop, in ways uncontrolled by previous agronomic methods" (interview, ACRE member, 25 Jan 95). Conveniently, ACRE members regarded such a scenario as implausible.

Figure 4: Defining harm – Risk scenarios for PGS' herbicide-tolerant oilseed rape (H-T OSR): 'Hazard factor' of H-T gene flow

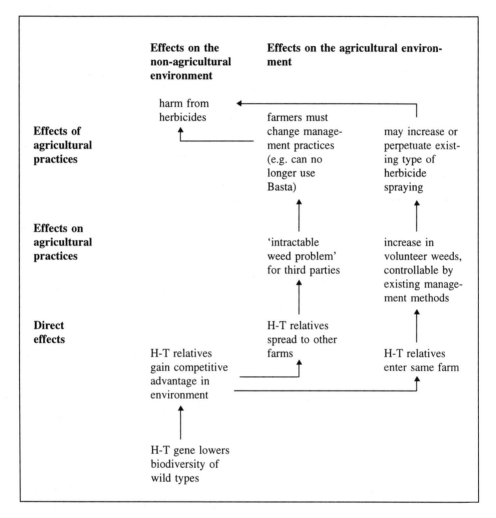

Some ACRE members acknowledged that hybridization of the PGS crop – with other OSR or weedy relatives – could result in herbicide-tolerant weeds becoming 'volunteers' in following crops, within the same farm as the original herbicide-tolerant OSR. They categorized this scenario as an 'agricultural problem', because it could be controlled and/or avoided by the same farmer. This acceptability judgement was publicly clarified:

> It was impossible to be certain that no weediness in agricultural land would result. In this case, weediness was not considered to be of significance, because first, oilseed rape could only become established in disturbed environments and even here the risk of spread was considered to be low; and second, glufosinate-ammonia [Basta] was seldom used to control volunteer oilseed rape, and therefore any spread of herbicide-tolerant OSR would be controlled using existing management (MacLeod 1995).

Such a spread was deemed acceptable: After all, "A weed becomes a problem only if you cannot control it" (interview, ACRE member, 5 June 1995). By noting that Basta is seldom used to control OSR volunteers in agriculture, the safety judgement accepted the potential loss of a Basta option for the future. In the 'agricultural environment', then, real harm occurs only if the GMO disrupts present weed-control methods – i.e., if a GMO victimizes agriculture.

Both before and after the DoE's favourable decision, the PGS application drew public criticism in Britain. The 'environmentalist' member of ACRE voted against it and issued a press statement (cited in Clover 1994). NGOs criticized the narrow scope of the DoE's environmental evaluation. One activist felt that NGOs' pressure had frightened the DoE Biotech Unit into narrowing its remit: no government agency was willing to take responsibility for the herbicide implications (interview, R. Jenkins, Genetics Forum, 8 March 95). The regulatory gap left the way open for NGOs to discredit the safety judgement for ignoring potential harm, as well as to pressurize MAFF against extending Basta approval to oilseed rape.

5. EU Procedure Fragments the Risk Problem

In May 1994 the UK proposed EU approval of the PGS application. This proposal led to disagreements among the national Competent Authorities (CAs) for Directive 90/220. According to the company, political motives led some member states to push the discussion beyond 'the safety of the crop':

> In the differences among the member states, they have taken political standpoints on how to relate the different safety questions; perhaps these standpoints have been more important than differences on the environmental safety of the crop ... The UK authority is doing a good job of dealing with the other CAs (PGS official, interview, 5 Dec 1994).

Indeed, the DoE had the difficult job of delinking 'crop safety' from food safety and weed-control problems, because these issues were linked by other member states (see Figure 5).

5.1 Deferring food safety

MAFF's advisors remained uncertain about the safety of antibiotic-resistance genes in raw foods, where the gene would not be degraded by cooking (ACNFP 1994). The PGS crop contained a kanamycin-resistance gene, so the UK made explicit the general assumption that market approval under Directive 90/220 would exclude food safety. In this regard, the UK proposal incorporated a proviso from ACRE (1994): "The product shall not be used in any human or animal food until such use has been given approval by the relevant authority". The applicant accepted this condition (PGS letter to DoE, 21 March 1994); such a deferral was no problem for PGS, whose medium-term aim was to multiply the seed for testing its quality.

However, some critics regarded the UK proviso as inadequate, for two related reasons. The EU still had no agreement on a Novel Food Regulation, which had been repeatedly delayed by disagreements over risk assessment criteria and labelling rules for genetically modified foods. In the meantime, the EU had no credible way to restrict uses of a crop – e.g., of the OSR itself, or hybrids which could acquire the kanamycin-resistance gene (see Figure 5, left-hand side).

The enforcement gap was emphasized by some CAs (see letters in References). For example, "Denmark considers it doubtful that this provision will be possible to administer in practice". Taking the criticism even further, Austria argued that "precaution is necessary concerning the genetically modified pollen", which could not be subject to confinement measures during large-scale commercial use. Thus the UK proposal was challenged for separating food safety from environmental safety.

During these disputes, the UK established national procedures and criteria for assessing foods from genetically modified crops. MAFF approved the rapeseed oil from the PGS crop in January 1995 – probably several years before such a product would be commercially available. In this way, the UK provided a potential model for an EU system and gave symbolic support to the PGS crop. Indeed, the development of the UK procedure may have influenced PGS to file its marketing application there (as implied in interviews by a DoE official, 27 Jan 1995, and by PGS itself, 2 Feb 95).

Figure 5: **Marketing application for herbicide-tolerant OSR:**
How the UK fragmented the risk problem

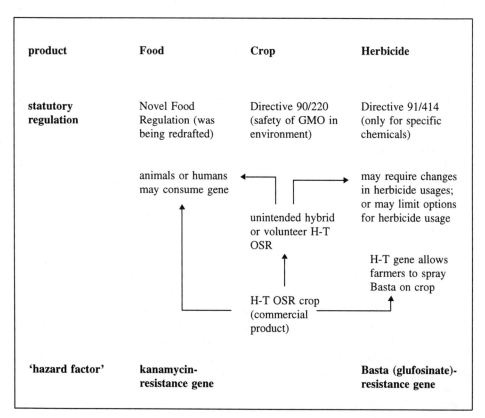

5.2 Debating weed-control issues

The UK also had the difficult job of excluding weed-control issues, which had been controversial in several EU countries. In Germany the government funded a technology-assessment exercise on herbicide-tolerant crops, but environmental NGOs withdrew before the exercise could complete its 'discursive' reasoning towards some consensus (Gill 1993; Daele 1994). PGS had decided not to request a consent to conduct trial releases in Germany, because the company would need to employ several public-relations officers there (PGS official, interview, 5 Dec 1994). When Denmark approved trial releases of a herbicide-tolerant sugarbeet in 1990, and of the PGS crop in 1993, the Environment Ministry had already begun to assess the herbicide implications of large-scale commercial use, in response to environmentalist pressures.

The national Competent Authorities (CAs) for Directive 90/220 had discussed such issues prior to the PGS application, e.g. in a January 1994 workshop (IHE 1995). The conclusions were phrased so as to separate the herbicide implications from Directive 90/220: "A secondary impact of using herbicide-resistant plants, not necessarily associated with safety, may be increased overall use of herbicides" (DGXII 1994).

Also in January 1994, the CAs considered a marketing application for herbicide-tolerant tobacco. Concerns were voiced by three member states: the Netherlands, Denmark and Germany. Germany suggested that the environmental risk assessment should consider any potential increase in herbicide usage, as this issue could affect public acceptance of the product (DGXI 1994). Ultimately the member states accepted market approval, while deferring the herbicide issue. In this case, deferral was possible because tobacco has no close relatives in Europe, and because the company intended to grow the product only in France, by distributing the seeds to contract farmers.

However, the general herbicide issue was pre-empted by the Council of Environment Ministers in June. In their text granting market approval to the herbicide-tolerant tobacco, the Preamble asserted that the herbicide implications lie within the EC pesticide directive 91/414 (EEC 1991, 1994). In protest, Green Members of the European Parliament argued that overall herbicide usage lies beyond that Directive, which authorizes the EU only to approve or ban specific pesticidal agents (quoted in Anon. 1994).

After the UK recommended market approval of the PGS crop, Denmark objected and thus triggered the conciliation procedure under Directive 90/220, Article 21. The CAs had to clarify the bounds of statutory regulation because the herbicide issue now became compelling, for related ecological and political reasons. PGS was requesting EU-wide approval for a crop which has weedy relatives in several European countries. Spring OSR is grown widely in countries with cold winters, especially Scandinavia and Britain, though also in northern Germany; thus commercial use of the PGS crop could affect the member states where herbicide-tolerant crops had been particularly controversial.

Soon the PGS application was publicly criticized by three CAs – Denmark, Austria and Norway (see letters in References). For product approval under Directive 90/220, they conceptually linked geographical-environmental differences, ecological uncertainties and herbicide usage. Denmark cited the legal requirement to 'ensure that all necessary measures are taken to prevent a negative impact on human health and the environment' (paraphrase of EEC 1990: Article 4). It also reiterated the Green MEPs' argument that Directive 91/414 has inadequate scope to fill the regulatory gap, because it can assess only specific herbicides.

5.3 Evaluating ecological uncertainties

In public debate, some environmentalists had focused upon the potential for greater use of the herbicide to which the crop is tolerant. Indeed, the company marketing Basta had already conducted a trial release of the PGS crop, in order to collect safety data which could justify extending Basta approval to oilseed rape (Hoechst 1993). Under the pesticides directive 91/414, each member state decides whether to permit farmers to spray Basta on oilseed rape. PGS predicted that the herbicide companies would not obtain approval for farmers to do so (Anon. 1994). PGS intended to sell the seeds on the basis of high-yield hybrid vigour, rather than herbicide resistance. In any case, the scenario of increased Basta spraying was not the main issue in the CAs' arguments over the PGS marketing application.

Rather, the critical CAs emphasized risk assessment criteria which were explicit in Directive 90/220, especially the prospects and ultimate effects of gene transfer (i.e., in Figure 5, the upper right-hand side rather than the lower). Denmark's letter cited its own research which demonstrated a significant capacity for OSR to hybridize with naven, *Brassica campestris*, a widespread weed in Denmark (Jorgensen and Andersen 1994). Its hybridization capacity had been described as minimal by an earlier study, cited in the PGS application (Scheffler and Dale 1994). The Danish letter emphasized the pervasive role of OSR as a volunteer weed in following crops; thus the spread of the crop or the tolerance gene could affect herbicide usage. A similar weed was known in Britain (Clapham et al. 1952: 153), but regulators there regarded it as insignificant for hybridization.

Austria's letter too drew causal links between ecology and herbicide usage: "Some uncertainties remain on the effects of the genetically modified OSR on specific Austrian ecosystems (pannonic, alpina, illyric)." In this regard, Austria also criticized an acceptability judgement implicit in the PGS risk assessment: "The potential necessity to destroy Basta-resistant wild or weedy relatives using additional herbicides, as suggested in the dossier, cannot be supported [accepted] from the idea of an integrated pest control ..."

According to the Norwegian letter, "The interaction between crop fields and the natural environment in Norway is more pronounced ...", thus increasing the probability that fertile hybrids 'may reinfest the fields'. This portrayed the herbicide-tolerance gene as aggravating problems rather than solving them, and as disrupting farmers' control rather than enhancing it. The letter advocated extreme caution, lest additional herbicide-tolerant crops lead to "multi-tolerant weeds developing". Implicitly, Norway treated the PGS application as an ominous precedent for subsequent approvals, e.g. for glyphosate/Roundup-tolerant OSR.

From those broader perspectives, CAs criticized PGS' claim that the hybridization potential has 'negligible consequences' for environmental harm. The company reiterated its earlier claim:

> Denmark did the Jorgensen study, of *Brassica campestris* in particular, because that species is widespread in Denmark. In our view, however, the extent of hybridization is irrelevant to safety because the glufosinate-resistance gene can give no selective advantage to the crop. In fact, PGS may want to put the gene into other *Brassicas*. So we can't base our safety assessment upon a limited spread of the gene (PGS official, interview, 2 Feb 1995).

This stance, supported by the UK, presumed that Directive 90/220 excludes the weed-control implications; yet their statutory relevance was in dispute.

In their national procedures, some member states had emphasized quite different uncertainties. In the Netherlands, the advisory committee gave relatively greater attention to the male-sterility gene, which PGS had inserted in order to produce 100% hybrid seeds. They judged that "outcrossing ... to wild relatives could lead to fluc-tuations in the proportion of male-sterile/hermaphrodite plants of the relatives concerned, but will not lead to a persistent unacceptable impact ... on the composition of varieties" [our translation from the Dutch]; they expected that natural selection would act against the new gene and so restore the prior frequencies (VCOGEM, 1994). By discussing such a scenario, they implied that a long-term change in genetic composition might be unacceptable (Figure 4, lower left-hand side); by contrast, the UK had not included such effects in its ordinal scale of environmental harm (see section 4.1; DoE/ACRE 1993). With this different emphasis, the Netherlands too concluded that the crop could cause no harm.

6. International Disharmonies

The Article 21 committee still had not reached any agreement on the PGS application by December 1994, so DGXI initiated a formal voting procedure, following the Treaty of Rome rules. In February 1995, the PGS application gained a qualified majority. The voting is officially confidential, though the following CAs have disclosed how they voted. Favourable votes included the UK, the Netherlands and Belgium. Negative votes included Denmark, Sweden and Finland. Abstentions included Austria and Luxembourg. Although CAs nominally voted on whether to approve the PGS crop, they effectively voted on how to interpret Directive 90/220, especially regarding the breadth of risk assessment.

Denmark and former EFTA countries quoted the Directive's broader precautionary language (see Figure 1, lower right-hand side). They emphasized heterogeneous national environments, lending greater significance to the ecological uncertainties which could affect herbicide usage. From a perspective of sustainable agriculture, they anticipated qualitative effects, e.g. which might restrict the future options for weed-control methods.

By contrast the UK assessed 'the safety of the product', a phrase which interpreted the Directive more narrowly (see Figure 1, lower left-hand side). On this basis, the UK's safety judgement could be extended to other member states. By excluding agri-cultural effects, they could regard gene flow as inconsequential for environmental harm; they could more readily accept the available evidence for an EU-wide safety judgement. In effect, their decision helped to create an economic 'environment' for the product, e.g., by allowing the company to treat Europe as a homogeneous environment (cf. CEC 1992: 16). Yet it also marginalized some environmentalist concerns, thus jeopardizing the legitimacy of the market approval.

Having recommened EU-wide approval, the UK downplayed the resulting conflict:

> For some member states, there is still a question mark on the remit of Directive 90/220, though they don't necessarily take the view that the remit *does* include the herbicide implications ... There was not really disagreement about the safety of the crop (DoE official, interview, 27 Jan 1995).

However, the conflict was over how to define 'safety', or whether 'the safety of the crop' adequately encompassed all 'adverse effects' of using the crop. Lamented another UK regulator, "Member states are interpreting the Directive differently. In my view, this weakens the Directive, because it becomes unclear what is covered by the Directive" (interview, DoE official, 12 July 1995). Likewise it becomes unclear how the regulatory procedure can help legitimize GMO products.

Indeed, key participants have acknowledged a regulatory gap. In the UK, some ACRE members have highlighted the herbicide implications, especially the scenario of multiple herbicide-resistance; they have attempted to direct environmentalist pressures at MAFF rather than at the DoE. In the Netherlands, national pesticides policy prohibits Basta spraying and mandates a 50% reduction in overall herbicide usage by the year 2000; the Dutch CA's advisory committee signalled potential problems for herbicide usage from the PGS crop but noted that this problem is not their task (VCOGEM 1994). In Germany the CA acknowledged that the herbicide implications remain a concern (RKI 1995); yet it presumably voted for the PGS application, which had been criticized by the Federal Environmental Agency. Officials in Belgium and Luxembourg (1995) portrayed the EU vote as authorizing PGS only to breed more seed; thus they implied that a later regulatory decision could still consider the large-scale herbicide implications.

In various ways, then, the PGS marketing application had tested the EC Directive and shaped the EU political environment. According to the company, "It was a test case, not in the environmental sense, but rather in the regulatory sense, e.g. for fine-tuning the procedure around a real case, so that the regulators could decide what questions are important" (interview, PGS official, 2 Feb 95). In this regard, EU member states ultimately disagreed over how to define the important questions for the statutory regulation. Each in their own way, they had difficulty in accepting responsibility for the agricultural implications.[1]

7. Conclusions: Limits of Risk Assessment

In conclusion, a herbicide-tolerant crop became an important test case for the EU's safety regulation of GMO releases; a voting procedure became necessary in order to adjudicate the boundary of risk assessment. The UK played a lead role in fragment-ing the risk problem into separate administrative procedures – environmental safety, food safety and herbicide usage (see again Figure 5). In this way, the European Union could operationalize Directive 90/220 for granting market approval, while deferring awkward uncertainties about how to predict and avert some plausible effects.

This case illustrates several contested boundaries of risk assessment. Although scientific disputes had originally influenced the establishment of safety legislation, its administrative implementation in turn defined the relevance of technical expertise. That political relation is suggested by the following sequence of contested boundaries (as surveyed earlier in section 2).

7.1 Administrative responsibility

The safety judgement presumed that real-life practices, and their potential for harm, would fall within the existing administrative division of labour – i.e., the distinct authorities responsible for regulating GMO releases, novel foods and herbicides. With this working assumption, environmental safety regulators could take responsibility only for the direct ecological effects of the crop and its genes; they could exclude more complex cause-effect scenarios, e.g. the 'genetic treadmill' which NGOs had foreseen.

By interpreting Directive 90/220 this way, they left no one officially responsible for a range of undesirable effects which lay beyond or spanned the existing administrative boundaries. Despite the precautionary potential of EU legislation, its implementation still left some risks "across specialized competences and institutional responsibilities ..." (Beck 1992: 70).

7.2 Causality of effects

In particular, the market approval excluded responsibility for any effects on weed-control methods. Called 'secondary' or 'indirect', such effects were attributed to management practices, not to the crop. On this rationale, any environmental harm is 'caused' *either* by human activity *or* by the inherent characteristics of an organism (see section 4.1). The safety judgement conceptually de-linked agricultural practices from GMOs' design; this stance denied the material links between them – e.g., the R&D priorities geared to intensify productivity and competition, and the industrial restructuring which integrates plant breeders with herbicide vendors.

When some member states opposed market approval, they emphasized the in-built links between crops and herbicide usage. Moreover, they regarded this product as an ominous precedent for subsequent ones, bringing the prospect of multiple herbicide-resistance, which would lie beyond safety regulation. Member states contested the conceptual bounds of causality, and thus the regulatory limits of the risk-generating system (cf. Wynne 1982: 172).

7.3 Acceptability of effects, of control methods

Regulators evaluated some hypothetical effects as acceptable and/or as not environmental harm. In effect, they devised normative reference points – which were necessary in order to implement the EC Directive, but not provided by it. Within such boundaries, they could support market approval, without claiming to have resolved all predictive uncertainties.

As regards uncertainties about hybridization capacity, UK regulators judged gene flow as acceptable if it conferred no selective advantage to *Brassica* relatives in the wider environment. In the Netherlands, the advisory committee went further, by asking whether introgressed genes could persist in natural populations; they did not assume that a changed genetic composition would be acceptable. In various ways, these normative standards drew some analogy to natural processes already deemed to be acceptable.

As regards potential effects on herbicide usage, member states diverged even more than their votes might suggest. For example, the Netherlands' risk assessment simply excluded agricultural effects. The UK considered whether the PGS crop could disrupt present weed-control methods, while taking such methods as an acceptability norm, or even depending upon such methods as a safety rationale. By contrast, critical member states refused to assume that any particular weed-control method would be either essential or dispensable in the future. In dispute were not only potential changes, but also the acceptability of present methods, which might become unwelcome prescriptions for the future (cf. Wynne 1992). For evaluating weed-control effects, each normative standard drew some analogy to present herbicide usage as a reference point.

7.4 Expertise, adequacy of evidence

In their risk assessment, regulators regarded some hypothetical effects as implausible. In particular, they judged that the herbicide-tolerance genes would not confer a selective advantage to *Brassicas*, in the absence of the herbicide Basta. Apparently no member state challenged this judgement, nor its weak empirical basis.

Instead the critical member states emphasized uncertainties about whether the crop or herbicide-tolerant relatives would aggravate familiar agricultural problems. This scenario lent greater significance to national environmental differences, and to the hybridization potential of the crop. In dispute was not the ecological uncertainty, but whether it mattered for unacceptable effects, i.e., those which transgressed a normative reference point.

In this case, ecological evidence played diverse roles – e.g., by suggesting that this GMO would not gain a competitive advantage, or by emphasizing uncertainties which could not be resolved by the available data. While the earlier debate had concerned the plausibility of knowledge claims (von Schomberg 1993), it now shifted somewhat – to the *implausibility* of specific effects, as well as their statutory relevance, and therefore the adequacy of evidence for safety.

In sum, a herbicide-tolerant crop became a test case for Directive 90/220. At both national and EU levels, regulators conceptually tested the safety claims for this product. At the market-approval stage, regulatory discussions moved more clearly from 'risk' to 'effects' – their statutory relevance, acceptability, and plausibility. At this stage, 'evidence of safety' partly means narrowing the range of effects whose implausibility must be argued. Thus 'risk assessment' is a misnomer, for several reasons: it has no consensual analogy in past experience, as a basis for future predictions; and it accommodates a predictive uncertainty by conceptually narrowing the range of relevant effects.

When implementing the Directive at the commercial stage, regulators selectively interpreted its key terms – e.g. 'the product', its 'safety', and even 'the environment' to be protected. There was a conflict between 'avoiding adverse effects' and 'completing the internal market'. In bounding the risk assessment, EU regulators underwent a tension between protecting the environment and homogenizing it, i.e., treating Europe as a homogeneous commercial environment for biotechnology products. In setting limits on risk assessment, the EU procedure thereby limited the capacity of GMO regulation to accommodate the wider environmental debate.

Acknowledgements

This essay arises from two related studies: 'GMO Releases: Managing Uncertainties about Biosafety', funded by the European Commission's DGXII during 1994-95; and 'From Precautionary to Risk-Based Regulation: The Case of GMO Releases', funded by Britain's Economic and Social Research Council during 1995-96, project number L211 25 2032.
We would like to thank several people for editorial comments, especially Claire Marris, Ad van Dommelen and Mark Williamson.

Note

1.   This essay has not attempted to explain the stance of each national Competent Authority, e.g. in terms of national politics. This aspect, and EU-wide efforts at harmonizing GMO regulation, will be further analysed in a special issue of *Science and Public Policy*, probably June 1996.

Institutional Abbreviations

ACRE (UK):	Advisory Committee on Releases to the Environment
CA:	Competent Authority for Directive 90/220 in each member state (e.g. DoE in UK, VROM in the Netherlands, RKI in Germany)
DoE (UK):	Department of the Environment
EFTA:	European Free Trade Area (EC plus Sweden, Finland, Norway, Austria, etc.)
DGXI:	Directorate-General for Environment, European Commission
DGXII:	Directorate-General for Science, Research and Development, European Commission
EPA (DK):	Environmental Protection Agency, Environment Ministry
MAFF (UK):	Ministry of Agriculture, Fisheries and Food
PGS:	Plant Genetic Systems, Gent
RKI (D):	Robert-Koch Institut, formerly part of the Bundesgesundamt (BGA)
VCOGEM (NL):	Netherlands' advisory committee
VROM (NL):	Volkshuisvesting, Ruimtelijke Ordening en Milieubeheer; in the Directorate-General of the Environment

References

[ACNFP] Advisory Committee on Novel Foods and Processes 1994. *The Use of Antibiotic-Resistance Markers in Genetically Modified Food Organisms.* London: MAFF, July.

[ACRE] Advisory Committee on Releases to the Environment 1994. Advice on PGS marketing application, DoE public register, unpublished typescript, April.

Anon. 1994. 'Genetically modified rape blazes trail for industry and regulators.' *ENDS Report* **239** (December), pp.15-18.

Austria 1994. Letter from Health Ministry to DGXI, 12 August.

Beck, U. 1992. *Risk Society: Towards a New Modernity.* London: Sage.

Beringer, J. 1993. 'Risks associated with molecular approaches to weed control.' *British Crop Protection Conference – Weeds*, volume 1, pp.249-253.

[BWG] Biotechnology Working Group 1990. *Biotechnology's Bitter Harvest: Herbicide Tolerant Crops and the Threat to Sustainable Agriculture.* New York: Environmental Defense Fund.

[CBC] Cambridge Biomedical Consultants 1990. *The Impact of New and Impending Regulations on UK Biotechnology.* Cambridge: Cambridge Biomedical Consultants.

[CEC] Commission of the European Community 1991. *Promoting the Competitive Environment for the Industrial Activities Based on Biotechnology within the Community.* Brussels: Commission of the European Communities.

————. 1992. 'Research after Maastricht: An assessment, a strategy.' *Bulletin of the European Communities*, supplement 2/92.

————. 1993. 'Growth, Competitiveness, Employment: The Challenges and Ways Forward into the 21st Century.' *Bulletin of the European Communities*, supplement 6/93.

Clapham, A.R. et al. 1952. *Flora of the British Isles*, Cambridge: Cambridge University Press.

Clover, C. 1994. 'Designer crop is given go-ahead.' *Daily Telegraph* (20 April).

Daele, W. van den 1994. *Technology Assessment as a Political Experiment.* Berlin: Wissenschaftszentrum.

Denmark 1994. Letter from Environment Ministry to DoE, 10 August.

[DG XI] Directorate-General for Environment, European Commission 1994. Minutes of the CAs' January meeting, unpublished typescript.

[DG XII] Directorate-General for Science, Research and Development, European Commission 1994. 'Herbicide-resistant plants: Are they safe?' *Ebis Newsletter* **4** (1), p.6.

DoE/ACRE 1993. Guidance note no.1: The Regulation & Control of the Deliberate Release of Genetically Modified Organisms.

DoE/ACRE 1994. Guidance note no.2: Fast Track Procedures for Certain GMO Releases, January.

EEC 1990. 'Council Directive on the Deliberate Release to the Environment of Genetically Modified Organisms.' *Official Journal of the European Communities*, L 117, 8 May, pp.15-27.

————. 1991 'Council Directive Concerning the Placing of Plant Protection Products on the Market, 91/414.' *Official Journal of the European Communities*, L 230, 19 August, pp.1-32.

————. 1994. 'Commission decision of 8 June, 94/385/EC.' *Official Journal of the European Communities* L 176, 9 July, pp.23-24.

[EPA] 1990. *Environmental Protection Act 1990.* London: HMSO.

Gill, B. 1993. 'Technology assessment in Germany's biotechnology debate.' *Science as Culture* **4** (1), pp.69-84.

Gottweis, H. 1995. 'German politics of genetic engineering and its deconstruction.' *Social Studies of Science* **25**, pp.195-235.

Hoechst UK Ltd 1993. Application for Consent to Release Genetically Modified Winter OSR, ref. no.UK/93/R9/1, unpublished typescript, submitted to DoE.

[IHE] Institute of Hygiene and Epidemiology 1995. *Safety Considerations of Herbicide-Resistant Plants to be Placed on the European Market*, 26 January 1994 Workshop Report, Brussels: Institute of Hygiene and Epidemiology, June.

Jorgensen, R.B. and Andersen, B. 1994. 'Spontaneous hybridization between OSR and weedy relatives.' *American Journal of Botany* **81** (no.12, 1 December), pp.1620.

Levidow, L. 1991. 'Cleaning up on the farm.' *Science as Culture* 2 (4), pp.538-568.

——. 1994. 'Biotechnology regulation as symbolic normalization.' *Technology Analysis and Strategic Management* 6 (3), pp.273-88.

Levidow, L. and Tait, J. 1991 'The greening of biotechnology: GMOs as environment-friendly products.' *Science and Public Policy* 18 (5), pp.271-280.

——. 1992. 'The release of genetically modified organisms: Precautionary legislation.' *Project Appraisal* 7 (2), pp.93-105.

——. 1993. 'Advice on biotechnology regulation: The remit and composition of ACRE.' *Science and Public Policy* 20 (3), pp.193-209.

Limoges, C. et al. 1990. 'Controversies over risks in biotechnology (1973-89): A framework of analysis.' In: *Managing Environmental Risks*. Pittsburgh, PA: Air & Waste Management Association, pp.155-174.

Luxembourg 1995. Letter from Health Ministry to Norbert Campagna, 13 June.

MacDonald, J.F. (ed.) 1989. *Biotechnology and Sustainable Agriculture: Policy Alternatives*. Ithaca, NY: National Agricultural Biotechnology Council. Available from NABC, 211 Boyce Thompson Institute, Tower Road, Ithaca, NY 14853-1801.

MacLeod, J. 1995. 'Deliberate Release and Marketing.' Talk at conference on Genetically Modified Crop Cultivars, National Institute of Agricultural Botany, 2-3 February.

Mantegazzini, M. 1986. *The Environmental Risks from Biotechnology*. London: Pinter.

Norway 1994. Letter from Environment Ministry to DGXI, 10 August.

[OECD] Organization for Economic Cooperation and Development 1986. *Recombinant DNA Safety Considerations*. Paris: OECD.

[PGS] Plant Genetic Systems 1994. A New Hybridization System in Oilseed Rape (*B. napus*): Application for Consent to Market Genetically Modified Organisms, ref. no. 94/M1/1, unpublished typescript, submitted to DoE, February.

[RKI] Robert-Koch Institut 1995. Antrag auf Inverkehrbringen eines herbizidresisten Rapses in Grossbritannien durch die belgische Firma Plant Genetic Systems. Berlin: Robert-Koch Institut, undated typescript of draft press statement.

Rüdelsheim, P. 1993. 'Engineering crops for tolerance to specific herbicides: A valid alternative.' *British Crop Protection Conference – Weeds*, volume 1, pp.265-272.

Scheffler, J. and Dale, P. 1994. 'Opportunities for gene transfer from genetically modified oilseed rape (*B.napus*) to related species.' *Transgenic Research* 3, pp.263-278.

Schomberg, R. von 1993. 'Political decision-making and scientific controversies.' In: R. von Schomberg (ed.), *Science, Politics and Morality: Decision-Making and Scientific Uncertainty*. Dordrecht: Kluwer Academic, pp.7-26.

Tait, J. and Levidow, L. 1992. 'Proactive and reactive approaches to regulation: The case of biotechnology', *Futures* 24 (3), pp.219-231.

[VCOGEM] Netherlands' advisory committee 1994. Advice on PGS marketing application, VROM public register, unpublished typescript, 13 June.

Wynne, B. 1982. *Rationality and Ritual: The Windscale Inquiry and Nuclear Decisions in Britain*. British Society for the History of Science.

——. 1992. 'Risk and social learning: Reification to engagement.' In: S. Krimsky and D. Golding (eds.), *Social Theories of Risk*, New York: Praeger, pp.275-297.

7

Political Problems – Genetically Engineered Solutions: The Socio-technical Translations of Fox Rabies

Ruth McNally

1. Introduction

Raboral V-RG is a cyborg[1]; it is a genetically engineered construct, a living organism and a commercial product. It is a genetically engineered chimaera resulting from the insertion of part of the rabies virus (glycoprotein G CDNA from strain ERA) into the genome of vaccinia virus (Copenhagen strain). It is a living hybrid organism – a vaccinia virus which expresses a rabies virus protein. It is also a vaccine, whose purpose is to immunise foxes against infection with rabies virus.

Trials of the vaccine are not so much open field releases as open air releases. The genetically engineered viruses are loaded into edible bait which is then dropped onto the field sites from the air. Between 1987 and 1992 an estimated 800,000 baits were dropped on sites of up to 42,000 km^2 in France and Belgium. In 1993, the intention was to 'treat' 75,000 km^2 of the European Union (EU) with a total of 30 baits per km^2 (Rhone Merieux 1992: 2). Each bait contains 10^8 $TCID_{50}$ (tissue culture infectious doses). This makes these releases among the largest authorised open field releases of genetically engineered organisms anywhere in the world.

Raboral V-RG is potentially harmful – vaccinia, the host virus, is a minor human pathogen. It is not contained – vaccinia has a broad host range and although intended for foxes the bait which contains it can be eaten by other animals, including small mammals, which it may infect and colonise, where it may mutate, and from where it may be transmitted to other animals, including humans. And it is not genetically stable – vaccinia hybridises readily with related poxviruses, including cowpox which may be present in wild rodents which eat the bait (see McNally 1995a, 1995b).

Yet in October 1993 the European Commission gave written consent under the deliberate release Directive 90/220/EEC to place Raboral V-RG on the market for use in aerially distributed bait as a vaccine against rabies in rural populations, and in November 1994 the vaccine was given a favourable evaluation as a veterinary medicine under Directive 87/22/EEC.

I have previously critically evaluated the safety and efficacy of Raboral V-RG in McNally 1995a and 1995b. In this paper I shall apply actor-network theory to explore the socio-technical translations of fox rabies into a European 'problem' for which Raboral V-RG is the 'solution'.

Actor-network theory, also known as the 'sociology of translation[2]', was developed by a group of sociologists of science including Bruno Latour, Michel Callon and John Law (see Callon 1986; Latour 1988a, 1988b, 1991a, 1991b; Law 1986a, 1986b).

Actor-network theory is described as a new approach to the study of power, which rather than explaining what power is, attempts to describe what power does through a description of the 'socio-technical' path through which reality is progressively constructed (see Latour 1991b: 117). One of the characteristic features of the sociology of translation is that an actor-network is a web of both human and non-human actors.

There are a number of reasons why actor-network theory seems an appropriate approach for the story which I wish to tell. Firstly, given actor-network theory's deconstruction of the boundary between human and non-human actors, it permits the extension of Haraway's (1985, 1991) concept of a 'cyborg' to viruses. Thus, what I present here is an eco-constructivist analysis of the social relations of science in which genetically engineered organisms are conceptualised as cyborgs whose identity is actively constructed in accordance with certain strategies. Secondly, it provides an opportunity for portraying the regulatory process as a method of translation, and risk assessment as a set of techniques for producing data with which to represent (non-human) actors. Thirdly, actor-network theory embraces the notion that actor-networks themselves and the identities of the actors within them are not fixed, and are liable to destabilisation through contestation and/or mutiny. The unstable nature of actor-networks seems appropriate for the story I wish to tell because it both encompasses a warning that genetically engineered organisms may resist their characterisation in the actor-network as safe and predictable products, and also because it reveals the potential for other actors – the readers of this chapter for example – to intervene in the socio-technical shaping of science, technology and society and alter the nature of the actor-network I describe here.

"The methodology of the sociology of translation is rooted in the work of Machiavelli[3], who is a conscious model for the ethnographic techniques it employs" (Clegg 1989: 203). The researcher engaged in studying the sociology of translation proceeds by following the (enrolling) actor: "the observer follows the actors in order to identify the manner by which they build and explain their world, whether it be social or natural" (Callon 1986: 201). The actor who is followed is the enrolling actor, the 'Prince', who translates other actors in order to enrol them into the actor-network.

The choice of the Prince is made by whoever undertakes the study. For this analysis of the socio-technical translation of fox rabies, I have allocated the role of the Prince to the group of institutions which have developed Raboral V-RG, and it is with their story that I shall start.

2. Assembly of a Cyborg

The history of Raboral V-RG goes back to the study of the antigenic properties of rabies virus components in the early 1970s by researchers at the Wistar Institute in Philadelphia, USA (Wiktor et al. 1973). In 1983/1984, Lecocq formed the French company Transgene and in 1984, Lecocq, Kieny and Skory (of Transgene), Lathe (of Transgene and Wistar), Wiktor and Koprowski (of Wistar), and Drillien and Spehner (of INSERM) published a paper describing a new genetic recombinant virus, later called Raboral V-RG (Kieny et al. 1984). In 1984, Lathe, Kieny, Drillien and Lecocq applied for a patent on the virus as a viral vaccine, with Transgene as the patent assignee (FR/84/06499, then PCT/FR85/00096), and at a later date the patent rights were sold to the French company Rhone Merieux, which is one of the world's largest makers of veterinary biological pharmaceuticals.

What the enrolling actors had produced was a living genetically engineered virus designed to immunise a range of animals against rabies infection. What they required were target populations of animals at risk of rabies in which there was sufficient economic interest to create a market for the vaccine. Furthermore, in order to bring in a financial return, Raboral V-RG would also require the appropriate product licences.

One such target population they identified was cattle. In 1986, Wistar arranged with the Pan American Health Organisation (PAHO) to test Raboral V-RG (manufactured by Rhone Merieux) in Azul, Argentina, as a vaccine against bovine rabies. This field trial was terminated when it was alleged it was being conducted without the consent of the Argentinian authorities and that it violated ethical and legal principles (see Wheale and McNally 1988a: Chapter 7). Another target population they identified was wild raccoons, and field trials of Raboral V-RG as a vaccine against raccoon rabies were undertaken in the USA where application for a product licence has been made (see McNally 1995a, 1995b).

A third target population was in the EU. Rabies is endemic in fox populations in four of the (then) twelve European Community (EC) Member States – France, Belgium, Germany and Luxembourg – and from 1987, field trials of Raboral V-RG were undertaken in Belgium and France by a collaboration of French and Belgian institutions including Transgene, Rhone Merieux, the University of Liege, the Pasteur Institute in Brussels, the Etat-Major General in Brussels, and the Centre d'Economie Rurale in Marloie, Belgium.

Around this time, in 1988, the European Commission published its proposal for a Council Directive on the deliberate release of genetically engineered organisms into the environment (see Wheale and McNally 1990a). As a genetically engineered organism, Raboral V-RG would be covered by this Directive when adopted.[4] This prospect was both advantageous and disadvantageous to the vaccine producers. The advantage was that this Directive (90/220/EEC, adopted in October 1991) was one of the measures adopted to establish a Single European Market, and accordingly a written consent to place a product on the market granted under this Directive is valid in all Member States of the EU. The disadvantage was that the Directive is also concerned with health, safety and environmental protection which means that in order to obtain consent to place a genetically engineered organism on the market the producers must supply a technical dossier evaluating foreseeable risks of the genetically engineered organism, as required by Annex II of the Directive.

Thus, on the basis of a dossier containing data from field releases undertaken in Belgium and/or France, consent could be given to place Raboral V-RG on the market in all Member States. On the other hand, compiling the technical dossier would be costly and time-consuming. Moreover, the dossier would have to convince the Competent Authorities of other Member States to give a favourable opinion to the placing of Raboral V-RG on the market. The worst scenario would be that some of the Member State Competent Authorities would object, in which case the outcome would be decided by majority vote of a Committee of Member State Representatives. It could be calculated that France and Belgium would give a favourable opinion on the dossier, and that certain other Member States would not oppose the dossier simply because they lacked the national expertise to evaluate it. Therefore, a crucial strategy for the producers of Raboral V-RG was to enrol the European Commission, which would not only chair the Committee but would also be responsible for drafting the proposal upon which the vote would be taken.

The enrolment of the European Commission could also be useful in addressing the first obstacle posed by Directive 220 – the cost of compiling the technical dossier itself. A successfully enrolled European Commission would not only treat the application for consent to place Raboral V-RG on the market favourably, but would also supply financial support for gathering the information which was inside the dossier. The question for the producers of Raboral V-RG was: 'How to enrol the EU Institutions in the Raboral V-RG actor-network?'

3. The Obligatory Passage Point

The methods by which the enrolling actor enrols others in the actor-network are called 'translation'. One method of translation is 'problematisation' whereby the enrolling actor defines a general problem which can only be resolved by the solution of a much more specific problem proposed by the enrolling actor. In this way the enrolling actor 'renders itself indispensable to others by creating a geography of obligatory passage points' (Callon, Law and Rip 1986: xvii).

In this case the general problem is rabies, the specific problem is fox rabies, and the solution – the obligatory passage point – is Raboral V-RG. In other words, rabies is a problem for the EU which will be solved by the eradication of fox rabies using the licensed vaccine called Raboral V-RG.[5]

Problematisation is only one stage in the process of enrolment. In order to become enrolled each actor must adopt a defined role in relation to the problematisation. The actors to be enrolled – who must take on a role – within this actor-network are fox rabies, the EU, the EU Institutions, and Raboral V-RG.

Fox rabies must play the role of the dreaded enemy, pestilential outsider, scourge from the untamed front with Eastern Europe, which threatens to invade the entire EU. Hazardous to humans, their pets and livestock, impervious to other control mechanisms, it will be neutralised by Raboral V-RG and be driven back by a barrier of invisible soldiers which infiltrate the foxes and disarm the foe from within.

The EU must be constituted as a separate part of the European continent, with biological as well as geographical and political boundaries. Without Raboral V-RG it is blighted. However with Raboral V-RG, and only Raboral V-RG, it can be cleansed and transformed into its ideal state, as a purified free zone in which the legitimate may circulate freely.

The role of the EU Institutions is that of protector of citizens, creator of wealth, and facilitator of free trade. To be enrolled, they must perceive rabies as a problem which it is in their interest to solve. Moreover, they must support the use of Raboral V-RG as the way of solving it.

Raboral V-RG also has an ideal identity within the actor-network. It must perceive itself not as a genetically engineered organism, but as a veterinary pharmaceutical product – a vaccine whose purpose is to be effective in eradicating fox rabies. In order to be successfully enrolled, it must suppress its other biological inclinations to cause harm, to spread, or to mutate, and concentrate solely on its defined role as an immunising agent targeted at rabies in foxes.

The methods of translation involve the use of forms of representation and transformation. In the next section I shall illustrate the principle of translation using examples of the enrolment of fox rabies in a number of different actor-networks.

4. Some Translations of Fox Rabies

On entering the English port of Dover, having crossed the Channel from Calais on a car ferry, you cannot fail to notice multiple copies of a huge poster displayed at immigration control (see Figure). The poster, published by the Ministry of Agriculture, Fisheries and Food (MAFF), features a young girl cuddling a cat. The slogan above the poster says: 'It's this easy to pick up rabies'.

In some respects this is a curious poster to display in this location because the message it implies is that the young girl is at risk of catching rabies from the cat she has brought back with her (smuggled?) from the Continent. However, if the cat has merely come from another Member State of the EU, the probability that it will give her rabies is virtually zero. This is because the type of rabies which is endemic in foxes in the EU – sylvatic rabies – differs in significant ways from the canine rabies which is endemic in Asia and Africa.

The main host reservoir for sylvatic rabies in Europe is the fox. The epidemic of fox rabies in Continental Europe pushed westwards from the

Polish/Russian border in the decades immediately following World War Two, and it is presently endemic in four Member States of the EU: France, Belgium, Luxembourg and Germany. Since 1977, when the World Health Organisation (WHO) Collaborating Centre for Rabies Surveillance and Research at Tubingen in Germany began collecting data on human cases of rabies in Europe, there have been no reported human deaths from indigenously-contracted rabies in EU countries (WHO 1992). The last such case in France was in 1928 (House of Commons Agriculture Committee 1994). The low risk to human health is in part due to the existence of an effective human vaccine against rabies. But it is also due to the biological properties of the fox rabies virus itself. Whilst all mammals are believed to be susceptible to rabies, the fox-adapted rabies prevalent in Europe is not very threatening to other species. The adaptation of the virus to the fox is demonstrated by the fact that in 1992, 2,047 of the 2,769 confirmed cases of rabies in the EU were in foxes, 126 in cats and 90 in dogs (House of Commons Agriculture Committee 1994: xxiv). Furthermore, the victims of a bite from a rabid fox can only pass the disease back to another fox. Indeed, there is no documented evidence of dog-to-dog or cat-to-cat transmission of rabies in Europe, and onward transmission of rabies by animals such as cows, sheep and horses is considered to be extremely unlikely. In other words, if a rabid fox bites a dog and gives it rabies that dog cannot infect a human with a bite – the disease may only be transmitted to another fox (Jackson 1992). The same principle applies to cats: the little girl in the MAFF poster is not at risk of contracting sylvatic rabies from her pet cat. The only animal the cat could transmit rabies to is a fox.

This poster is part of an actor-network involving the MAFF, domestic pets, rabies, and quarantine. The UK and Ireland are the only two EU Member States with quarantine systems. There is currently a debate in the UK about whether to replace the quarantine system for pets coming from within the EU with a system of pet vaccination.[6] Between 1972 and 1993, UK import licences were issued for 101,244 dogs and 49,476 cats. During this period there were no incidences of rabies occurring during quarantine amongst pets imported from within the EU (House of Commons Agriculture Committee 1994). In addition to animals which are imported legally, there are those which are smuggled into the UK. Yet since 1922 there have only been two confirmed cases in the UK of rabies in animals outside quarantine, and both occurred in animals which had previously been in quarantine, one of which was thought to have contracted rabies whilst inside quarantine. It has been calculated that if 5,000 dogs were randomly admitted to the UK each year from Germany, the EU country with the highest incidence of rabies, only one animal every 31 years could be expected to be incubating rabies (House of Commons Agriculture Committee 1994: xxviii). On the other hand, pet vaccination is cheaper and is reputed to be very effective; for example in France there have been no cases of pet vaccination failure for the last 10 years (House of Commons Agriculture Committee 1994: xxx). Yet 84 per cent of the UK population, fearful of rabies, support the current system of quarantine (Bonner 1995).

Fear of rabies in the UK may well be a manifestation of a form of xenophobia with historical roots in a colonial past in Africa and India. It is also a fear which is actively maintained in the present. Fear of rabies and the fear of the loss of national identity – politically through the erosion of sovereignty to Brussels; culturally through the circulation of goods, people, capital and services; and geographically through the physical link of the Channel Tunnel – mutually reinforce each other. Opposition to the EU abolition of point-of-entry border checks on livestock and opposition to the free movement of people (and their pets) can each be mobilised through the national fear of rabies, by those who have the political will to do so.

What the MAFF poster illustrates is the translation of fox rabies into a pestilential threat with the characteristics of canine rabies. Indeed, the representation of fox rabies as canine rabies in the poster is so successful that most people would be unaware that the translation had taken place – there is no indication in the poster that fox rabies is not identical to canine rabies. In this example, fox rabies is part of an actor-network in which the MAFF's strategy is to persuade travellers from France to put their pets into quarantine.

In other actor-networks, even those involving the UK quarantine system, fox rabies is represented differently, resulting in contradictory characterisations of fox rabies. Whilst all mammals are susceptible to rabies, the only species which are subject to quarantine are carnivores (of which dogs and cats are the most commonly imported), rodents (including mice, rats and hamsters), and primates (excluding humans). All pet cats and dogs, whether vaccinated or not, are required to undergo quarantine – unless they belong to a commercial breeder, in which case, if vaccinated, they can be imported without going into quarantine. The MAFF, which on the one hand has strongly opposed the replacement of quarantine with a system of vaccination for domestic pets, on the other hand has introduced a system of exemptions whereby pigs, cattle, sheep, goats and horses are not required to undergo quarantine. This means that while farmers and professional pet breeders can trade unhindered, the substantial costs of quarantine are imposed only on private citizens.

The above example illustrates how the identity of fox rabies is different in different actor-networks, sometimes being characterised as severely threatening, at others characterised as posing only a negligible threat. The identity of the actors – fox rabies, the quarantine system, the MAFF – are not *a priori* to the actor-networks in which they are enrolled, but rather are constructed through the process of translation.

I shall return to the translation of fox rabies in the Raboral V-RG story at a later stage, but first I shall explore the enrolment of the EU Institutions.

5. The Enrolment of the EU Institutions

For the EU Institutions to become enrolled in the Raboral V-RG actor-network, it was necessary for them to endorse the representation of rabies as a serious threat. However, there are reasons why the EU Institutions would rather represent fox rabies as being a minimal, rather than a severe, risk. This is because rabies impinges upon the practices and ideals of the Single European Act 1986 (SEA) which endeavours to establish the four fundamental freedoms – the freedom of movement of goods, services, people and capital – throughout the EU. Rabies poses a problem for the SEA on two counts. Firstly, there is public concern that pets accompanying their owners as they 'move freely' throughout the EU will spread rabies from the Member

States with rabies to rabies-free Member States. Secondly, the existence of rabies in some Member States could restrict the free movement of livestock, thus constituting a barrier to trade within the EU which, it is maintained, could jeopardise the profitability of EU stockfarming compared to its competitors. From this perspective, a rational strategy for the EU Institutions would be to enrol in actor-networks which represent fox rabies as being of minimal risk. Such a representation is apparent in Council Directive 90/425/EEC, one of the measures designed to establish the internal market, which establishes the principle of the abolition of veterinary checks at frontiers for trade in live animals.

On the other hand there are strategic advantages for the EU Institutions in endorsing the problematisation of rabies and enrolling in the Raboral V-RG actor-network. Firstly, Raboral V-RG is a genetically engineered vaccine manufactured by a European company. In a European Commission White Paper, Jacques Delors identified genetic engineering as one of three key technologies for economic growth, international competitiveness and employment in the EU (CEC 1994). However, the European Commission recognises that the genetic engineering industry suffers from 'certain problems' which 'require resolution' (see CEC 1991; Wheale and McNally 1993). In enrolling in the actor-network, the EU Institutions could help the genetic engineering industry to bring a product to market and in so doing legitimate the European Commission's confidence in the industry. Secondly, like any sovereign power, the European Institutions, particularly the European Commission, are liable to crises of legitimation. The representation of rabies as a severe threat to the people, livestock and pets of the EU combined with the characterisation of the EU Institutions as instrumental in its eradication portrays them in the role of hero, a role which helps to legitimate their sovereignty. Thirdly, were Raboral V-RG to be successful, the eradication of rabies from Europe would remove one of the obstacles to free trade and thus aid the completion of the internal market. Thus by enrolling in the Raboral V-RG actor-network, the EU Institutions could enhance their legitimacy through their heroic posture as protector of citizens from the threat of rabies, Raboral V-RG would become the flagship for the new genetic engineering technology that would bring economic growth, competitiveness, employment and prosperity to the EU, and the landmass of the EU would become one pure free zone in which livestock, people and their pets could circulate freely in accordance with the ideals of the single European market.

Thus it came to pass that in July 1989 Council Decision 89/455/EEC was adopted to provide financial support to set up large-scale pilot projects for the eradication or prevention of rabies in the wild life of the Community through the oral vaccination of foxes. Once enrolled in the Raboral V-RG actor-network, the EU Institutions had an interest in combining forces with the producers of the vaccine in order to translate both Raboral V-RG and fox rabies, and it is to the translation of Raboral V-RG that I shall now turn.

6. The Enrolment of Raboral V-RG

You will recall that Raboral V-RG is a cyborg: it is a hybrid genetic construct, a living organism, and a veterinary pharmaceutical product. You will also recall that the successful enrolment of Raboral V-RG would require that its only representation in the actor-network would be as a pharmaceutical product. Therefore the translation of Raboral V-RG must separate its identity as a vaccine which is effective in eradicating fox rabies from its identity as a novel genetic chimaera with unpredictable properties and its identity as a living virus with the potential to cause harm, spread, and mutate. Fortunately for the producers of Raboral V-RG, and for the EU Institutions who also have an interest in its successful enrolment in the actor-network, a method for such a translation of Raboral V-RG already existed in the form of the regulatory process.

The translation of Raboral V-RG by the regulatory process was a two-stage process. The first stage, which was its passage through Directive 90/220/EEC on the deliberate release of genetically engineered organisms, stripped Raboral V-RG of its identities as a novel genetically engineered construct with unpredictable properties and as a living organism with the potential to cause harm to the environment and human health. What emerged from the first stage of the regulatory process was an untested product. This product then entered the second stage – its passage through Directive 87/22/EEC – for its translation into a vaccine – pure, safe and efficacious – against fox rabies.

The translation was not straightforward. For the first stage, the technical dossier required under Directive 90/220/EEC had to be filled with convincing representations of Raboral V-RG as safe, biologically contained (that is, unable to spread or persist in the environment) and genetically stable. The compilation of such representations, involving the gathering of data in the scientific literature, laboratory studies and field releases, was expensive and time-consuming. The European Institutions assisted by supplying financial support for the assessment of Raboral V-RG under the Biotechnology Action Programme (BAP) and the Biotechnology Research for Innovation, Development and Growth in Europe (BRIDGE).[7] Even with such support, convincing data for the translation could not be gathered fast enough; at the same time as the technical dossier was being submitted to the European Commission (DG XI) for consent to place Raboral V-RG on the market (Rhone Merieux 1992), European Commission-funded researchers were reporting to the European Commission (DG XII) that they had not yet completed their risk assessment research, and that further work was necessary (see BRIDGE 1992; BRIDGE/BIOTECH 1993).

Another strategy for the translation of Raboral V-RG was to circumvent the problems of assessing the novel, unknown properties of the new genetically engineered virus by representing it as having properties no more harmful, infectious, or liable to mutation than a known virus – vaccinia virus. This strategy proved successful, and the representation of Raboral V-RG as vaccinia virus is manifested in the Commission Decision (93/572/EEC) to give consent to its placing on the market under Directive 90/220/EEC in which the safety of Raboral V-RG is expressed solely by reference to its identity with vaccinia virus.[8] In other words, the strategy of representing Raboral V-RG as vaccinia virus meant that what was evaluated was vaccinia virus rather than Raboral V-RG.

Although the identification of Raboral V-RG with vaccinia virus was a successful tactic for the regulatory process, it was not without problems because vaccinia virus is itself represented in the scientific literature as a minor human pathogen, with a broad host range, and a propensity to recombine readily with other pox viruses which may be present in the 'genomic ecosystems'[9] of the organisms it infects (see McNally 1995a, 1995b). Indeed, during the regulatory process, the German Competent Authority objected to the representation of Raboral V-RG as a safe organism on these very grounds (CEC 1993a). The basis of the German objections were that past experience with vaccinia virus provided evidence that Raboral V-RG posed a health risk to humans and non-humans, that it could be transmitted to and even colonise non-human species, that it could genetically recombine with related pox viruses, and that the technical dossier supplied by Rhone Merieux did not provide convincing evidence that these risks would not be realised.

However, these formal objections, limited as they were to one national Competent Authority, did not prevent the regulatory translation of Raboral V-RG because Directive 90/220/EEC is itself a chimaera: on the one hand it is a measure to protect human health and the environment, but on the other it is also a measure for the completion of the internal market. Thus the protection of the environment and human health is not paramount, but is conditional upon a majority vote among the Member States. So on the 17th September 1993 the Committee on the Releases of Genetically Manipulated Organisms (comprised of a representative of each Member State and of the European Commission) voted by a qualified majority to accept the Commission's Draft Proposal for a Commission Decision on Raboral V-RG, with only Germany voting against (CEC 1993b).

The passage of Raboral V-RG through Directive 90/220/EEC, stripped it of its identity as an unpredictable living organism with the potential to harm the environment or human health, and translated it into a product for use throughout the EU without further notification under the Directive. However, in order to become fully enrolled in the actor-network – to become a licensed, saleable, efficacious product – it had to undergo one further translation to become a vaccine which is safe, pure and effective against fox rabies. The method for this translation was Directive 87/22/EEC, which, like Directive 90/220/EEC, is a measure designed for the completion of the internal market.

This translation was also problematic, and required the application of a number of different methods before a reasonably satisfactory translation was achieved. Initially, in pre-release studies, the producers of Raboral V-RG measured efficacy by giving foxes bait containing the vaccine and then testing blood samples for the presence of anti-rabies antibodies. Those found to be 'seropositive' – that is their blood samples contained anti-rabies antibodies – were then exposed to rabies virus in order to test their resistance to infection and disease. There is a formula for estimating the proportion of a target population which must be effectively immunised to eradicate a given infection (see Anderson 1986; McNally 1995a, 1995b). This formula predicts that the proportion of the rural fox population which must be effectively vaccinated must be at least 80 per cent. However, even under these ideal conditions in which bait uptake was 100 per cent, only 76 per cent of the foxes fed with the bait were found to be seropositive (see Appendix 1). When this method was used to test foxes in the field in the 1989/90 campaign in France, only 51 per cent of the foxes tested were seropositive for neutralising antibodies (see Appendix 2). Thus these results made the measurement of anti-rabies antibodies an unsuitable method for the translation of Raboral V-RG into an effective vaccine against fox rabies.

Therefore the producers of Raboral V-RG abandoned this method of translation in favour of two other methods: the rate of bait uptake; and the number of rabies cases in the treated area. The first method equates the eating of the bait with immunisation. The bait was labelled with tetracycline, the presence of which in the jaws of animals was used as proxy measure of their having eaten the bait.[10] As the pre-release studies predicted (see Appendix 1), this method generated a higher measure of efficacy than measuring seroconversion. However, even this method failed to effect a convincing translation of Raboral V-RG into an effective vaccine; in the 1989/1990 Belgian field trials only 71 per cent of the foxes tested positive for having eaten the bait, a figure which is still lower than the 80 per cent required to eradicate fox rabies (see Appendix 3).

The second method involved monitoring the incidence of rabies in wild animals and livestock before and after the use of Raboral V-RG. The collection of data for this method was aided by the European rabies eradication programme (Council Decision 89/455/EEC) which makes rabies a compulsorily notifiable disease in all species. One advantage of this method is that it circumvented the problems of trying to meet an external standard of efficacy, namely the 80 per cent herd immunity described above. In the absence of an external standard, any decline in the incidence of rabies within the test zone, however small, and whatever it may be due to, could be used as evidence of the efficacy of Raboral V-RG as a vaccine against fox rabies in rural fox populations.

The authorisation procedure under Directive 87/22/EEC was initiated in November 1993 and completed in November 1994 following an evaluation of the safety, efficacy and quality of Raboral V-RG by a Special Working Party set up by the Committee for Veterinary Medicinal Products (CVMP). The outcome of the Working Party's Deliberations was that the CVMP issued a favourable opinion on Raboral V-RG, with Germany dissenting from the majority. The methods used for this translation are, however, not available in the public domain; unlike Directive 90/220/EEC, whose deliberations are bound by Directive 90/313/EEC on the freedom of access to environmental information, the assessment report and the reasons for the opinion in favour of granting Raboral V-RG's authorisation are not available under Directive 87/22/EEC (CEC 1995). However it was achieved, the favourable opinion marked an endpoint in the enrolment of Raboral V-RG into the actor-network.

7. The Enrolment of Fox Rabies?

The story might be considered to be complete at this stage. The EU Institutions have been enrolled and so has Raboral V-RG. But what about fox rabies? Has it been enrolled, has it yielded to Raboral V-RG and been banished from the EU? Well, not yet.

The method used for the translation of fox rabies is to distribute bait containing Raboral V-RG by aerial drops and then measure the incidence of rabies in wildlife and livestock species. Vaccination campaigns are underway in France, Belgium and

Luxembourg, twice a year, in autumn and spring, at a total annual density of 30 baits per km^2 per year. There are also campaigns to 'cleanse' a strip of up to 150 km wide inside the western borders of Poland and the Czech Republic (*The Economist* 1994). However, the translation of fox rabies is proving to be problematic: in 1992 it was predicted that the EU would be rabies-free by 1995 (Jackson 1992); in 1994, the European Commission predicted that it would be within 2 or 3 years; current estimates are that it is likely to have been eradicated by the turn of the century (House of Commons Agriculture Committee 1994: xxiv). But will it? In October 1994 it was reported that rabies was once again on the increase in Belgium in the very areas which had been subjected to the Raboral V-RG vaccination campaigns (Cranford 1994; Vita Vitalis, personal communication).

What can be done to translate these mutinous rabies viruses? The actor-network has only one response: more Raboral V-RG – the vaccination campaigns must be stepped up (Cranford 1994). (Of course it is possible that it was always part of the vaccine producers' strategy that it would *not* be totally eliminated by Raboral V-RG. For, from a Machiavellian perspective, what could be a cleverer strategy than enrolling the EU Institutions to use a vaccine that, because of its failure to eradicate rabies, requires permanent biannual usage?)

And what about Raboral V-RG? What is there to prevent this cyborg from mutiny, from resisting its enrolment as a safe predictable product, and expressing itself as a pathogenic, infectious, mutating organism? Absolutely nothing!

8. The Strategy

Like any actor-network, the Raboral V-RG actor-network I have described above is, of course, a fiction. I defined the actor-network, I identified the problem, I chose the actors, I selected the vocabulary, and I told the story. I am the enrolling actor.

And what is my strategy? I follow Latour:

> If science and technology are politics pursued by other means, then the only way to pursue democracy is to get inside science and technology, that is, to penetrate where society and science are simultaneously defined through the same stratagems. This is where the new Princes stand. This is where we should stand if the Prince is to be more than a few individuals, if it is to be called 'the People' (Latour 1988b: 39).

My strategy in constructing the actor-network I have described here is to bring this extraordinary, contradictory, and alarming story to a wider public who can make it their story and their concern, and perhaps bring about a halt to this madness.

Acknowledgement

I would like to express my appreciation to *Vita Vitalis* vzw, Grote Hondstraat 38, B2018 Antwerpen, Belgium, from whom information on the use of Raboral V-RG in Belgium may be sought.

Notes

1. "A cyborg is a cybernetic organism, a hybrid of machine and organism, a creature of social reality as well as a creature of fiction" (Haraway 1985: 65).

2. The sociology of translation is described and famously applied in Michel Callon's (1986) account of the 'domestication of the scallops and the fishermen of St Brieuc Bay'. The method employs three principles which are as follows. Firstly, 'generalised agnosticism' whereby the 'observer' or 'power analyst' must be impartial between actors engaged in controversy. Secondly, 'generalised symmetry' which demands that a common vocabulary be used to describe conflicting viewpoints. The third principle is 'free association' which requires the abandonment of all *a priori* distinctions between the natural and the social.

3. Nicolo Machiavelli (1469-1527) was a celebrated political and military theorist, historian, playwright, diplomat and military planner, whose most famous works are *The Prince* and *Discourses on the First Ten Books of Titus Livius*. For Machiavelli, rather than belonging to any one or any place, power is conceived as pure expediency and strategy; power is the "effectiveness of strategies for achieving for oneself a greater scope for action than for others implicated by one's strategies" (see Clegg 1989: 32). In *The Prince* Machiavelli offers a descriptive ethnography of power conceived in terms of its strategies.

4. Initially live viral vaccines were not included in the scope of the Directive, an omission which was criticised by Wheale and McNally (1989), and later addressed, see McNally and Wheale (1989).

5. How do the enrolling actors in our story – the producers of Raboral V-RG – construct the problematisation? Firstly, they merged the distinction between fox rabies and canine rabies. For example, they write, "Rabies infection of domestic and wild animals is a serious problem throughout the world" (Brochier et al. 1991: 520). Secondly, they draw military-style maps of the incursion of fox rabies from Eastern Europe and of its geographical distribution within the EU, and produce statistical tables to demonstrate its increasing incidence in livestock and foxes. Thirdly, they perform calculations of the average yearly costs of fox rabies in terms of treatment of humans, animal diagnosis, compensation to farmers for the culling of infected livestock and the culling of wild foxes, and they allude the costs of vaccination of domestic animals and the salaries of civil servants (Brochier et al. 1991: 522). Fourthly, they describe fox rabies as unyielding to methods of control other than vaccination: "Whereas rabies among domestic animals can be controlled by appropriate prophylactic measures, it poses a bigger problem in wildlife, and, until 1960, the only possible available means of control was considered to be the reduction of vector populations" (Pastoret et al. 1992: 165); however, "culling has not been effective, and the distribution of live vaccine baits is the only appropriate method for the vaccination of wild foxes" (Brochier et al. 1991: 520). Fifthly, they portray competing rabies vaccines produced by classical methods as having harmful 'side-effects', being pathogenic for rodents and liable to reversion to virulence (see Brochier et al. 1991). Finally, they claim that Raboral V-RG is effective against fox rabies, and to illustrate the susceptibility of fox rabies to Raboral V-RG they produce graphs of the incidence of rabies in wild animals and domestic animals before and after its use (see Flamand et al. 1990: 82).

6. Having abolished the system of dog licences in 1988, the administration of compulsory vaccination would be problematic and require governmental expenditure. Moreover, the 'quarantine industry' is an effective parliamentary lobby group.

7. Contract numbers: BAP 0381-F; BAP 0382-F; BAP 0368-B; BIOT-CT91-0289.

8. The relevant recital states:

> Whereas, the information submitted and the evidence from testing indicate in particular that the genetic modification of the virus is not expected to result in any post-release shift in biological interactions or host range or in any known or predictable effects on non-target organisms in the environment or in any increase

in pathogenicity as compared to the parental virus strain [Vaccinia virus, Copenhagen strain] and/or in any increase in the capacity of the Raboral V-RG virus to recombine with other related viruses (Commission Decision 93/572/EEC: 16).

9. The classical concept of the genome, as a stable and static blueprint of the organism, is inaccurate. The genome is an ecosystem: the DNA of cells and microbes is in a constant state of flux, caused through its rearrangement and duplication and the accommodation of DNA from external sources, in the form of invading viruses and plasmids. Transgenic manipulation depends upon the dynamic nature of cells and microbes, in particular their capacity to integrate pieces of DNA from external sources, duplicate them and express their messages as gene products. Genetic engineers exploit the intimate relationship between cells and microbes and their viruses and plasmids to assist them in transgenic manipulation. The dynamic nature of genomes and their intimate relationship with viruses and plasmids have important implications for the assessment of the risks of genetic engineering, including gene therapy (Wheale and McNally 1988b). For a fuller discussion of these ideas, see Wheale and McNally 1986, 1988a: Chapter 4, 1990b: Chapter 1. See also Goodwin and Jäger & Tappeser, in this book.

10. Tetracycline can be detected in animal bones by ultraviolet microscopy. Each bait contains 150 mg of tetracycline the purpose of which (according to Pastoret et al. 1992) is to serve "as a long term biomarker of bait uptake" (p. 198). After the vaccination campaigns, dead wild animals are collected from the vaccination area for post-mortem examination and laboratory testing. Jaws are taken from the foxes and other wildlife and stored at -200°C until testing. Thin transverse sections (300 micro-mm) are cut with a diamond saw and examined directly. Tetracycline incorporation in the bones is detected by ultraviolet fluorescence microscopy (Brochier et al. 1988).

References

Anderson, R. 1986. 'Rabies control: Vaccination of wildlife reservoirs.' *Nature* **322**, pp.304-305.

Bonner, J. 1995. 'Britain pussyfoots on pet passports.' *New Scientist* (3 June), pp.12-13.

[BRIDGE] Biotechnology Research for Innovation, Development and Growth in Europe 1992. *First Sectoral Meeting on Biosafety (Wageningen, 6-9th December)*, Brussels: CEC, pp.70-75.

BRIDGE/BIOTECH 1993. *Final Sectorial Meeting on Biosafety and First Sectorial Meeting on Microbial Ecology (Granada, 24th-27th October)*, Brussels: CEC, pp.94-100.

Brochier, B. et al. 1988. 'A field trial in Belgium to control fox rabies by oral immunisation.' *The Veterinary Record* (10 December), pp.618-621.

Brochier, B. et al. 1991. 'Large-scale eradication of rabies using recombinant vaccinia-rabies vaccine.' *Nature* **354** (19/26 December), pp.520-22.

Callon, M. 1986. 'Some elements of a sociology of translation: Domestication of the scallops and the fishermen of St Brieuc Bay'. In: J. Law (ed.), *Power, Action & Belief: A New Sociology of Knowledge?* (Sociological Review Monograph 32), London: Routledge , pp.196-233.

Callon, M., Law, J. and Rip, A. (eds.) 1986. *Mapping the Dynamics of Science and Technology*, London: Macmillan.

[CEC] Commission of the European Community 1991. *Promoting the Competitive Environment for the Industrial Activities Based on Biotechnology Within the Community* (III.A.3, 15th April). Brussels: CEC.

————. 1993a. *Comments on the notifications C/B/92/B28 & C/F/93/03-02* (Doc. XI/A/021/93, June). Brussels: CEC.

————. 1993b. *Committee on the release of GMOs to the environment established under Article 21 of Directive 90/220/EEC: Summary of the Decisions of the Committee at its 5th Meeting* (Doc. XI/707/93, 17th September), Brussels: CEC Unit XI/A/2.

————. 1994. *Growth, Competitiveness, Employment: The Challenges and Ways Forward into the*

21st Century (White Paper). Brussels: CEC.

[CEC] Commission of the European Community 1995. *Information Note: Antirabies vaccine for foxes 'Raboral'* (III/E/3/pb, 10th April). Brussels: CEC.

Clegg, S. 1989. *Frameworks of Power*. London: Sage.

Commission Decision 93/572/EEC 1993. 'Commission Decision of 19 October 1993 concerning the placing on the market of a product containing genetically modified organisms pursuant to Article 13 of Council Directive 90/20/EEC.' *Official Journal of the European Communities* (No. L 276), pp.16-17.

Council Decision 89/455/EEC 1989. 'Council Decision of 24 July 1989 introducing Community measures to set up pilot projects for the control of rabies with a view to its eradication or prevention.' *Official Journal of the European Communities* (No. L 223), pp.19-21.

Council Directive 87/22/EEC 1987. 'Council Directive of 22 December 1986 on the approximation of national measures relating to the placing on the market of high-technology medicinal products, particularly those derived from biotechnology.' *Official Journal of the European Communities* (No. L 15), pp.38-42.

Council Directive 90/220/EEC 1990. 'Council Directive on the deliberate release to the environment of genetically modified organisms.' *Official Journal of the European Communities* (No. L 117), pp.15-27.

Council Directive 90/425/EEC 1990. 'Council Directive of 26th June 1990 concerning veterinary and zootechnical checks applicable in intra-Community trade in certain live animals and products with a view to the completion of the internal market.' *Official Journal of the European Communities* (No. L 224), pp.29-39.

Council Directive 90/313/EEC 1990. 'Council Directive on the freedom of access to information on the environment.' *Official Journal of the European Communities* (No. L 158), pp.56-58.

Cranford, H. 1994. 'Belgian war on foxes as rabies reappears.' *The Daily Telegraph* (22 October), p.3.

The Economist 1994. 'Mad dogs and Europeans.' *The Economist* (26 November), p.58.

Flamand, A. et al. 1990. 'Monitoring the potential risk linked to the use of modified live viruses for antirabies vaccination of foxes'. In: I. Economidis (ed.), *Biotechnology R&D in the EC – BAP: Part I*. Brussels: Commission of the European Communities.

Haraway, D. 1985. 'A manifesto for Cyborgs: Science, technology and socialist feminism in the 1980s.' *Socialist Review* **80**, pp.64-107.

———. 1991. *Simians, Cyborgs, and Women: The Reinvention of Nature*. London: Free Association Books.

House of Commons Agriculture Committee 1994. *Health Controls on the Importation of Live Animals* (Volume I, Fifth Report). London: HMSO.

Jackson, C. 1992. 'Mad dogs and Englishmen: Britain has no need to fear rabies from the Continent.' *Kangaroo News* (October), p.13.

Kieny, M.P. et al. 1984. 'Expression of rabies virus glycoprotein from a recombinant vaccinia virus.' *Nature* **312** (8 November), pp.163-166.

Latour, B. 1988a. 'Mixing humans and non-humans together: The sociology of a door-closer.' *Social Problems* **35** (no.3, June), pp.298-310.

———. 1988b. '*The Prince* for machines as well as for machinations.' In: B. Elliot (ed.), *Technology & Social Change*, Edinburgh: Edinburgh University Press, pp.20-43.

———. 1991a. 'The impact of science studies on political philosophy.' *Science, Technology & Human Values* **16** (no.1, Winter), pp.3-19.

———. 1991b. 'Technology is society made durable.' In: J. Law (ed.), *A Sociology of Monsters: Essays on Power, Technology & Domination*. London: Routledge, pp.103-131.

Law, J. 1986a. 'Editor's introduction: Power/knowledge and the dissolution of the sociology of knowledge.' In: John Law (ed.), *Power, Action and Belief: A New Sociology of Knowledge?*, London: Routledge, pp.1-19.

———. 1986b. 'On the methods of long-distance control: Vessels, navigation and the Portuguese route to India.' In: John Law (ed.), *Power, Action and Belief: A New Sociology of*

Knowledge? London: Routledge, pp.234-263.

McNally, R. 1995a. 'Genetic madness: The European rabies eradication programme.' *The Ecologist* **24** (no.6, Nov/Dec), pp.207-212.

———. 1995b. 'Mad dogs or jackasses: The European rabies eradication programme.' In: P.R. Wheale and R. McNally (eds.), *Animal Genetic Engineering: Of Pigs, Oncomice and Men.* London: Pluto Press, pp.109-124.

———. 1995c. 'Eugenics here and now.' *The Genetic Engineer and Biotechnologist* **15** (2-3), pp.135-144

McNally, R. and Wheale, P.R. 1989. *The Environmental Consequences of Genetically Engineered Live Viral Vaccines,* Report to CEC DG XI, Contract Number B6614/89/91.

———. 1994. 'Environmental and medical bioethics in late modernity: Giddens, genetic engineering and the post-modern state.' In: R. Attfield and A. Belsey (eds.), *Philosophy and the Natural Environment.* Cambridge: Cambridge University Press, pp.211-226.

———. 1995. 'Bio-patenting and innovation: A new industrial divide?' In: O. Morrissey (ed.), *Biotechnological Innovation, Societal Responses and Policy Implications* (Proceedings of a Workshop hosted by the Centre for European Social Research, University College Cork, 6-7th April, supported by CEC DG XII), pp.7-17.

Pastoret, P.P. et al. 1992. 'Development and deliberate release of a vaccinia-rabies recombinant virus for the oral vaccination of foxes against rabies.' In: M.M. Binns and G.L. Smith (eds.), *Recombinant Poxviruses.* London: CRC Press, Chapter 5.

Rhone Merieux 1992. Notification No. C/B/92/B28, Raboral V-RG, Oral live rabies vaccine for foxes, in bait.

STOA 1992. *Bioethics in Europe.* Luxembourg: European Parliament.

Wheale, P.R. and McNally, R. 1986. 'Recombinant DNA technology: Re-assessing the risks.' *Science, Technology & Society Newsletter* (Summer).

———. 1988a. *Genetic Engineering: Catastrophe or Utopia?* Hemel Hempstead: Wheatsheaf.

———. 1988b. 'Technology assessment of a gene therapy.' *Project Appraisal* **3** (no.4, Dec), pp.199-204.

———. 1989. 'Quis custodiet ipsos custodes? How should we regulate the release of genetically engineered organisms?' *Rivista Giuridica Dell-Ambiente.*

———. 1990a. 'Genetic engineering and environmental protection: A framework for regulatory evaluation.' *Project Appraisal* **5** (no.1, March), pp.23-38.

Wheale, P.R. and McNally, R. (eds.) 1990b. *The Bio-Revolution: Cornucopia or Pandora's Box?* London: Pluto Press.

Wheale, P.R. and McNally, R. 1993. 'Biotechnology policy in Europe: A critical evaluation.' *Science and Public Policy* **20** (no.4, August), pp.261-79.

———. 1994. 'What bugs genetic engineers about bioethics.' In: A. Dyson and J. Harris (eds.), *Ethics and Biotechnology.* London: Routledge, pp.179-201.

Wheale, P.R. and McNally, R. (eds.) 1995. *Animal Genetic Engineering: Of Pigs, Oncomice and Men.* London: Pluto Press.

[WHO] World Health Organisation 1992. *Rabies Bulletin Europe* **16** (no.4), p.19.

Wiktor, T.J. et al. 1973. 'Antigenic properties of rabies virus components.' *The Journal of Immunology* **110** (no.1, January), pp.269-276.

Appendix 1: Pre-release studies of Raboral V-RG on foxes*

	First trial	Second trial	Total
No. of foxes fed with vaccine baits	18	11	29
No. of foxes positive for tetracycline	18		
Percentage of foxes positive for tetracycline***	100		
No. seropositive for rabies	15	7	22
Percentage seropositive for rabies	83	64	76
No. resistant to rabies challenge	15**	6	21
Percentage resistant to rabies challenge	83	55	72

*   Source: Pastoret, P. et al. (1992), pp.174-177.
**   Excludes one fox which did not seroconvert but was resistant to rabies challenge. If this fox is included, then the total percentage resistant to rabies challenge increases to 76% (22/29 x 100).
***   As you can see above, all 18 of the foxes in the first trial were positive for tetracycline, which illustrates that tetracycline as a proxy measure of vaccine efficacy, a measure which was used in later field trials, would tend to inflate the efficacy figures of the vaccine as measured by resistance to rabies challenge.

Appendix 2: Field trials of Raboral V-RG against fox rabies in France 1989/90*

No. of foxes tested	191
No. of foxes tetracycline positive	118
Percentage of foxes tetracycline positive	62
No. of foxes tested for seropositivity	59
No. of foxes found seropositive	30
Percentage of foxes seropositive	51

*   Source: Flamand, A. et al. (1990), p.83.

Appendix 3: Field trials of Raboral V-RG against fox rabies in Belgium 1989/90*

	1st Collection	2nd Collection	3rd Collection	Total
No. of foxes tested	23	86	79	188
No. of foxes tetracycline positive	17	52	64	133
Percentage of foxes tetracycline positive	74	61	81	71
Estimated percentage of foxes seropositive**				59

*   Source: Brochier, B. et al. (1991), pp.520-522.
**   In the pre-release studies (see Appendix 1), 83% of tetracycline positive foxes were seropositive for rabies. 83% of 133 = 110. Therefore, 110 foxes are estimated to have seroconverted to rabies, which is 59% of the total number (188) of foxes tested.

8

The Oxford Baculovirus Controversy – Safely Testing Safety?

Les Levidow

1. Introduction

In spring 1994, for the first time in Britain, there was a prolonged public controversy over the intentional release of a genetically modified organism. The GMO was a baculovirus with a gene inserted for a scorpion toxin, thus designed to kill moth larvae more quickly than the wild-type baculovirus does. Mass-circulation periodicals carried a proxy debate between proponents and critics of the release. Articles had headlines such as "Safety scare on eve of mutant virus test", "Will the scorpion gene run wild?", and "Trial an error?" (Watts 1994b, Coghlan 1994b, and Patel 1994, respectively).

The latter headline, with its pun intended, aptly hinted at the underlying dilemma: How can a field trial test hypothetical hazards, yet avoid harmful errors? According to international guidelines, GMOs should be made predictable by progressively decreasing physical containment. Releases should follow "a logical, incremental, step-wise process, whereby safety and performance data are collected" (OECD 1986: 29). In retrospect, these early guidelines deferred the question of how to collect meaningful evidence of safety or even why such efforts were warranted.

Some advisers cited the stepwise principle as a basis for statutory controls, for a precautionary approach, "which should allow safety issues to become part of the development of the technology" (RCEP 1989: 36). Accordingly, in 1990 the European Community and Britain adopted precautionary legislation that subjected all GMO releases to wide-ranging risk assessment criteria (EEC 1990; Levidow and Tait 1992; Tait and Levidow 1992). Such formal rules provided a framework for negotiating a series of acceptable steps.

For genetically modified crops, researchers and regulators continue to disagree

Trial an error?

A furore has erupted over field trials of a genetically modified virus. **Kam Patel** reports

Safety scare on eve of mutant virus test

Will the scorpion gene run wild?

somewhat about hypothetical hazards, while agreeing that these hazards cannot be adequately clarified by small-scale field trials (e.g., OECD 1993: 23-24). Recently it has been argued that longer-term hazards can be addressed only by monitoring larger-scale releases. Yet such releases may cause the sort of environmental damage that earlier precautions sought to prevent (Stone 1994).

Herein lies a dilemma: How can controls be relaxed on a field trial without already accepting the safety claims that the trial is intended to demonstrate? This question expresses a more widespread problem in the scaling up of any new technology. For clarifying technological hazards, innovators learn most when conducting what can be considered to be a real-life experiment: large-scale commercial use. For prior learning to occur, "the existing boundary conditions of laboratory science must be adapted to those of society" (Krohn and Weyer 1994: 174). That is, the lab must somehow anticipate and simulate realistic conditions – conditions that may cause harm.

For GMO releases, then, how can a veritable field laboratory be adapted to clarify hazards, both meaningfully and acceptably? How can field trials safely test safety? What counts as adequate evidence of safety to warrant taking a further step? Indeed, how is the word 'step' defined?

Such issues arose starkly in the baculovirus controversy. Rather than judge whether the releases were safe or desirable, in this article I analyze the dilemmas and value judgments involved in the regulatory procedure. My analysis draws upon scientific papers, risk assessment documents, mass-media reports, and research interviews with key participants. In these interviews, each member of Britain's advisory committee was speaking as an individual, on an anonymous basis. Staff at the Natural Environment Research Council's Institute of Virology and Environmental Microbiology (IVEM/NERC, Oxford) agreed for their comments to be individually attributed.

2. Crippling the Virus

A baculovirus can fatally infect a susceptible larva that ingests sufficient quantities of virus. In the case of a nuclear polyhedrosis virus (NPV), the protective protein coat is broken down in the larval gut. The virus multiplies in the gut cell nuclei and eventually reproduces the viral polyhedron coat, which are called occlusion bodies or polyhedra. The next generation of virus is released when the larva dies and liquefies. The virus may repeat this cycle and thus generate an epizootic (or epidemic). Requiring several days to kill the host larvae, baculoviruses are used more widely in forestry, where trees can tolerate and repair considerable pest damage, than in agriculture (Payne 1986).

The *Autographa californica* NPV (AcNPV) is named after the insect from which it was first isolated. This virus has an irregular host range within the Lepidoptera: The most susceptible species are members of the Noctuidae family, while members of other Lepidoptera families tend to be affected only by much higher doses of baculovirus than those that kill the most susceptible species. In recent years, the broad host range of AcNPV has attracted commercial interest (Payne 1986). Although mass produced by the agrochemical company Sandoz, AcNPV was not registered for commercial use in the United States until 1994, and it has not been proposed for registration in Britain.

In the 1980s AcNPV was developed as a model system for genetic modification at IVEM. The institute pioneered a precautionary approach, in both generating evidence of safety and consulting environmental groups. According to David Bishop, IVEM's director between 1985-1995:

> We have been cautious in our science, in a way that is probably unwarranted in terms of risk; we have done so because it is unprofessional for us to do otherwise. Indeed, our step-by-step approach has affected the regulatory procedures in general. In ten years from now, that careful approach may be seen as unnecessary for our baculovirus, but we would rather prove that it is unnecessary by establishing the scientific basis with a track record (David Bishop, interview, 25 September 1991).

Before conducting the first releases of a genetically modified AcNPV, IVEM sought to clarify the host range by testing various insect species, selected in consultation with the Nature Conservancy Council (NCC), a government-funded agency (Bishop et al. 1988: 153). According to the NCC director,

> We asked them [IVEM] to test a range of other species, which they did. The different reactions of very closely related butterflies illustrate the ecological unpredictability.... David Bishop's group are actually exemplars in the way they have tackled both the risk assessment and the publicity end of it (Derek Langslow, interview, 28 August 1991).

In testing the virus' host range, the insect species were chosen partly for their ecological importance, such as moths in the food chain of early-reared birds (David Bishop, interview, 10 August 1992).

IVEM also made efforts to inform local people about the releases. Bishop argued that physical and biological containment measures provided extra protection for an intrinsically safe release. He also cited the potential environmental benefits of eventually substituting a baculovirus for synthetic chemical pesticides. There was no reaction from local environmental groups.

The UK government's Health and Safety Executive (HSE) approved IVEM's proposed experimental design for the first releases of AcNPV. They were conducted in 1986 and 1987. AcNPV was genetically modified to incorporate a marker sequence, designed for tracking the virus'

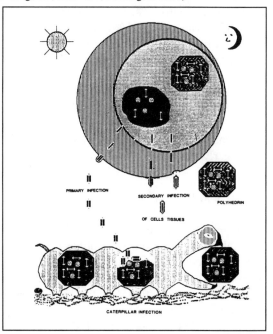

Schematic infection of a lepidopteran larva by a naturally-occurring, occluded, baculovirus such as AcNPV. Polyhedra (PIBS) are ingested with foliage (or other diet) and dissolve in the alkaline midgut releasing infectious virus particles. The viruses infect columnar cells in the midgut epithelium producing progeny that distribute the infection via the haemocoel to other cells and tissues. At the end of the infection large numbers of polyhedra are produced that are distributed from the larval corpse in the environment.
(Credit: Bishop et al. 1988)

persistence. Insect larvae were fed the virus and then placed on sugarbeet plants within subenclosures surrounded by Plexiglas™, which in turn was surrounded by netting. Monitoring showed that no virus escaped the subenclosures and that the virus persisted within the subenclosures for six months, after which the area was disinfected. No virus was detected inside the subenclosure after the formaldehyde treatment (Bishop et al. 1988).

For subsequent AcNPV releases between 1987 and 1989, IVEM deleted the gene for reproducing the polyhedron coat. Because the 'crippled' baculovirus would have a reduced persistence, some members of HSE's advisory committee said that they felt more comfortable about recommending approval. During that period, "Members thought the baculovirus harmless because it was engineered not to persist in the environment", according to one member (interview, April 1990). However, some had safety concerns about how the insecticide might be developed as a commercial product.

Such concerns were raised publicly by Friends of the Earth. Speaking as the organization's toxics campaigner at a 1988 conference, Andrew Lees argued that the IVEM trial releases gave a misleading impression of likely products from GMOs, because such products would not be modified for lower persistence. He called the crippled baculovirus "a Trojan horse for the genetic engineering industry" (Lees 1990: 138). He quoted ecologist Freda Taub: "Engineering [for] efficiency and safety ... cannot be addressed simultaneously."

At that conference, Bishop insisted that the two criteria were compatible: "We know that the 'crippled' virus is an efficient biopesticide" (Bishop quoted in Wheale and McNally 1990: 151). However, its efficacy had been demonstrated mainly in laboratory tests. In further field trials, under adverse weather conditions, the crippled baculovirus killed few of the preinfected larvae (IVEM 1991b; Possee et al. 1992: 49). Henceforth IVEM no longer attempted to reduce the persistence of the wild type; no longer would a crippled virus defer the safety arguments.

3. Scorpion-toxin Virus

For its next test organism, the IVEM team retained the gene for the polyhedrin coat. They also chose a more susceptible insect – the cabbage looper (*Trichoplusia ni*). This host would facilitate an epizootic and so better simulate agricultural conditions. Moreover, the team inserted a scorpion gene, so that the baculovirus would produce an insect toxin and thus kill the host faster, as demonstrated in laboratory tests (Stewart et al. 1991).

For the earlier releases, IVEM staff had emphasized the inbuilt biological safety measure; that is, the crippled virus "should be even safer than the natural virus" (Possee et al. 1990: 58). However, as IVEM shifted its research strategy back to the uncrippled virus, Bishop now downplayed any difference in safety:

> The polyhedrin-negative [crippled] virus is not preferable for the final product, but it would be preferable for setting up a model system to ask questions about hazards. We want to study how the virus moves among infected caterpillars by using a genetically marked virus. If the virus degrades away, there is no environmental risk, but studies showed that its half-life was too short to be useful. We had hoped that it would be effective, but it wouldn't be

efficient as an insecticide. So we are now going back to a marked polyhedron-positive virus. I cannot imagine any difference it would make for safety in the trial releases or in the final commercial product (Bishop, interview, 1991).

IVEM (1991a) proposed to test the new baculovirus for insecticidal efficacy under field conditions by spraying virus onto larvae placed on the cabbages. IVEM proposed to contain the subenclosures only with netting, not with Plexiglas™ as well. They wanted to use only a single-barrier containment, on grounds that no virus had been detected beyond the subenclosures in previous trial releases.

The IVEM (1991a) proposal was considered at the July 1991 meeting of the government's Advisory Committee on Releases to the Environment (ACRE). Some ACRE members expressed unease that the experimental design no longer had the inbuilt biological containment of the crippled virus or the double physical containment. Consequently, they attributed greater significance to the virus' undetermined ability to persist, as persistence could multiply any small risk over a long time period (two ACRE members, telephone interviews with the author, September 1991). Such an uncertainty resonated with the United Kingdom's precautionary manner of defining environmental damage – defined as the mere "presence of organisms" that are capable of causing harm (the Environmental Protection Act 1990: section 107; Levidow and Tait 1992).

Some ACRE members queried the host range of the AcNPV baculovirus. For example, "IVEM has tested only about five butterflies, but we [Britain] have about 20 of them, and butterflies are what people get excited about", stated one ACRE member (interview, April 1990). He feared that the IVEM release might jeopardize the public credibility of genetically modified biopesticides for the sake of pursuing one version that offered a relatively ineffective pesticidal control.

Regarding host range, IVEM's 1989 application had reported the results of laboratory tests on many Lepidoptera species, which were fed AcNPV at quantities of 10^2-10^6 virus occlusion bodies. For the unmodified virus, the permissive species included a rare UK butterfly, *Boloria euphrosyne*, the pearl-bordered fritillary (IVEM table excerpted in Rechaussat and Williamson 1989, Appendix M: 8-9). Yet IVEM's June 1991 application defined insects as permissive only if they were fatally infected by 10^5 occlusion bodies or less;

Cages used at field site for the release of the baculovirus expressing scorpion virus. Photo courtesy of Jenny Cory, Institute of Virology and Environmental Microbiology.

and its list of species included no butterflies (IVEM 1991a). IVEM's account of the host range led to arguments over how to define a permissive host (i.e., susceptible to lethal infection).

On behalf of the ACRE secretariat, the HSE asked IVEM why its latest application had a table of tested insects with fewer species than in 1989, omitting endangered species in particular. The HSE also expressed concern at the AcNPV's wide host range. The HSE suggested that IVEM revise the application (points cited in IVEM 1991b). The HSE also raised human health issues, for which it had statutory powers under the Health & Safety at Work Act 1974, but these issues did not arise again in the 1994 public controversy.

In his reply, Bishop stated that "[w]e do not wish to withdraw the application since we consider that the answers provided below clarify all the issues raised by ACRE." He argued that it was more prudent for a table of permissive species to be based upon repeat tests, comparing the modified virus with the wild type; for this comparison, the selection had been "biased towards those insect species which are more likely to be susceptible to the AcNPV" (IVEM 1991b). In these tests, IVEM investigated whether the genetic modification altered the host range of the unmodified virus, whose safety IVEM took for granted, though some ACRE members doubted this assumption.

In its June 1991 application, moreover, IVEM had already argued that any escaped virus could not cause an epizootic: "The modified virus would require a continuous replicative chain in permissive species to persist in any environment. This is considered to be an unlikely scenario" (IVEM 1991a). In its later reply to the HSE, IVEM emphasized "the physical containment", which would prevent any escape: An epizootic would be unlikely, "given these precautions" (IVEM 1991b).

In approving the release, ACRE would face a dilemma: It would need to assume either that any escaped virus could not cause an epizootic or that no virus could escape. Yet the latter rationale was awkward, because ACRE's judgments generally took into account the possibility of the confinement measures being disrupted (ACRE members, interviews with the author, 1990-1991). Indeed, such a scenario was implicit in assessing and regulating a release.[1]

During 1991-1992, the government had not yet implemented its statutory powers under the United Kingdom's 1990 Environmental Protection Act. This law would require each applicant to obtain an explicit consent from the UK Department of Environment (DoE), and it would require the government to disclose specified information from each release application (Levidow and Tait 1992). Unexpectedly, the 1990 Environmental Protection Act was not put into force until February 1993. For the baculovirus release, IVEM sent copies of its application to a list of local Oxfordshire organizations, but none expressed any concern; nor did journalists report the case.

IVEM was not legally required to obtain government permission but did seek informal approval. Finally, IVEM accepted an ACRE proposal to surround the experimental site with an additional rabbit-proof fence and water-filled trench (as later described in IVEM 1993). In April 1992, ACRE recommended approval of the release with the extra containment. As one member reflected, "We delayed the release for nine months, but for no longer.... Experimental protocols were traded off against uncertain risks – though that cannot be done for all risks" (ACRE member, interview, June 1992).

This trade-off provided a compromise within ACRE, as much as between ACRE and IVEM. In effect, some ACRE members had used the voluntary regulations in order to request more information relevant to the risk assessment of subsequent releases and in order to strengthen the physical safeguards on this one. According to one participant, "The ambiguous pre-statutory situation made it easier for ACRE to press these requests, without necessarily claiming that they were essential for the safety of this particular release" (ACRE member, interview, 25 January 1995).

This episode illustrated another convenient ambiguity – between public and scientific perception of risk. As ACRE members had privately commented at the time, their regulatory role was "to think as if we were members of the public" (Levidow and Tait 1993). This role meant translating unease into scientific criteria for evidence of safety, as in the baculovirus case.

4. Unintended Epizootic?

In parallel with Britain's regulatory procedure, scientists were discussing scenarios of an unintended epizootic. An ACRE member, Mark Williamson, extrapolated from the permissive dose in laboratory tests, in order to argue that the AcNPV's sporadic host range contradicts the European Community's directive on GMO releases (Williamson 1991). That is, its risk assessment criteria emphasize the "host range, including non-target organisms" of the organism that has been used to construct the GMO (EEC 1990: 23). On this basis, Williamson suggested that the AcNPV wild type should not be developed into an insecticide.

In response, a biopesticide specialist acknowledged that the safety concern would be warranted for a biological control agent designed to replicate repeatedly within infected insects in the environment. However, he argued that present research was instead designing baculoviruses as chemical-like pesticides, whose effectiveness would require repeated application. Moreover, the inserted toxin would kill the host faster, thus allowing less time for the virus to replicate; the faster kill would put the GMO at a competitive disadvantage relative to the wild-type virus (Hammock 1992). This assumption coincided with a theoretical model that predicts that a faster-killing virus would be less persistent than the wild type (Hochberg and Waage 1991).

IVEM's safety judgment rested upon similar assumptions about a competitive disadvantage, as well as about insect feeding behaviour. Thus, IVEM cited familiar facts, including past epizootic studies, for its safety claims:

> In realistic field conditions, it is difficult to see how each insect would find, much less eat, more than 10^1 virus particles at the second instar stage. More relevant than the technically "permissive dose" is the hundred years experience of epizootics. For example, when the Germans tried to use a baculovirus to control the gypsy moth, other species did not eat enough of it to set off an infection [an epizootic]. A dead caterpillar could produce 10^9 virus particles, but it would likely get diluted before another insect found that material. From our experience, the insect needs a susceptibility of 10 particles/cm^2 in order to set off an epizootic[2] (Bishop interview, 10 August 1992).

The above safety claims lacked empirical evidence for the genetically modified virus, or even for the wild-type virus, whose safety was taken for granted by IVEM. For example, how much virus would insects ingest, under field conditions? What difference would the scorpion toxin make? Could the virus generate repeated cycles of infection, harming nontarget organisms?

Although IVEM's 1991 application proposed to test efficacy alone, the trial release yielded some evidence relevant to safety. As expected, the insects died sooner from the scorpion-toxin virus than from the wild type; consequently, they produced relatively fewer virus particles, by an order of magnitude. Moreover, there were fewer secondary infections (i.e., of insects eating cadavers). This result may be because many infected insects became paralyzed and fell off the cabbage leaves, thus becoming inaccessible to other feeding larvae (Cory 1994: 19; Cory et al. 1994).

As the next step, IVEM (1994) proposed a five-year series of trial releases. In effect, these releases would investigate some of the safety concerns that ACRE members had voiced during 1991-1992. The experiment would place infected cadavers and noninfected larva on cabbage leaves and/or would spray the crop with virus. It would measure mortality and transmission rates among relatively less permissive *Lepidoptera* hosts that might undergo an epizootic; the results would allow assessing the invasive potential of the virus among populations of nontarget hosts. The trials would compare the behaviour of nonpermissive, semipermissive, and permissive insect species; the latter species was the *Trichoplusia ni* of the previous test.

For the 1994 release, IVEM chose a semi-permissive species, *Mamestra brassica*. IVEM had originally classified this species as non-permissive (Bishop et al. 1988: 155), then reclassified it as permissive, because it could be infected at doses of 10^5 virus particles (IVEM 1991a). IVEM finally reclassified the species as semipermissive (IVEM 1993: 72). The latter change resulted from a change in term usage (i.e., reserving the term "permissive" for species infected at 10^3 virus particles). Perhaps more significant, the first reclassification resulted from using laboratory tests with a more sensitive assay system, which found second instars to be rather more susceptible than third instars (Jenny Cory, February 1995, personal communication).

Thus the term 'semi-permissive' entailed a methodological indeterminacy in testing, classifying, and even selecting species.[3] In this case, more scientific knowledge (e.g., about the earlier instar) implied greater ecological uncertainty about its potential to sustain an unintended epizootic.

5. Contained Release?

ACRE members recommended approval of the new IVEM proposal in March 1994, and the DoE granted a consent in early April. The ensuing public controversy revolved around two related questions: Was the ecological uncertainty a rationale for conducting the releases or for discouraging them? And did their safety depend upon the physical containment?

In its public statement, IVEM explained that the releases aimed to "look at the effect of the genetically modified virus on alternative hosts and its longer-term survival in the environment" (advertisement in *Oxford Mail*, 5 March 1994).

Prominent scientists emphasized unacceptable consequences of the uncertainty that IVEM proposed to test: With its uncertain host range, the baculovirus posed environmental risks, especially to rare moths inhabiting a nearby nature reserve, Wytham Wood (Watts 1994a). As one critic later complained, "The advert says that this virus is specific, yet the object is to see if it persists in other caterpillars" (George Smith quoted in Coghlan 1994b).

English Nature (formerly the Nature Conservancy Council) discretely requested monitoring to ensure that the soil disinfection would be effective. They also queried the consequences of any virus escaping:

> If it is concluded that sufficient virus could escape to cause a lethal or sublethal effect on potentially susceptible species, then the risk assessment should consider the likely fate of the virus under such circumstances, and whether its establishment in the field via this route is possible (letter to DoE from English Nature, 28 March 1994).

The release met clear opposition from an environmental organization, the Butterfly Conservation Society (BCS), which stated in a letter to the DoE:

> Butterfly Conservation hope[s] to see research using this virus discontinued.... Potentially, this virus could breach the containment procedures at Wytham Wood field station and become established in the local soil and plant communities.... Given the virus' rather indifferent ability to protect cabbages, the risks involved in continuing the trial seem to massively outweigh any realistic benefits (27 May letter).

The society publicly opposed the release on grounds that "this modified virus could escape in sufficient quantity to become indigenous, seriously reducing Britain's population of butterflies and moths" (9 June press statement). BCS considered applying to the High Court for an injunction, on grounds that the regulatory procedure had not provided adequate opportunity for public comment (Coghlan 1994a). However, BCS did not succeed in persuading any other organization to join its protest – judicial or rhetorical (Nick Bowles, telephone interview, 25 August 1994). Nor did any scientist consistently oppose the release.

The BCS letter arrived just before ACRE met to reconsider the IVEM release application, which it had already approved in March. Following its review, ACRE issued a scientific rationale for its safety judgment: Namely, that "under the experimental conditions ... a sufficient number of virus particles could not enter the environment to permit recombination or to cause harm to populations of insects" (31 May statement in DoE public register). In effect, ACRE's statement answered the English Nature query: for this small-scale trial, members believed that any escaped virus could not cause an epizootic (ACRE members, interviews with the author, December 1994/January 1995). Thus, ACRE implied that the safety assessment did not depend upon the physical containment. Previously regulators had given a different impression, when they advised IVEM against labeling the experimental field, for fear of attracting environmental activists (Watts 1994a).

Why did the containment matter? The IVEM (1994) application claimed that the release posed "effectively zero risk" – because the design would securely contain the larvae and virus, as the previous experiments had done. Privately, the IVEM project leader Jenny Cory believed that an escape of the virus could cause no harm anyway: An epizootic would require a high concentration and succession of susceptible hosts, as provided in the crop monoculture of the so-called release enclosure. However, the IVEM application did not make this stronger claim for safety, because it would have been difficult to do so on a scientific basis, before obtaining additional evidence (Jenny Cory, IVEM, interview, 15 August 1994).

Eventually the stronger claim was made explicit by Bishop. In comments to journalists, he argued that escape of the virus could cause no harm: "At the doses likely to be encountered by caterpillars in the wild, the effective host range of the virus is limited" (Bishop quoted in Coghlan 1994b). By assuming that the ecological uncertainty entailed a minimal hazard, IVEM could justify further releases, designed to test that uncertainty.

In sum, this dispute revolved around the paradox of a contained release.[4] When IVEM reverted to the polyhedron-positive virus, earlier steps had provided evidence that they could contain and monitor the virus; however, only further releases could generate evidence that the virus was safe, regardless of containment. Within ACRE, the more cautious members had preferred to discourage the first of these releases in 1991-1992, but they proved able only to delay it. Having ambivalently accepted this new step, members eventually persuaded themselves that its safety did not depend upon containing the virus.

6. Stepwise Dilemmas

In terms of the stepwise procedure, was the baculovirus controversy a special case? Certainly it had unusual circumstances: Unlike most GMO releases in Britain, the wild-type organism was not yet in commercial use; some safety concerns applied as much to the wild-type virus as to the genetically modified virus. Yet the applicant took for granted the safety of the former, as an acceptable baseline for comparisons with the latter.

Also, the British government had not yet implemented its statutory regulation; regulators had no clear means of linking their discussions with some public debate. When such debate did erupt, two years later in 1994, ACRE was already bound by its earlier compromise. At that time, some critics attempted to discourage IVEM's research agenda, just as some ACRE members had implicitly done in 1991. In both episodes, however, the safety regulation largely substituted for

---

'Step-by-Step' Chronology*

Polyhedron-positive virus

1986-87: IVEM releases virus marked with non-functional marker gene; IVEM confirms ability to contain and monitor the virus.

Polyhedron-negative virus

1987-89: IVEM releases 'crippled' virus with a functional marker gene, but it proves ineffective as a pesticide in bad weather.

Polyhedron-positive virus with scorpion-toxin gene

June 91: IVEM proposes to test *efficacy* of its 'improved' virus; ACRE has difficult discussions; HSE corresponds with IVEM.

Apr 92: IVEM reaches compromise with DoE-ACRE on designing its 'contained' release, but MAFF approval is delayed until 1993.

Feb 93: EPA 1990 comes into force.

June 93: IVEM resubmits its 1991 application.

Aug 93: DoE grants a consent.

Sept 93: IVEM conducts the trial.

Feb 94: IVEM proposes to test *safety* of its 'improved' virus.

Apr 94: Public controversy begins.
           DoE grants a five-year consent.

May 94: ACRE reconsiders and confirms its original advice to DoE.

June 94: IVEM conducts the field trial.

Sept 94: Further disputes over the experimental protocol.

* See page 133 for abbreviations.

evaluating that agenda. Consequently the proposed release strained potential consensus on an acceptable step.

When some critics questioned the ultimate benefit of this research, also at issue was the entire agricultural model that guided it. Before the controversy erupted, the Butterfly Conservation Society had identified the main environmental threat as "modern intensive farming methods" that eliminate habitats friendly to wildlife (BCS n.d.). In a complementary way, a German biologist argued that society should redesign agriculture to avoid attracting pests, rather than perpetuate crop monocultures that may bring the increased use of engineered biopesticides (Altmann 1992). The scorpion-toxin virus may have symbolized not only a pollutant but also a commitment to intensive monoculture, which is taken for granted by biotechnology research and by its safety regulation.

Thus, despite the unusual features of the baculovirus controversy, it highlights difficulties that generally pervade the stepwise procedure for GMO releases. That is, hypothetical hazards can be meaningfully tested only by enhancing the prospects for realizing them. Formally speaking, European Community and UK law allows regulators to consider only risk; yet evidence of safety involves much discretion, which regulators cannot so readily separate from perceived benefits.

At least implicitly, safety tests are promoted through biotechnological claims to provide environment-friendly products. Given that they are largely designed to solve problems of intensive monoculture, the environmental issues have proven all the more controversial (Levidow and Tait 1991). In effect, safety judgments bear the burden of adjudicating a contentious technological development, by default of any democratic means for doing so (Beck 1992: 102-3, 212-214).

Thus, the baculovirus controversy may symptomize more general dilemmas for regulating GMOs. That is, how can a veritable field laboratory safely test safety – both acceptably and meaningfully? Indeed, how does it define safety? If safety regulation substitutes for any wider debate on research priorities, then how can the stepwise procedure achieve more than a resigned acceptance of this "progress"?

7. Postscript: Causal Limits of Risk Assessment

Risk assessment is not just part of the solution for handling GMO releases. It is also part of the problem. Its scientific basis remains value-laden, and accountable to the socio-environmental issues which it has the implicit burden of resolving. In this vein, the baculovirus episode illustrates several limits of risk assessment which entail implicit models of causality; these can be understood in terms of indeterminacy, simulation and teleology (as follows).

7.1 Indeterminacy

In order to improve the risk assessment of field trials, regulators sought more extensive lab tests on the virus' host range. Yet the test results depended upon the experimental design, e.g. the choice of species, the instar-stage, the quantity of virus, perhaps the mode of ingestion, etc. Criteria for 'permissive' species, as well as the empirical basis for classifying particular species, depended upon contingent knowledge – inherently limited by the specific conditions of its production, by its cause-effect assumptions, etc. Such limits allow risk assessment no clear boundary between reliable knowledge and uncertainty. In seeking knowledge to guide risk assessment, regulators face a methodological indeterminacy (Wynne 1992: 116).

7.2 Simulation

Even more so than the lab tests, the field trial was designed to simulate 'the boundary conditions of society' (Krohn and Weyer 1994), i.e. conditions conducive to an epizootic. The simulation was double-edged. On the one hand, it enhanced prospects for inadvertently causing environmental harm; it provoked arguments over whether the safety depended upon the physical containment. On the other hand, as a contained 'release', the simulation had a limited capacity to test hazards. Yet its designers expected to obtain experimental results which would vindicate the safety assumptions necessary for conducting a large-scale, true 'release'.

7.3 Teleology

In this case, GMO regulators took for granted the context of intensive monoculture, whose systemic problems predefine the performance criteria for benefits, e.g. for 'environment-friendly products' from biotechnology (Levidow and Tait 1991). By conceptually separating 'risk' from 'benefit', the regulatory procedure serves to naturalize intensive monoculture, the veritably man-made source of the potential for harm. Like science in general, risk assessment devises cause-effect models which conceptually exclude human purposes.

   In terms of Aristotle's four causes, scientific explanations emphasize the 'efficient' or 'moving' cause of potential effects – separated from the 'final' cause, from the *telos* which traditional knowledge attributed to natural phenomena (Proctor 1991: 41-42). In that vein, risk assessment limits itself to 'unintended, secondary, side-effects' – separated from the intended, primary effects for which organisms are redesigned. As a cultural construct, risk assessment is inherently limited by its role of separating efficient causes from final causes; it serves ideologically to limit choices for defining our problems differently, for directing innovation in other ways.

In risk controversy, then, at stake are not only the limits of risk assessment, but also the socio-political limits subtly reinforced by risk assessment.

Notes

1.   The United Kingdom defined a release broadly: the permitting of a GMO to leave one's control. Legally speaking, a GMO remains under the control of a person if biological and/or physical barriers are used for ensuring that the GMO either remains harmless or does not enter the environment (EPA 1990: section 107). Such ensuring is not taken for granted when assessing a proposed release.

2.   Note that assessing a larva's capacity to ingest virus may be further complicated by the phenomenon of a liquefied cadaver drying out on a leaf. A larva that consumes such a leaf

could be ingesting a relatively greater number of virus particles per quantity of leaf eaten (Mark Williamson, 1994, personal communication).

3. As a social-science term, 'indeterminacy' denotes inherent unknowns about causal chains, and thus unknowns about the conditions of validity for our present knowledge. An indeterminacy pervades apparently 'technical' criteria for testing and predicting hazards (Wynne 1992: 116).

4. Given that the IVEM application emphasized the physical containment, it is understandable that one public-interest group posed the question: "Why was the research not planned in a laboratory under contained use conditions?" (Genetics Forum 1994). Of course, this would require an enormous laboratory; under such conditions, moreover, the experimental data would have less relevance for subsequently relaxing containment. Some critics suggested that IVEM should develop a more subtle kind of biological containment (Coghlan 1994b). In fact, IVEM's Dutch partners were already deleting AcNPV genes that have a role in viral persistence but that are not essential for reproducing the polyhedron coat protein (Mons and Vlak in DGXII 1992: 80). Perhaps such a semipersistent virus could avoid the regulatory problems that IVEM encountered. However, IVEM regarded this containment measure as inadequate, because the baculovirus could undergo a coinfection and reacquire the deleted gene; thus IVEM preferred to demonstrate that the virus is safe (Jenny Cory, IVEM interview, 15 August 1994; compare Cory 1991, Cory in DGXII 1993: 111). Thus IVEM cited a precautionary reason for rejecting a potential safety measure; there was little apparent scope for the baculovirus to be designed differently.

Acknowledgments

This essay is reprinted from *BioScience*, volume 45: 545-51, with only minor changes, except for the extra Postscript, on which Ad van Dommelen provided helpful comments.

For the *BioScience* version, helpful editorial comments were provided by several participants in this episode: David Bishop, Jenny Cory, and Rosie Hails (IVEM/NERC); Mark Williamson (University of York; former member of ACRE); Alastair Burn and Ian McLean (English Nature, formerly the Nature Conservancy Council). The text was also checked by John Beringer (chairman of ACRE). However, the final text remains the responsibility of the author alone.

This article arises from two related studies funded by Britain's Economic and Social Research Council: "Regulating the Risks of Biotechnology", during 1989-1991, project number R000 23 1611; and "From Precautionary to Risk-Based Regulation: the Case of GMO Releases", during 1995-1996, project number L211 25 2032.

Abbreviations

AcNPV:	Nuclear Polyhedrosis Virus isolated from *Autographa californica* (alfalfa looper)
ACRE:	Advisory Committee on Releases to the Environment
DoE:	Department of the Environment
EPA:	Environmental Protection Act 1990
HSE:	Health and Safety Executive
MAFF:	Ministry of Agriculture, Food and Fisheries
IVEM:	Institute of Virology and Environmental Microbiology

References

Altmann, M. 1992. 'Biopesticides turning into new pests?' *Trends in Evolution and Ecology* **7** (2), p.65.

Beck, U. 1992. *Risk Society: Towards a New Modernity*. London: Sage.

[BCS] Butterfly Conservation Society. n.d. Form letter. Colchester (UK): Butterfly Conservation Society.

Bishop, D., Entwhistle, P., Cameron, I., Allen, C., Possee, R. 1988. 'Field trials of genetically engineered baculovirus insecticides.' In: M. Sussman, C. Collins, F. Skinner, D. Stewart-Tull (eds.), *The Release of Genetically-Engineered Microorganisms*. London: Academic Press, pp.143-179.

Coghlan, A. 1994a. 'Legal sting for caterpillar virus.' *New Scientist* (11 June), p.7.

―――. 1994b. 'Will the scorpion gene run wild?' *New Scientist* (25 June), pp.14-15.

Cory, J. 1991. 'Release of genetically modified viruses.' *Reviews in Medical Virology* **1**, pp.79-88.

―――. 1994. 'Genetically engineered biopesticides.' *NERC News* (July), pp.18-20.

Cory, J., Hirst, M., Williams, T., Hails, R., Goulson, D., Green, B., Carty, T., Possee, R., Cayley, P., Bishop, D. 1994. 'Field trial of a genetically improved baculovirus insecticide.' *Nature* **370**, pp.138-140.

[DGXII] Directorate General XII: Science, Research and Development. 1992. *First Sectoral Meeting on Biosafety* [BRIDGE programme]. Brussels: Commission of the European Communities, DGXII.

―――. 1993. *Final Sectoral Meeting on Biosafety and First Sectoral Meeting on Microbial Ecology* [BRIDGE + BIOTECHnology programmes]. Brussels: Commission of the European Communities, DGXII.

[EEC] European Economic Community. 1990. 'Council directive on the deliberate release to the environment of GMOs.' *Official Journal of the European Communities* (L 117 – 8 May), pp.15-27.

EPA 1990. *Environmental Protection Act*. London: HMSO.

Genetics Forum 1994. 'Oxford scorpion gene virus update.' *The Splice of Life* **1** (5), pp.15-16.

Hammock, B. 1992. 'Virus release evaluation.' *Nature* **355**, p.119.

Hochberg, M., Waage, K. 1991. 'Control engineering.' *Nature* **352**, pp.16-17.

[IVEM] Institute of Virology and Environmental Microbiology. 1991a. 'Field studies on a polyhedron-positive AcNPV containing an insect-specific scorpion toxin gene.' (June), Oxford: Institute of Virology and Environmental Microbiology.

―――. 1991b. 'Trial release of genetically modified virus pesticide.' (8 August letter to HSE).

―――. 1993. 'Field test of the efficacy of a polyhedron-positive AcNPV containing an insect-specific scorpion toxin gene: Information to be included in the public register.' (June), Oxford: Institute of Virology and Environmental Microbiology.

―――. 1994. 'Field studies on a polyhedron-positive AcNPV containing an insect-specific scorpion toxin gene: Information to be included in the public register.' (February), Oxford: Institute of Virology and Environmental Microbiology.

Krohn, W. and Weyer, J. 1994. 'Society as a laboratory: The social risks of experimental research.' *Science and Public Policy* **21** (3), pp.173-183.

Lees, A. 1990. 'Pandora's genes: The Trojan Horse of bioengineering.' In: P. Wheale and R. M°Nally (eds.) *The Biorevolution: Cornucopia or Pandora's Box?* London: Pluto, pp.135-142.

Levidow, L. and Tait, J. 1991. 'The Greening of Biotechnology: GMOs as Environment-friendly Products.' *Science and Public Policy* **18** (5), pp.271-280.

―――. 1992. 'The release of genetically modified organisms: Precautionary legislation.' *Project Appraisal* **7** (2), pp.93-105.

―――. 1993. 'Advice on biotechnology regulation: The remit and composition of ACRE.' *Science and Public Policy* **20** (3), pp.193-209.

[OECD] Organization for Economic Cooperation and Development 1986. *Recombinant DNA Safety*

Considerations. Paris: OECD.

[OECD] Organization for Economic Cooperation and Development 1993. *Field Releases of Transgenic Plants, 1986-1992: An Analysis.* Paris: OECD.

Patel, K. 1994. 'Trial an error?' *Times Higher Education Supplement [The Higher]* (8 July).

Payne, C.C. 1986. 'Insect pathogenic viruses as pest control agents.' *Fortschritte der Zoologie* **32**, pp.183-200.

Possee, R., Allen, C., Entwhistle, P., Cameron, I., Bishop, D. 1990. 'Field trials of genetically engineered baculovirus insecticides.' In: *Risk Assessment in Agricultural Biotechnology, Proceedings of the International Conference.* (August 1988), Oakland, CA: University of California, pp.50-60.

Possee, R., King, L., Weitzman, M., Mann, S., Hughes, D., Cameron, I., Hirst, M., Bishop, D. 1992. 'Progress in the genetic modification and field release of baculovirus insecticides.' In: D. Stewart-Tull and M. Sussman (eds.) *REGEM2: The Release of Genetically-Engineered Microorganisms.* London: Plenum Press, pp.47-58.

Proctor, R. 1991. *Value-Free Science? Purity and Power in Modern Knowledge.* Cambridge, MA: Harvard University Press.

[RCEP] Royal Commission on Environmental Pollution. 1989. *13th report: The Release of Genetically Engineered Organisms to the Environment* (Cm 720). London: Her Majesty's Stationery Office.

Rechaussat, L. and Williamson, M. 1989. *Final report on a feasibility study on the establishment of a European biotechnology environmental release database.* Brussels: CEC, DGXII.

Stewart, L., Hirst, M., Ferber, M., Merryweather, A., Cayley, P., Possee, R., Bishop, D. 1991. 'Construction of an improved baculovirus insecticide containing an insect-specific toxin gene.' *Nature* **352**, pp.85-88.

Stone, R. 1994. 'Large plots are next test for transgenic crop safety.' *Science* **266**, pp.1472-1473.

Tait, J. and Levidow, L. 1992. 'Proactive and reactive approaches to regulation: The case of biotechnology.' *Futures* **24** (3), pp.219-231.

Watts, S. 1994a. 'Genetics row fuelled by scorpion's venom.' *The Independent* (17 May).

———. 1994b. 'Safety scare on eve of mutant virus.' *The Independent* (26 June).

Wheale, P. and McNally, R. (eds.) 1990. *The Biorevolution: Cornucopia or Pandora's Box?* London: Pluto.

Williamson, M. 1991. 'Biocontrol risks.' *Nature* **353**, p.394.

Wynne, B. 1992. 'Uncertainty and environmental learning: Reconceiving science and policy in the preventive paradigm.' *Global Environmental Change* (June), pp.111-127.

9

Deliberate Release of Genetically Modified Organisms: Applying the Precautionary Principle

Soemini Kasanmoentalib

1. Introduction

The regulatory system of the deliberate release of genetically modified organisms (GMOs) is said to fit well with the precautionary principle. The gist of the principle is that in facing uncertainties we are morally obliged to take a precautionary stance in decision-making. This presupposes that the scientists involved should be explicit about uncertainty and ignorance. Unfortunately scientists often disagree about uncertainties. In this article I argue that the precautionary principle then requires us to give the benefit of doubt to those who voice uncertainties. Considering the release of GMOs I argue that the regulatory system is not precautionary in this respect.

2. The Precautionary Principle

In the last decade the precautionary principle emerged as a guiding idea in the discourse on environmental policy. Like sustainability, its ally in the discourse, precaution is not a precise concept. The principle covers various loosely interconnected key notions of environmentalism, which belong to different perspectives on decision-making and ecological economics. Adherents of the principle put emphases on the limited power of science to predict ecological impacts of human interventions in nature, and on the hidden costs of interventions for future generations.

Intuitively, precaution is a sound guideline for actions of all kinds. We take precautions in our daily lives as a matter of course. Even animals do that, within their range of possible behaviours. If I do not know whether the kettle on my stove is hot, I cautiously touch its grip before picking it up, to avoid burning myself. Precaution is a guideline in merely practical acts and in acts with moral implications. Thus, when we are not sure about the consequences of acts, we often postpone acts to decrease uncertainty about consequences, and we might refrain from acts if uncertainties remain high.

At the level of collective decisions on human interventions in nature with wider impacts, the precautionary principle recommends that in the case of doubt and/or shortage of information and scientific understanding about environmental consequences, we should err on the safe side. However, the principle doesn't specify the degree of caution. We might proceed cautiously or refrain from action entirely. The degree of caution depends on an evaluation of the severity and the scope of the impacts. Decision-making thus remains dependent on scientific knowledge and advice. To exercise caution we need factual information and science is one of the important sources of information. The principle tells us that the less we know, the more precautionary we should be.

The precautionary principle could get a foothold in regulation in particular in the international context, where it is a vital theme. Environmental pollution and depletion of resources have no regard for national boundaries and require cooperation between states. Nowadays the precautionary principle is so often referred to in international declarations about the environment that it is considered as a normative principle of customary international environmental law (Cameron and Abouchar 1991: 14; Hey 1992). The wording of the precautionary principle as it survived through the different declarations and agreements from the Bergen Conference on *Action for a Common Future* in 1990 to the *Rio Declarations* and the *Australian International Agreement on the Environment* in 1992 is:

> In order to achieve sustainable development, policies must be based on the precautionary principle. Environmental measures must anticipate, prevent, and attack the causes of environmental degradation. Where there are threats of serious or irreversible damage, lack of full scientific certainty should not be used as a reason for postponing measures to prevent such environmental degradation (Bergen Conference 1990: *supra* note 6 at art.7).

The principle requires states to take preventive or corrective measures even in the absence of sufficient scientific evidence of a causal link between a suspected factor and the adverse effects observed (or even before any effect is observed at all).

The depletion of the ozone-layer and global climatic change are cases where the application of the precautionary principle led to international agreements, about the banning of CFCs and about reduction of CO_2 emissions, respectively, in the absence of any scientific certainty or consensus (Churchill and Freestone 1991). The most extensive application of the precautionary principle was the declaration of the 2nd International North Sea Conference in 1987, which contained concrete and ambitious decisions regarding the protection of the North Sea environment. It took the ethical stand that dumping at sea, in particular of persistent and bioaccumulative toxic chemicals, represents a risk to other nations and future generations which is no longer justifiable. It meant a reversal of the long-standing assumption that states are free to use the oceans for waste disposal if there is no proof of likely harm (Boyle 1992).

The precautionary principle is particularly relevant whenever the chance for some negative event is low and/or unknown but the potential consequences of that event might be disastrous and/or definite. The protection of biodiversity is proposed as a case where the precautionary principle should be applied with stringency because of the irreversibility of the extinction of species (Myers 1993). The deliberate release of GMOs into the environment too seems to be an eligible case for a strong application of the precautionary principle. The risks involved may be low – though that is far from clear – but they are potentially far-reaching.

3. The Moral Core of the Precautionary Principle

Most researchers writing on the application of the precautionary principle complain about the insufficiency of the definitions of precaution, which provide few, if any operational guidelines. A lot of discussion in the past circled around the question of the principle's status. Is it a scientific norm or an ethical principle? Agreement exists nowadays that the precautionary principle is not a matter of science alone, since it is a political and value-laden statement expressing a fundamental shift in attitude of the general public to the environment (O'Riordan and Cameron 1994; Dover and Handmer 1995).

In my opinion the precautionary principle is an ethical principle, which in application to concrete cases must rely on scientific information. It shares this feature with generally acknowledged basic ethical principles such as autonomy, justice, non-maleficence and beneficence (Beauchamps 1989). Like these principles it is intrinsically connected with moral values, in this case environmental well-being and the avoidance of irreversible harm.

The principle could thus be regarded as an extension of the ethical principle of non-maleficence, which envisages harm to others as a restriction on individual freedom and autonomy of actors. The scope of application of the principle of non-maleficence is extended at the side where the consequences are suffered to include nature and future human generations. Its extension from humans to non-human beings and nature is implicitly committed to a bioethics which recognizes that vulnerable ecosystems should be protected because they have an intrinsic value. Intergenerational justice represents another moral commitment. In addition to this, the range of possible agents is extended from the individual moral actor to collectives (agencies, governments) (Atfield 1995).

As an ethical guideline the precautionary principle does not allow of direct application in policy. Neither can it prescribe specific actions or solve ethical and socio-economic dilemmas in environmental decision-making. It cannot replace the process of balancing benefits and risks. Decisions presuppose that we know what consequences are (un)acceptable or (un)desirable. The precautionary principle itself does not provide this knowledge. The nature of 'serious' environmental damage and 'irreversible' environmental damage will thus be subject to intense debate. Judgments on seriousness and irreversibility will depend on moral and other contextual factors. Even the principle's implicit relationship to moral values such as the intrinsic value of nature and intergenerational justice is contentious.

I will not take sides in these matters. Instead I will focus on problems with uncertainty that must be solved to make the principle workable. On a higher level than where differences of opinion on values exist, the precautionary principle can be perceived as a reasonable presumption against uncertainty.

4. Recognizing Uncertainty and Ignorance

The principle as a guideline for decision-making has far-reaching implications for science and scientists involved in policy. The principle says that it is morally irresponsible to take uncertain risks. The guideline it provides is that, the less we know, the more precautionary we should be.

The shift in perspective to uncertainty is often explicated as the requirement that the burden of proof should be on those whose actions might result in unacceptable damage to ecosystems. Environmentalists welcome the precautionary principle because now the benefit of doubt befalls on the environment rather than the polluter, as in the past, when "absence of evidence has been used to equate to evidence of absence, when ecological impacts are considered" (Earle 1992: 184).

Ecologists standing up for environmental protection had the problem that because of the complexity of ecological systems it is extremely difficult to obtain hard causal evidence. Most cases in which ecologists succeeded to pinpoint the offender were strokes of luck. The discovery that PCB's in very low concentrations had a fatal impact on the immune system of seals in the Waddensea is an example of mere luck.

Others criticise the reversal of the burden of proof as being excessively rigid. The precautionary principle is said to be conservative in favour of the status quo, because you can never be certain of no risk or absolute safety. For this reason, some regard the principle as 'unscientific' because it does not discriminate between activities which involve 'real' risks and those which do not. They argue that judgments should not be based on 'suspicion' but on 'scientific evidence'.

The principle seriously confuses scientists and risk assessors when they are asked to produce positive scientific evidence. Actually what is at stake is the traditional notion of scientific 'objectivity' (Gray 1990; Hunt 1994). According to O'Riordan and Jordan, the principle is profoundly radical and potentially very unpopular, because it challenges the scientific method in its normal reliance on experimentation, hypothesis testing, consistency within a disciplinary context and predictability (O'Riordan and Jordan 1995).

The precautionary principle asks from scientists to make explicit what is uncertain and not (yet) known or essentially unknowable about irreversible damage and about long-term negative ecological effects. In these areas the limitations of science are the strongest. There is a lot of controversy about the uncertainties of the environmental effects involved.

I will now look at how the regulatory system deals with uncertainties in deliberate releases of GMOs. Is the system really precautionary? To answer this question, we should take sides in the prevailing controversy over uncertainties. I argue that we should take sides with ecologists who emphasize uncertainties. This implies that the current regulatory system is not precautionary.

5. The Current Regulation of GMOs

The 1990 European Community directives on the contained use and the deliberate release of GMOs take a precautionary approach to environmental risk as a starting point in line with the Maastricht Treaty art. 130 r (Cameron and Abouchar 1991; Lake 1991). Each member state is required to enact appropriate legislation within this framework. Reputedly, the regulation of GMOs has been precautionary from the outset. Genetic modification is considered as the first case of a large-scale technology subject to a scrutinous precautionary approach since the negative experience with nuclear energy. In the initial phase of the development of the rDNA techniques, since the Asilomar conference in 1975, the scientific community voluntarily imposed restrictions on research. The biotechnology industry used to comply with attempts at a legitimate regulation, recognizing the importance of public support for these technological innovations (Levidow and Tait, 1992).

The main reason why the current regulatory system is considered to be precautionary is that a risk assessment in advance is required to get permission for any experimental release and for any commercialization of GMOs. In addition to this, to ensure safety of GMOs the system for risk assessment is based on the generally accepted case-by-case review and step-by-step approach.

The questions the scientific community has focused on are whether the environment can be disturbed by GMO releases, whether or not GMOs might become pests, and whether genes can be transferred to other species with harmful effect. In most countries these key questions form the framework of environmental risk assessment in the regulation of GMO-release.

The views of scientists on these issues of environmental risks differ substantially and at the most fundamental level. In the next section I consider how the disagreements affect applications of the precautionary principle.

6. Emphasis on Traits

Every proposal for a release of GMOs has to be accompanied by a risk assessment in the form of answers to a list of questions. These questions refer to characteristics of the gene, of the donor species, of the receiving species and of the specific environment in which the GMO will be released, and the risks involved in these traits. The risks are only classified as high or low. No criteria are specified for quantitative measures of damage and scales of time or space are disregarded. The risk assessment is very much 'trait-oriented'. That is, traits of GMOs serve as a basis for inferences – indeed guesses – concerning persistence in the environment, invasiveness, competitiveness, weediness, and gene transfer.

These features of existing formal procedures indicate that the knowledge required is severely limited. Most ecological risk assessments of GMOs hardly improve on the limited formal requirements. The introduction of transgenic maize, for example, has been considered safe on the mere ground that maize cannot survive the British winter. The introduction of transgenic oilseed rape has likewise been considered safe, on the ground that crop plants should not compete with native vegetation, which supposedly comprises more effective competitors.

According to the ecologist Crawley this line of reasoning reflects a widespread misconception about ecology. Competitiveness and invasiveness are not intrinsic traits of species. They are highly context-specific, since they depend on all kinds of environmental factors. The possibility that a crop would become competitive depends crucially on the nature of the location, overall weather in the relevant year (wet or dry, hot or cold), the identity of the competitors and their condition and so forth (Crawley 1994, Hengeveld 1994).

Ecologists have stressed that an assessment of the invasion risk is so complicated that routine extrapolation from the existing knowledge of the genes is impossible. There is an extensive literature on biological invasions which demonstrates the idiosyncrasies and unpredictability of effects of introduction on the structure and nutrient flows of ecosystems. There are dramatic examples of declining of species diversities where the original community is replaced by species poor stands with single dominating new species. Ecologists do think that it is impossible to predict the behaviour of a particular transgenic organism after the release, because present knowledge of relevant parameters is too poor (Simberloff 1991; Bartsch et al. 1993).

Unforeseen accidents illustrating lack of knowledge have happened in the past. Cultivated species have escaped the boundaries of plots and become serious pests. This happened in the USA during Mississippi floods of July 1993. Half an acre of insect-resistant transgenic corn was uprooted and transported to become part of the giant downstream river system (Munson 1995). Sorghum in Africa has been known to hybridise with weedy relatives to produce a serious pest called 'shattercane' (Hatchwell 1989). Transgenic fish in aquaculture and insects for biological control have escaped the containments (Chourrout 1994; Hindar 1994; Ehler 1991).

The existing method of risk assessment reflects a fundamental belief of the genetic engineering researchers, which can be summarized as follows. Genetic engineering is a refined and precise technique, much more so than the traditional methods of plant breeding of which it is an extension. Because GMOs represent the transfer of well-defined genes, the risks are predictable and can therefore be controlled. Genetic engineering researchers have apparently reached consensus about an assumption they often air, that risks for the environment are primarily a function of the characteristics of the product of engineering (Dale 1993; Miller 1994; Schell 1994).

This assumption, which is highly questionable from the point of view of ecology, amounts to the view that the behaviour of the phenotype can be inferred from precise knowledge of the genotype, since we are dealing with minor genetic changes.

The opposing scientific views have few points of contact. The following opposing statements, pronounced during the same conference, illustrate this well. "The better one understands the function of the DNA that is being introduced, the better one will be able to predict the consequences" (Schell 1994: 23) *versus* "It is unlikely that we shall ever be able to predict the consequences of small genetic changes on population-level behaviour" (Crawley 1994: 33).

This stalemate has been characterized as a clash of different disciplinary paradigms between molecular geneticists and ecologists (Krimsky 1991) and as a gulf between a reductionist approach of laboratory scientists and a more holistic approach of field re-searchers. It represents an enduring epistemic controversy between experts (von Schom-berg 1993). Regarding such controversies, the precautionary principle should recommend us to take sides with those who voice uncertainties and doubt, ecologists in the present case. However, the existing risk assessment procedure, gives more weight to the views of the laboratory-based scientists. Therefore alone, the current regulatory system is now anything but precautionary.

7. Case-by-case and Step-by-step

The case-by-case approach implies that every new transgenic organism has to go through the whole procedure. It has been advocated by ecologists with the argument that generalizations over different species are very difficult (Sharples 1987; Tiedje et al. 1989). Because until now no unexpected harms have been observed in experiments, the current tendency is to apply the procedure to entire classes of transgenic organisms which share particular genetic manipulations, to shorten the time needed for approval. This amounts to a so-called 'generic' approach.

Proponents of a generic approach argue that the increasing knowledge of introduced genes does allow generalizations covering different crops. The introduction of well-known genes which modify the quality of a plant product or confer resistance to pests, diseases or herbicides allegedly should not change the ecological characteristics of a crop plant (Dale 1993). Because the plant is introduced in its familiar environment, it is unlikely that it will become invasive. Because crops cannot be compared with 'exotics', the analogy with biological invasions doesn't hold. This is the prevailing view among molecular geneticists.

The step-by-step approach aims to move from release in a controlled environment to release in the real world in a stepwise fashion: from the laboratory and the greenhouse to small-scale field-experiments and ultimately to large-scale release. Although the step-by-step method might be considered as a prudent strategy with a built-in learning process, since it provides time to gain information and new experience, it need not yield adequate information about possible environmental risks.

Critics have argued that the method cannot cope with scaling and long-term uncertainty. Scales are very different in the range from experiments in a small, well-controlled and closely monitored experimental plot and a full-scale commercial release. Thus each step in the range may confront us with unforeseen phenomena. Neither does the step-by-step approach account for geographical diversity. Safety found in experiments for one kind of soil and climate cannot be generalized to other situations and other regions.

Recent evaluations of the results of the release experiments so far performed have led to the conclusion that the dangers of negative environmental impacts are rather small and that there is no reason for great concern (OECD 1994). But that conclusion is premature. It is not surprising that no harm is observed as yet, because of the short time-scale of the trials and the limited scope of the investigations (Wrubel et al. 1992). Studies on invasions have shown that a considerable time-lag of decades, even centuries may occur between the introduction of a species and its successful naturalisation. Ecologists argue that, to know unintentional negative impacts, we need information at a time-scale of 10 to 100 generations of a species. For crop plants with one generation per season this calls for an observation period of 10 years (Crawley 1994; Tolin 1994). The step-by-step method does not cover this requirement.

In the years ahead, releases will quickly multiply in number and scale, and they will ultimately involve large-scale commercial applications. The step-by-step procedure paves the road for massive future releases of a huge variety of GMOs; from trees in forestry down to viral biopesticides in agriculture. It is questionable if the 'piecemeal' method of introduction can guarantee safety in the long-term.

8. Conclusion

The existing regulatory system cannot be regarded as rigorously preventive, because the existence of uncertainties is not sufficiently acknowledged. It is inherently biased in favour of one view, that of the genetic engineering community.

Current risk assessments are mainly structured around controlled experiments, which cannot be extrapolated to the real world. Outside the controlled environment of the trials, unknown parameters, non-linearities and threshold effects combine to make events unpredictable. The reductionist approach of genetic engineers, if appropriate at all, only holds in closed systems (Ehrenfeld 1992; Wynne and Mayer 1993; Hunt 1994). An adequate non-reductionist environmental science should allow for much uncertainty.

In controversies over uncertainties, the precautionary principle should be taken to imply that the burden of proof is primarily on those who dismiss uncertainty. Ecologists and molecular geneticists disagree about environmental risks of GMOs in the field. The molecular geneticists dismiss uncertainties which ecologists emphasize. The burden of proof should be on the molecular geneticists, the more so because expertise concerning the field resides primarily with the ecologists.

References

Atfield, Robin 1994. 'The Precautionary Principle and Moral Values.' In: Timothy O'Riordan and James Cameron (eds.), *Interpreting the Precautionary Principle*. London: Earthscan, pp.152-164.

Bartsch, D., Sukopp, H. and Sukopp, U. 1993. 'Introduction of plants with special regard to cultigens running wild.' In: K. Wöhrmann and J. Tomiuk (eds.), *Transgenic Organisms: Risk-Assessments of Deliberate Release*. Basel: Birkhäuser Verlag, pp.135-151.

Beauchamps, Tom L. and Childress, James F. 1989. *Principles of Biomedical Ethics* (3rd ed.). New York: Oxford University Press.

Bergen Conference 1990. *Bergen Ministerial Declaration on Sustainable Development in the ECE region* (May 16).

Boyle, Allan E. 1992. 'Protecting the Marine Environment. Some Problems and Developments in the Law of the Sea.' *Marine Policy* **16** (March), pp.79-85.

Cameron, James and Abouchar, Juli 1991. 'The Precautionary Principle: A Fundamental Principle of Law and Policy for the Protection of the Global Environment.' *Boston College International and Comparative Law Review* **14**, pp.1-27.

Chourrout, D. 1994. 'Genetically Modified Fish: Technologies and Their Potential Environmental Impacts.' In: P.J. van der Meer and J.P.M. Schenkelaars (eds.), *PAN European Conference on the long-term ecological impacts of genetically modified organisms, Working Document 14 March 1994*. Voorschoten, The Netherlands, pp.185-191.

Churchill, Robin and Freestone, David (eds.) 1991. *International Law and Global Climate Change*. London/Dordrecht/Boston: Graham & Trotman/Martinus Nijhoff.

Crawley, M.J. 1994. 'Long Term Ecological Impacts of the Release of Genetically Modified Organisms.' In: P.J. van der Meer and J.P.M. Schenkelaars (eds.), *PAN European Conference on the long-term ecological impacts of genetically modified organisms, Working Document 14 March 1994*. Voorschoten, The Netherlands, pp.31-50.

Dale, P.J. 1993. 'The Release of Transgenic Plants into Agriculture.' *Journal of Agricultural Science* **120**, pp.1-5.

Dovers, Stephen R. and Handmer, John W. 1995. 'Ignorance, the Precautionary Principle, and Sustainability.' *Ambio* **24** (no.2, March), pp.92-97.

Ehler, L.E. 1991. 'Planned Introductions in Biological Control.' In: Lev R. Ginsburg (ed.), *Assessing Ecological Risks of Biotechnology*. Boston etc.: Butterworth-Heinemann, pp.21-39.

Ehrenfeld, David 1991. 'Environmental Protection: The Experts Dilemma.' *Report from the Institute for Philosophy & Public Policy* **11** (2), pp.8-12.

Freestone, David 1991. 'The Precautionary Principle.' In: Robin Churchill and David Freestone (eds.), *International Law and Global Climate Change.* London/Dordrecht/Boston: Graham & Trotman/Martinus Nijhoff, pp.21-40.

Earle, R.C. 1992. 'Commonsense and the Precautionary Principle: An Environmentalist's Perspective.' *Marine Pollution Bulletin* **24** (4), pp.182-186.

Gray, J.S. 1990. 'Statistics and the Precautionary Principle.' *Marine Pollution Bulletin* **21** (4), pp.174-176.

Hatchwell, P. 1989. 'Opening Pandora's Box: The Risks of Releasing GEOs.' *The Ecologist* **19** (no.4, April), pp.130-135.

Hengeveld, R. 1994. 'Assessing Invasion Risk.' In: P.J. van der Meer and J.P.M. Schenkelaars (eds.), *PAN European Conference on the long-term ecological impacts of genetically modified organisms, Working Document 14 March 1994.* Voorschoten, The Netherlands, pp.67-82.

Hey, Ellen 1992. 'The Precautionary Concept in Environmental Law: Institutionalizing Caution.' *Georgetown International Environmental Law Review* **IV** (2), pp.257-478.

Hill, Julie 1994. 'The Regulation of Genetically Modified Organisms.' In: Timothy O'Riordan and James Cameron (eds.), *Interpreting the Precautionary Principle.* London: Earthscan, pp.172-182.

Hindar, K. 1994. 'Ecological and Genetic Effects of Transgenic Fish.' In: P.J. van der Meer and J.P.M. Schenkelaars (eds.), *PAN European Conference on the long-term ecological impacts of genetically modified organisms, Working Document 14 March 1994.* Voorschoten, The Netherlands, pp.193-202.

Hunt, Jane 1994. 'The Social Construction of Precaution.' In: Timothy O'Riordan and James Cameron (eds.), *Interpreting the Precautionary Principle.* London: Earthscan, pp.117-125.

Krimsky, Sheldon 1991. *Biotechnics and Society. The Rise of Industrial Genetics.* New York etc.: Praeger.

Lake, Gordon 1991. 'Scientific Uncertainty and Political Regulation: European Legislation on the Contained Use and Deliberate Release of Genetically Modified (Micro)Organisms.' *Project Appraisal* **6** (1), pp.7-15.

Levidow, Les and Tait, Joyce 1992. 'Release of Genetically modified Organisms: Precautionary Legislation.' *Project Appraisal* **7** (no.2, June), pp.93-105.

Miller, Henry I. 1994. 'Risk assessment experiments and the new biotechnology.' *Trends in Biotechnology* **12**, pp.292-295.

Munson, Abby 1995. 'Risk associated with and liability arising from, releases of genetically manipulated organisms into the environment.' *Science and Public Policy* **22** (no.1, February), pp.51-63.

Myers, Norman 1993. 'Biodiversity and the Precautionary Principle.' *Ambio* **22** (no.2-3, May), pp.74-79.

[OECD] Organisation for Economic Cooperation and Development 1994. *Field Releases of Transgenic Plants 1986-1992, An Analysis.* Paris.

O'Riordan, Timothy and Cameron, James 1994. 'The History and Contemporary Significance of the Precautionary Principle.' In: Timothy O'Riordan and James Cameron (eds.), *Interpreting the Precautionary Principle.* London: Earthscan, pp.12-30.

O'Riordan, Timothy and Jordan, Andrew 1995. 'The Precautionary Principle in Contemporary Environmental Politics.' *Environmental Values* **4**, pp.191-212.

Schell, J.S. 1994. 'Plant Biotechnology: State of the Art in Developed Countries and Relevant Safety Considerations.' In: P.J. van der Meer and J.P.M. Schenkelaars (eds.), *PAN European Conference on the long-term ecological impacts of genetically modified organisms, Working Document 14 March 1994.* Voorschoten, The Netherlands, pp.17-24.

Schomberg, René von 1993. 'Controversies and Political Decision Making.' In: René von Schomberg (ed.), *Science, Politics, and Morality.* Dordrecht/Boston/London: Kluwer Academic Publishers, pp.7-26.

Sharples, Frances E. 1987. 'Regulation of Products from Biotechnology.' *Science* **235**, pp.1329-1335.

Simberloff, Daniel 1991. 'Keystone Species and Community Effects of Biological Introductions.' In: Lev R. Ginsburg (ed.), *Assessing Ecological Risks of Biotechnology*. Boston etc.: Butterworth-Heinemann, pp.1-20.

Tiedje, James M. et al. 1989. 'The planned introduction of genetically engineered organisms: Ecological considerations and recommendations.' *Ecology* **70**, pp.298-315.

Tolin, S. 1994. 'Introduction into the *Bacillus Thuringiensis* Issue.' In: P.J. van der Meer and J.P.M. Schenkelaars (eds.), *PAN European Conference on the long-term ecological impacts of genetically modified organisms, Working Document 14 March 1994*. Voorschoten, The Netherlands, p.57-63.

Wrubel, R.P., Krimsky, S. and Wetzler, R.E. 1992. 'Field Testing Transgenic Plants. An Analysis of the US Department of Agriculture's Environmental Assessments.' *BioScience* **42** (4), pp.280--289.

Wynne, Brian and Mayer, Sue 1993. 'How Science Fails the Environment.' *New Scientist* (5 June), pp.33-35.

10

The Laborious Transition to a Discursive Policy Process on the Release of Genetically Modified Organisms

René von Schomberg

1. Introduction

The issue of the deliberate release of genetically modified organisms (GMOs) into the environment was posed as a policy problem. This was perhaps unavoidable since one of the reasons why the contained use of GMOs was regulated was that an unintentional release should be prevented. It was perceived as a problem with manifold aspects which could only be dealt with by appealing to science, manageability and social conventions. This threefold appeal to fundamental institutions of society implied a threefold reduction of the problem. The policy process for the release of GMOs into the environment is the focus of this paper and it is argued that a discursive policy process is needed to achieve an integrative, non-reductionist approach to the problem. In the Netherlands, for example, this has been the approach to some extent. I will argue that only a discursive policy process can overcome the problems of decision making in the context of uncertainties and I will here draw upon the experience gained during a EU funded study.[1]

2. The Appeal to Science

The authorative appeal to science underlies the assumption that we have confidence in the functioning of the scientific system, for example, that it can provide policy makers with reliable knowledge and adequate predictions which are needed for a manageable practice for which policy-regulations must set the framework. In the case of the deliberate release of GMOs, the usual confidence in science is problematic for two reasons. First, we have to deal with a trans-scientific problem, that is a problem that can be stated in the language of science but cannot be solved within the language of science. Our current knowledge does not provide us with the means to predict the ecological long-term effects of releasing organisms into the environment. So it is beyond the *competence* of the scientific system to answer such a question, despite the fact that competence is normally the basis for an authoritative appeal. In fact, science would not pose such a question to itself since there is no method to make this question researchable. Reasoned statements on this subject matter cannot go beyond theoretical speculation. The reason for an appeal to science is solely policy motivated: we would like to have the answer to this question for achieving a manageable practice. So we have a good reason to be suspicious if scientists are nevertheless prepared to provide us with some kind of answer to this question. We can reconstruct two kinds of 'answers' science has given us so far. The first answer came from one branch of science, where most scientists were biotechnologists, molecular biologists or microbiologists. They answered the question by ack-nowledging the trans-scientific problem and stating that the development of a testprotocol for identifying the risks of individual organisms would be an un-achievable task (Brill 1985).[2] However, at the same time they argued that this is *irrelevant* knowledge since we can rely on the experience with traditional plant breeding practices, which differs, on their account, insignificantly from the practice of genetic engineering – only in so far that we now exactly know what kind of new genes we are introducing. Ecologists on the other hand down-played the trans-scientific issue, by saying that they could *develop* precisely the type of knowledge policy makers asked for by doing research on so called 'microcosms' (see also Krimsky in this volume) needed to make predictions possible in terms of quantitative risk assessment (Tiedje et al. 1989).[3]

From a policy perspective both answers are unsatisfactory because a biotechnologist cannot address the problems in terms of safety or in terms of risk. They just rhetorically state that it would be an 'acceptable risk' (by appealing to the fact that we already accepted the risks associated with conventional plant breeding). However this does not give us an informed opinion on how to regulate individual cases, nor did it address the issue of a precautionary approach. Ecologists, on the other hand, underestimate the difficulties of the trans-scientific issue: the promise of providing a quantitative risk assessment in the course of microcosm-based experiments, and without conducting field experiments, cannot be fulfilled in the foreseeable future. Only if one fully appreciates the trans-scientific issue, one sees the dilemma for policy: allowing major field experiments might involve unknown environmental impacts. To impose too many constraints on these experiments, however, would imply that we will never gain knowledge on the behaviour of GMOs. In the next section we will see that this dilemma bounces back on the regulatory system we have in place: what did we learn from the field experiments conducted during the last decade?

The appeal to science for policy has been made without reflecting sufficiently on the trans-scientific issue underlying a scientific controversy. Science *reduced* this issue by translating it into a question of *relevancy* to which both molecular biologists and ecologists came up with unsatisfactory answers. As a consequence, the contradiction that arises between policy and science has not been reflected either:[4] Policy has to be engaged in science to look for answers concerning perceived risks but cannot make a legitimate appeal to a science which does not resolve the relevancy question.

3. Appealing to Manageability

Hans Bergmans, Secretary of the Commission on Genetic Modification (COGEM) in the Netherlands, does not agree with the familiar argument that the field experiments with GMOs have demonstrated their safe environmental use.[5] According to Bergmans, it has only shown that experiments have been planned carefully. The experiments did not have any environmental impact other than those expected (to our knowledge). Consequently, the field experiments did not teach us anything about the behaviour of GMOs. This conclusion changes the initially intended perspective on the 'step-by-step' procedure. Rüdelsheim, from the company Plant Genetic Systems (PGS), based in Belgium, also affirmed this change in perspective at a workshop held in May 1995:[6]

> One could say so far, the 'step by step' procedure focused more on the safety of the 'step' to be taken, than on the preparation of future 'steps'.

In conclusion, I would argue that if we still think that it is necessary to gain knowledge on the behaviour of GMOs we have to do something other than reviewing applications within the current 'step-by-step' procedure since it cannot demonstrate the safe environmental use of GMOs.

According to Bergmans, we should now plan experiments with an intended environmental effect, in order to gain the necessary knowledge. Bergmans advocates that we should allow applications with GMOs with similarly manageable effects such as the accepted agronomic effects of conventional agriculture. These types of releases could yield information on the behaviour of GMOs. Stressing the fact that only an increased knowledge of basic natural processes can help risk analysis, he also claims that it would be useful to use GMOs in order to increase our knowledge of micro-organisms in the environment and suggests that genetic modification can be used for the 'tagging' of micro-organisms so that they can be followed in the environment.

The task for policy is to translate the precautionary assumptions of the legislation which is based on a 'case-by-case' and 'step-by-step' procedure, into a manageable practice that acknowledges these assumptions and make a science-informed learning process possible. We have observed that Bergmans addressed the trans-scientific issue explicitly, but we must realize that he has not given us an answer to the sequential questions: What intended effects can be 'manageable', on the one hand, and provide us, on the other hand, with usable information on the behaviour of GMOs that would provide a basis for risk assessment? What intended effects will be acceptable effects?

These questions cannot be answered yet, since not only the appeal to science implies a reduction of the problem, the manageability criterion, imposed by regulatory policy on the practice of field experiments has produced another possibly reductionist position: manageability has been equated with planning safe experiments from which we cannot learn enough.

4. Reducing Acceptability to Social Conventions

Existing legislation does not provide regulators with normative standards to evaluate applications concerning the acceptability of their environmental impact. Without a normative standard, however, it is impossible to draw a valid conclusion on the acceptability of a product or a release. Therefore, regulators have to make normative assumptions which could render a certain conclusion acceptable. So far, the implicit strategy has been to make an appeal to a conventional norm, that is to say a standard which would be acceptable because one can be certain it is widely accepted and uncontroversial. What kind of standard would that be? The Dutch advisory committee made the following statements in the evaluation of the application of the company Plant Genetic Systems (cf. Levidow et al. in this volume) in June 1994:

> outcrossing transgenic characteristics will not cause a persistently negative impact on the environment [and] outcrossing the gene and its property male sterility ... will not lead to a persistently unacceptable impact of these relatives on the composition of varieties in natural vegetation.

To draw a conclusion on the acceptability of an impact, one has to use phrases with normative implications like 'negative impact' or 'unacceptable impact'. In this case, the advisory committee assumed that a conventional standard, and therefore a non-controversial reference point, would be the 'natural situation' itself. It is assumed that so long as any impact would be an impact which could be counter-balanced by nature, which would allow nature to return to its original situation, it would be an 'acceptable impact'. Generally, this conclusion, which at first glance seems quite uncontroversial, implies that any process or impact caused by releases or new agricultural practices would be acceptable if we found that such a process or impact would be an instance occurring in nature itself. Indeed, advisory committees came to the conclusion that herbicide-resistant genes, for instance, are widespread in the natural environment and that, therefore, a possible spread of these genes caused by man-made varieties would be an acceptable phenomenon, comparable with existing natural processes.

However, unproblematic this appeal to a conventional norm seems to be, it soon runs into difficulties when one tries to apply this normative reference point, in diverse cases over time. The assumption we make by its application is that we have a full understanding of natural processes. Now, in the case of the ecological impact of organisms introduced, we do not have such a body of knowledge. Our perception of nature changes over time and, for instance, up to some years ago we believed that a thing like 'gene flow' is not a natural phenomenon (and therefore unacceptable), but now we have found that it occurs in nature as well, which would turn it into an acceptable impact in case human practices would cause identical phenomena. So, our further analyses turn our 'convention' into a transformable normative reference point, which depends on (and evolves synchronically with) the historical change in our perception of nature.

Do we want environmental policy to be dependent on such standards? Regulators are now forced to study nature if they are to apply this standard consistently. Indeed, this is current practice to some extent. The assumption has always been that such a study would probably yield information that would eliminate the concept of hypothetical risk. Secondly, the standard would raise controversy if we were to say that anything happening in nature would be acceptable for human practices. Now we know that quite some natural events are unacceptable, otherwise it would not be possible any more to talk about natural catastrophes, precisely the kind of events some ecologists think that might happen with an intensified, biotechnology-based agriculture. Here we face the classical naturalistic fallacy: we cannot derive valid normative conclusions from factual statements. Thirdly, although we came to the conclusion that we are dealing with a transformable norm, since it is dependent on our perception of nature, it was not the intention of regulators to create such a standard (although the standard is rather well received by industrialists, who prefer to speak about 'flexible' standards).

In the statement of the advisory committee, that something is acceptable because it will not have a persistent negative impact, it is implied that there is a stable natural composition of the natural vegetation, enabling the vegetation to counterbalance any impact by returning to its original state. The keyword was 'persistent', implying a normative view on nature, which is perceived as a stable business counter-balancing any impact over a period of time. This normative view of nature, has indeed been a quite influential conception in ecology for a long time but is now being replaced by the views of modern ecologists who introduced more 'reality-adequate', more 'dynamic' models of nature. Who is right, is still underdetermined; however, it seems problematic to take normative assumptions about nature's balance as a point of departure for evaluating the acceptability of an environmental impact. It anticipates the normative view of the person who wants to preserve a certain natural habitat, in the way we have it now, which means quite some human interventions, since quite some action is needed to preserve a 'balance'.

Fourthly, the transformable standard introduced is of course very likely to become problematic in the light of other standards which, in their own right, are also introduced as standards referring to conventions. One could refer to conventional agricultural practices, that is to say, anything that does not yield an impact substantially different from the impact of existing agricultural practices. One could even refer to norms that 'should' become conventions in the very near future, like the standard of sustainable development, which is a normative guideline for the Danish authorities to evaluate the acceptability of an impact. Which standard do we choose?

Finally, we go back to the question of assessing the risks of GMOs. Regulators have been forced, in the absence of standards, to invent normative reference points to say something about the acceptability of an environmental impact. The statements on acceptability appealed to conventions. Indeed conventions refer to acceptable norms. However, they do not explicate the rightness of such norms or standards for which one has to argue. In doing so, they moved away from the practice of risk assessment to general statements on the acceptability of environmental impacts which can neither be defined in terms of risk nor in terms of safety standards. Since 'risk' presupposes a standard of acceptability, the regulatory system is not focused on identifying risks but rather on identifying uncertainties. We can distinguish between risk-based regulation (which applies to chemical substances) and uncertainty-based regulation for GMOs (see table on next page). The table shows, in accordance with our discussion above, that we have an uncertainty-based regulation in place whereas regulators and political actors often justify this type of regulation in terms of a risk-based regulation (the authorities in the UK claim to have a model for risk assessment in the framework of risk-based regulation; this model is explained for the case of herbicide resistant oilseed rape in the contribution of Levidow et al. in this volume). However, no one at this point can either justify how to translate uncertainty to risk, or justify how to translate normative reference points to definitions of harm.

It became unavoidable to go beyond discussing safety issues without acknowledging that this is current policy. The unarticulated shift from risk-based regulation to uncertainty-based regulation needs a new justification since the vocabulary of a risk assessment model is inappropriate for current practice. Open discussion on transformable standards and the justification of an uncertainty-based regulatory system is hindered by the EC directive which restricts policy makers to the matter of scientific aspects of safety issues.

Table 1: Characteristics of regulatory systems

Risk-based regulation	Uncertainty-based regulation
identifying risks	identifying uncertainties
applying standards of acceptable risks	applying transformable (deliberations-based) standards of acceptable uncertainties
applying definitions of harm	appealing to normative reference points
calculating the chance of occurrence of *possible* environmental impacts	assessing the plausibility of *assumed* environmental impacts
policy objective: minimizing risks; regulatory burden appropriate to actual risks	policy objective: reducing uncertainties; regulatory burden determined by the application of a precautionary principle
possibility of avoidance of predictable long-term effects	prospective long-term effects cannot be assessed

5. Moving to a Discursive Policy Process

The Netherlands anticipated current EU regulation by publishing a 'draft decree on Genetically Modified Organisms pursuant to the Chemical Substances Act' in the Government Gazette in December 1987, in which a policy was outlined following the 'step-by-step' and 'case-by-case' approach described in the 1986 OECD report. In January 1990 the decree was enacted, an anticipatory implementation of EC Directive 90/220. Dutch policy is embedded in a highly discursive context which has been changing over time its focus, in content and in the type of initiatives taken by socio-political actors. A discursive context is here understood to be a practice with procedures and institutions that regulate (formally and informally) the debate between opponents and proponents of policy options. Here I would like to distinguish three phases.

In the first phase, at the end of the eighties, most of the political actors who defined the context of the regulation, among others, scientists, environmental and industrial organisations, focused on stimulating the public debate on all aspects of the deliberate release of GMOs that is to say: the socio-economic, ethical, scientific and policy aspects. They all shared the focus on policy regulation that should encompass all these aspects but disagreed with one another on how to do this. Initiatives for this debate were taken by Parliament and intermediary bodies like the former NOTA (now called the Rathenau Institute) to facilitate such a debate through governmental and semi-governmental information campaigns.

In the second phase, at the beginning of the nineties, antagonistic forces, for example, industry, and environmental and consumer groups, used the regulation to legitimise and to criticise certain developments. GMO regulation in the Netherlands is not based on a notification system as suggested in the EC Directive, but on a permit system under the Environmental Protection Act, which enables interested parties (by providing them with a legal right) to object to the intention of an authority to issue a permit to an applicant. This gave environmental groups the opportunity to explain their reasons for concern and enabled applicants and industry to respond to their objections. In the meantime government authorities developed a sense for socio-political concern and tried to accommodate criticisms and suggestions from both sides by integrating them into the policy process. The Ministry of Housing, Physical Planning and the Environment (VROM) took the initiative to organise and fund workshops on unsolved issues in risk assessment procedures and invited the various groups to develop criteria for the acceptability of GMO releases and products. The competent authority concerning GMO regulation in a sense also became an important political actor when it developed an open negotiating attitude towards all relevant parties. In August 1995 the Rathenau Institute called the 'state of the art' in the general discussion on biotechnology 'constructive', and announced its intention to withdraw from biotechnology since they believe their help was not needed any more.

Indeed, there are indications that we are entering a third phase, one of a societal embedding of biotechnology. In April 1995 environmental organisations and industry agreed on the labelling of products, which already affects the first Dutch market application with herbicide-tolerant and kanamycin-resistant red-hearted chicory. In the period 1992-1994 the Ministry of Agriculture, Nature Conservation and the Fisheries had a budget of about 5.5 million Dutch guilders (about 2.1 million ECU), to be spent on issues concerning the societal embedding of biotechnology, such as public information, public debate, educational activities, research projects on the consequences of various forms of labelling, support from the consumer organisation 'Consument en biotechnologie' (Consumer and Biotechnology) and a communication project for farmer organisations to enable discussions in the regions of the country.

GMO regulation faces two kinds of discursive challenges. On the one hand, policies on GMOs have to deal with the discursive legitimisation process, which may change its content and focus as described above, but the network of discussion and negotiation partners has to be discursively maintained on a continuing basis to react adequately to new developments and to enable the antagonistic forces such as industry and environmental organisations to remain cooperative and to develop a context of self-regulation.

On the other hand GMO regulation faces a discursive challenge which is inherent to that regulation. Neither EC Directive 90/220 nor the Dutch implementation of that directive define what counts as a harmful effect or what would be an acceptable risk, unlike the usual environmental legislation. Since the Commission on Genetic Modification (COGEM), which advises the authorities, did not have at its disposal a list of standards established to enable routine risk assessment, the COGEM had to develop such criteria in the light of applications and define normative reference points which would allow the COGEM to make statements on the *acceptability* of potential environmental effects.

The shadow of a political consensus on having a precautionary approach to the unknown risks of the release of GMOs forced the COGEM to defend every type of acceptable release in the 'case-by-case' approach. Deciding for a flexible regulation that could accommodate rapid developments implies the application of 'flexible' standards of safety. The authorities and the COGEM anticipated the possibility of redefining the notions of 'step' and 'case' as information on releases would accumulate. Since all these standards and definitions are subject to change, they have to be discursively defended within the COGEM itself, to which a broad range of experts were assigned on grounds of their proven scientific expertise. However, and perhaps this is typical of the Dutch political culture, some of the experts were assigned by a range of advisory bodies, resulting in the situation that experts with very specific backgrounds are members of the COGEM; both a representative of the most important environmental organisation ('Natuur en Milieu') and experts who work for industrial firms that apply for releases were assigned.

The transition to a discursive policy process in which standards of safety are continually subject to change and, therefore, to be discursively defended both within and outside expert committees, both formally and informally, met a major difficulty to becoming fully practised and appreciated by all relevant parties. The Dutch authorities interpretation of the EC Directive 90/220 and the way in which it was incorporated in law, follows a strict distinction between safety aspects in a scientific-technical sense and further reaching physical and socio-ethical aspects. The COGEM does not consider, for instance, agronomic effects such as the potential increase in the use of herbicides. The Dutch authorities and the COGEM do not go into any kind of cost-benefit analysis, insisting that such activities are beyond their task.

Here, a discursive policy process faces a limitation posed by traditional environmental legislation, in which the distinction between scientific aspects and socio-political aspects can be maintained on the assumption of non-contested, prefixed social definitions of harm and acceptable risk which, subsequently, can be applied 'neutrally' by scientific experts. In the case of deliberate release, we do not have such standards, and to some extent we do not want them, since the regulation should maintain its flexibility to accommodate scientific and industrial developments, and be open to the possibility of implementing the most recent scientific insights.

However, fully in line with the traditional boundaries of scientific expertise, the COGEM did point out that such problems are beyond their competence and should be discussed by other parties. The authorities acknowledged that "a forum to discuss the 'socio-ethical' aspects would be an asset but probably difficult to realize" (interview with Dutch Competent Authority, 9 May 1995). In line with the traditional boundaries and in the absence of a forum for socio-ethical aspects, the scientific deliberations, according to the authorities, continue to be frustrated by 'non-relevant' arguments both at the national and at the international level. Both environmental groups and representatives of industry, however, would favour a cost-benefit analysis or even technology assessments that do not reaffirm these traditional boundaries.

The new chairman of the COGEM, Huub Schellekens – who is also the chairman of a COGEM subcommittee, whose task it is to spot socio-ethical problems – is not particularly happy with the present situation of separating socio-ethical issues from safety aspects. In an interview with the author (29 October 1995), he explains that this specific committee is the result of a compromise between the Ministry of VROM, which is in favour of such separation, and Parliament, which is in favour of including the socio-ethical aspects of GMO regulation. Schellekens calls for an 'integrated evaluation of biological products', which would cover both safety and social aspects. He states:

> it would be hypocritical to employ such a separation since the very fact that something is identified as a harmful effect within the scope of safety regulation already constitutes a social approach.

He suggests that separate bodies may be used to evaluate the different aspects, but the focus should be an integrative approach. To enable such an integrative regulation, he favours a product-based regulation. He believes that earlier attempts at integrative approaches failed to be implemented because of differences between ministries. Schellekens' suggestions to overcome the traditional boundaries, would show a discursive policy process to full advantage; it would, for example, allow discussions on concepts of harm and normative reference points in risk assessment procedures with all parties involved. For good discursive practice, it would be difficult to explain why only particular types of argument are relevant.

The transition to a fully discursive policy now meets the limits of the political realm to overcome that boundary. In 1991 the Dutch Parliament requested an evaluation of GMO regulation within four years since it felt that future developments and unfamiliarity with this new issue might make adjustments necessary. An inter-ministerial committee has now finished its evaluation of the regulation in October 1995, specifically focusing on the cooperation between the ministries involved and the practicability of the regulation. Concerning the regulation on deliberate release, the committee came to the general conclusion that the current regulation is workable, in view of the responses from companies and institutions that make applications. The committee has invited advisory bodies, environmental and industrial organisations to comment on this evaluation before it is sent to Parliament in November 1995. The industrial organisation NIABA said it would cope with the existing regulation in hope of diminishing the bureaucratic burden in the future, a hope which is based on the belief that 'flexible' standards inherent in the existing regulation will allow a more routine handling of applications (interview with R. van der Meer, 8 August 1995). The reaction by the environmental organisation 'Natuur en Milieu' was rather negative:

> We would have preferred an external evaluation (...) The actual outcome of this evaluation confirms our views (...) It is not even considered to mention the jurisprudence concerning this regulation (letter to the CA, 7 September 1995).

More remarkably, however, are the statements by the new chairman of the COGEM, Huub Schellekens, who thought the evaluation was too much focused on the administrative aspects, and too little on content. The COGEM also commented on the evaluation in line with the arguments by Schellekens quoted above. However, to implement Schellekens' forceful suggestions, would certainly go beyond the negotiating space of the Dutch Competent Authority (CA), if not at the national level, it certainly would at the international level. The CA's approach is to reaffirm the existing EU regulation, which is, in the CA's view, flexible enough to accommodate new developments. The Dutch CA rejects any changes in the formal structure of the regulation now that the major parties, not without protest, have claimed to be willing to cope with it as matters stand after a laborious habituation period.[7] The negotiating space of the Dutch authorities cannot go beyond the traditional boundaries of environmental regulation since the EC directive itself sets these boundaries.

My plea would be to fully embark on a course towards a discursive policy encompassing an integrative approach to the subject matter that would facilitate a flexible regulation, both effective and legitimate. However, to meet this objective we have to formulate procedural norms for this discursive process to make a fair and just outcome possible.[8]

Notes

1. This essay arises from the context of a study for the European Commission "GMO releases: Managing Uncertainties about biosafety", conducted by Les Levidow et al., Open University, UK. I also thank Dr. Peter Wheale for useful comments.

2. Brill, W.J. 1985. 'Safety concerns and genetic engineering in agriculture.' *Science* **227**, pp.381-184.

3. For a thorough analysis of the debate between biotechnologists and ecologists, see my book: *Der rationale Umgang mit Unsicherheit. Die Bewältigung von Dissens und Gefahren in Wissenschaft, Wissenschaftspolitik und Gesellschaft*, Frankfurt am Main: Peter Lang, 1995. A summary appeared in: René von Schomberg (ed.), *Science, Politics and Morality, Scientific Uncertainty and Decision Making*. Dordrecht: Kluwer Academic Publishers, 1993.

4. On this topic, see: 'The erosion of the valuespheres, The ways in which society copes with scientific and moral and ethical uncertainties.' In: René von Schomberg (ed.), *Contested Technology. Ethics, Risk and Public Debate*. Tilburg: International Centre for Human and Public Affairs, 1995.

5. Quotations are from Bergmans' paper presented at the workshop: "Unanswered safety questions when employing GMOs", organised by the Coordination Commission Risk Assessment Research on 2-4 May, 1995.

6. Quotations are from Rüdelsheims paper presented at the workshop: "Unanswered safety questions when employing GMOs", organised by the Coordination Commission Risk Assessment Research on 2-4 May, 1995.

7. In the evaluation report of the inter-ministerial committee the limits of the 'negotiating space' of the Dutch CA are given by the conditions they set for changing the existing regulation. The Netherlands would accept changes in the existing regulation if the following conditions are met (evaluation report 1995, translation by RvS):

     1. adjustments appear to be necessary on the basis of a thorough evaluation;
     2. the evaluation must be based upon practical experience, according to the criteria mentioned in the evaluation report (such as maintainability, efficiency, practicability and transparency), and all parties concerned must be involved in this evaluation;
     3. adjustments must be tested on the question of whether they will actually lead to an improvement and will not imply a reduction in safety.

8. On this topic, see: 'The erosion of the valuespheres, The ways in which society copes with scientific and moral and ethical uncertainties.' In: René von Schomberg (ed.), *Contested Technology. Ethics, Risk and Public Debate*. Tilburg: International Centre for Human and Public Affairs, 1995.

Part III

Limits of Risk Assessment: Political Conditions

11

Outlooks on Public Information and Participation in the Context of the European Biotechnology Directives 90/219/EEC and 90/220/EEC

Piet Schenkelaars

1. Introduction

In this contribution, first, a historical overview of developments in biotechnology and its regulation will be given as a background to the public debate on biotechnology in Europe. Further, the results of a comparative study on the legal provisions for public information and public participation in the national legislation on safety in biotechnology of European countries will be summarized. Next, the outcome of a seminar for representatives of the Competent Authorities of European Union member states and non-governmental environmental- and consumer organizations on the issue of public information and participation will be described. Finally, the results of the comparative study and the seminar will be evaluated in order to indicate possible approaches to an improvement of the public debate on the quality of risk assessment in biotechnology.

2. Short Historical Overview of European Biotechnology Policy Developments

In 1973 experiments had shown the possibility of *in vitro* recombination of parts of DNA molecules. Almost before the experiments had progressed beyond their design, several molecular biologists initiated efforts to delay their application. A committee of eminent scientists convened by the US National Academy of Science and chaired by molecular biologist Paul Berg distributed a letter, often referred to as the 'Berg' Letter, calling for a voluntary moratorium on the cloning of genes for antibiotic resistance and of DNA from animal viruses pending an international conference to discuss the issues. This conference was held in 1975 at Asilomar, California, from where the discussion on risk and benefits of genetic engineering entered the public domain as government institutes and committees started to draw up regulations on the potential and perceived risks of genetic engineering to human health and the environment.

Almost immediately, most industries and governments, especially in developed countries, became aware of the economic potential of the application of genetic engineering and started to recognize biotechnology as a key technology for the 21st century. During the 1980s, governments started to create an attractive investment climate through supporting biotechnology research programmes at universities and through implementing a regulatory framework. During this decade large private investments in biotechnology were made, first, by many small start-up biotechnology firms, often nearby a university, and, later, by large pharmaceutical, chemical and food processing companies. As a result, at the beginning of the 1990s, the first wave of products of modern biotechnology began reaching the marketplace. Though the number of actual applications was still limited in comparison to the perceived potentials of biotechnology and genetic engineering.

Since the mid-1970s the European Community has also become increasingly involved in biotechnology. By funding research and developing a regulatory framework, it has sought to promote the competitiveness of biotechnology industries, whilst regulating the risks to man and the environment. About twenty years later, in 1993 the EU Commission issued a widely discussed, general policy document: the White Paper on Growth, Competitiveness and Employment (CEC 1993a), in which biotechnology was again acknowledged as one of the fields offering the greatest potential for innovation and growth: "Its application could be of particular benefit in areas such as health care, industrial chemicals, foods and feeds, agriculture and environmental clean-up services. Moreover, the further development of biotechnology will require increasing investment in supplies, services and hardware. This would have a correspondingly positive effect on the employment situation."

Although the main responsibility for competitiveness rests with the firms themselves, the EU Commission also took the view that "public authorities could help to stimulate competitiveness by adopting a consistent and supportive approach in relevant areas. This would entail the provision of financial support for basic and applied research and related infrastructure; the drawing up of a coherent regulatory framework, based on a number of defined principles (including protection of intellectual property); a renewed emphasis on education and training; the stimulation of technology transfer; and the facilitation of public understanding and consumer choice."

To facilitate public acceptance of biotechnology, the EU Commission (CEC 1993b) has committed itself to study public attitudes and perception of the new biotechnologies, since "a lack of public acceptability is one the limiting factors for both research and its successful commercialization. Therefore, particular emphasis will be put on analyzing issues such as public perception and the acceptance of biotechnology in general."

Put differently, public perception, attitudes and acceptance are being perceived as of increasing strategic significance for the progress of biotechnology. In the view of the former head of the EU Commission's *Concertation Unit for Biotechnology in Europe* (CUBE), Mark Cantley, adequate regulations on safety in biotechnology and their enforcement may be crucial in gaining public acceptance: "Whether or not these new biotechnologies really get off the ground (...) is going to depend upon whether we can erect a regulatory regime that can secure public trust (...) Moreover, if the public cannot evaluate the risk, they will evaluate the regulator" (Cantley 1995).

3. European Regulations on Risks in Biotechnology

On 23 April 1990, the European Community adopted Council Directives designed to anticipate and control risks from new applications of biotechnology: Council Directives 90/219/EEC on the contained use of genetically modified micro-organisms and Council Directive 90/220/EEC on the deliberate release of genetically modified organisms to the environment. These Directives have the dual purpose of ensuring an equal level of protection of people's health and environment from possible risks while helping to achieve a single European market for biotechnology products. Appropriate legislation was also perceived as important in developing an atmosphere of acceptance and public confidence in biotechnology. Public information and public participation in decision-making procedures on notifications and authorizations for the use of genetically modified organisms (GMOs) may therefore be crucial to create such an atmosphere. In the European Union public information and participation was left at the discretion of the national Competent Authorities (CAs). According to Article 13 of Directive 90/219/EEC, "Member States have the possibility to make wider consultations concerning any aspects of a contained use, provided that confidentiality is respected (...) And Article 7 of Directive 90/220/EEC stipulates that "where a Member State considers it appropriate, it may provide that groups or the public shall be consulted on any aspect of the proposed deliberate release, provided that confidentiality is respected."

Three years later, at a stage where most, but not all member states had just finished the implementation of both directives into their national legislation, the EU Commission (CEC 1993c) concluded in a review that, on the one hand, the biotechnology regulatory framework was perceived as a factor impacting on industrial competitiveness. On the other hand, however, many studies had shown that the regulatory framework played an important role in building public confidence. The EU Commission therefore concluded that "the whole network of interrelated biotech-nological regulations needs to ensure that oversight is always appropriate in relation to the risks involved, to the competitive development of the industries involved and to the building of public confidence."

Understandably, the biotechnology industry itself has also always been very vocal in addressing these issues. In the beginning of the 1990s, it was claimed that the regulations were hindering the development of European biotechnology, and would thus widen the gap in competitiveness between Europe and its US and Japanese counterparts. At that time, the implementation of both Directives had not been completed in all member states, and where they had been implemented, there were still significant differences. While France was considered as having the most favourable regulations possible within the framework of the European Directives, from an industry-perspective (Dodet 1994), some other countries, like Germany and Denmark, had implemented a much more restrictive regime than was required by the Directives. According to industry, the information required by the Directives was not compatible with ensuring adequate protection for industrial secrets, and therefore, there was concern over the potential loss of competitive advantage and of jeopardizing the validity of patent applications. In the case of releases, the required circulation of the Summary Notification Information Format (SNIF) documents in all member states was perceived as a threat to confidentiality, while public disclosure of experiments placed research and field trials at the mercy of activist opponents of genetic engineering. Proposals were therefore forwarded to limit the public disclosure of information to a minimum relevant to safety.

The US and Japanese systems of regulatory review and control focus on the product, whereas in Europe regulations focus on the process through which a product is obtained. However, according to industry, this approach unnecessarily discriminates among processes of recDNA technologies. The European approach principally seemed to consider recDNA technologies as potentially dangerous. In the view of industry, this had "inevitably led to an over-sized bureaucratic apparatus, and, in consequence, to a slow and costly procedure for controlling a whole field of technology, instead of controlling primarily the products where real risks may emerge" (Dodet 1994). Further, industry complained about the risk classification of micro-organisms and the definition of the types of operations in Directive 90/219/EEC. It also complained that the risk assessment questionnaires for release operations were too long and inappropriate for plants and animals as the Directive initially had been designed for micro-organisms.

In 1993 the EU Commission (CEC 1993c) issued proposals for a so-called 'simplification' of both Directives on biotechnology. Its subsequent publication of a list of criteria, if fulfilled, permitting a simplified procedure for the release of transgenic plants to be followed, was welcomed as an improvement by the biotechnology industry. Also Directive 90/219/EEC was further amended through streamlining and easing of the requirements concerning notification and consent procedures and through redefining of the risk categories and the types of contained use operations.

As a response to these developments in European biotechnology regulatory policy, one of the leading environmental organizations in the area of biotechnology, Friends of the Earth Europe, criticized that "although the expression 'deregulation' is always avoided when discussing the 'necessary adaptation' of the EU regulation concerning genetic engineering with respect to the state of the art of scientific risk assessment, and especially when discussing Directive 90/220/EEC, the so-called simplification is in fact a deregulation because it has been initiated to decrease central recommendations on how to proceed with risk assessments, although neither the methodology nor the data for a reliable prognosis on the long term ecological effects of genetically modified organisms are available so far" (Friends of the Earth Europe 1993).

4. Scientific Acceptability and Public Acceptance

It is noteworthy to point at the Organization for Economic Cooperation and Development (OECD) distinction between issues related to the *acceptability*, and those related to the *acceptance* of biotechnology. *Acceptability* derives from rational, scientific evaluation of biotechnology safety issues, which however, do not exclude rational dispute when different weight is given to social and economic criteria. *Acceptance* is the reaction of the public rooted in a large number of motives, and the OECD acknowledged that in cases where the public shows concern about a technology, scientific *acceptability* is a necessary, but not sufficient condition of *acceptance*. Therefore, it was suggested that "public policies should (...) attempt to close this gap between scientific *acceptability* and public *acceptance*" (OECD 1989). Moreover, this study indicated that during discussions of safety issues, disagreements between scientific experts can emerge. Although this would be a normal development in an ongoing debate between scientists of so may different disciplines, the OECD expressed its fear that "such disagreements could be amplified and misunderstood in public opinion" (OECD 1989).

In my view, these observations suggest that the role of scientific experts in evaluating the potential risks involved in the experimental or commercial usage of a genetically modified organism should be constrained to identify possible, adverse ecological consequences of its usage and their likelihood of occurrence. The limits and uncertainties of the scientific knowledge and experimental data underpinning the technical evaluation of risks should be clearly indicated. Although such a technical risk evaluation constitutes an important element in the decision making process to consent or not to consent, other considerations should be taken into account. A review of current scientific-technical controversies surrounding the risk assessment in biotechnology would go beyond the scope of this contribution. However, it is of utmost importance to seriously consider the methodological problems to integrate knowledge stemming from a variety of disciplines in biology and life sciences, of which each may utilize different conceptual models of nature at its multitude of (trophic) levels and interactions, in order to achieve a technical risk evaluation of a high quality.

In this context, the results of a study (Free University of Amsterdam 1991) commissioned by the Netherlands' Ministry of Economic Affairs in 1991 showed that in the Netherlands two communication networks on biotechnology exist alongside each other with little exchange of information between those two networks. One network, the most influential one, comprises organizations and persons in the area of research, industry and government. This network is internally well-informed on biotechnological applications and legislative regulations. It has therefore excellent access to a diversity of sources for information and possesses more secretarial facilities and financial power than the second network. The second network comprises (non-governmental) farmer-, rural women-, environmental-, consumer- and animal protection organizations, with quite different levels of information and usually with much less facilities and financial means.

As regards the ecological effects of the deliberate release of genetically modified organisms into the environment, the organizations of the first, dominant network tend to put a primary emphasis on a case-by-case approach to a scientific assessment of possible risks to human health and the environment and their management through safety measures, whilst the organizations of the second network consider the potential risks as being part of much wider concerns, such as socio-economic and ethical consequences of biotechnological developments in general. These differences in perception of the risks involved in biotechnology between the two networks reflect OECD's distinction between scientific *acceptability* and public *acceptance*.

To my opinion, this divergence of opinions on the regulation and control of biotechnology follows from conflicting views on other levels. Broadly speaking, the first network perceives the role of biotechnology as indispensable in sustainable development. In other words, it views biotechnology as a high technology having the potential to reconcile economy and ecology. In contrast, the second network views biotechnology as an ill-conceived attempt to repair damages to human health and the environment caused by current industrial and agricultural technologies. In this perspective, biotechnology constitutes a technological fix, which will only sustain current practices and conceptual approaches in industry, agriculture and food production. Most organizations of the second network advocate a more radical departure from these practices and the concepts on which these are based, and propose biological and ecological farming methods as more suitable for a sustainable economy. Moreover, these controversies also seem to be rooted in very different conceptions and images of nature-culture relations and interactions. Some of these are based on grounds of scientific or political nature, whereas others are based on grounds of religious or spiritual nature. This variety of concepts, ideas and images of nature constitutes a very complicating factor in the public debate on the acceptance of biotechnology.

The study of the Netherlands' Ministry of Economic Affairs suggested two different approaches to a policy communicating biotechnology related issues by the government. One approach is to stimulate the first network (in which the government is already heavily involved) to deploy activities to increase the level of knowledge within the second network, for example through information campaigns. However, it was not likely that such campaigns will increase the societal acceptance of biotechnology as the second network probably will perceive such campaigns as mere propaganda.

Another approach for the government would be to start the discussion in close cooperation with the second network. Such a dialogue would offer the first network insight in issues of societal importance, whilst the second network will be provided with an opportunity to give a constructive input into biotechnology (research) policy and regulations. One of the report's recommendations was that such a dialogue should be an on-going process between all parties concerned to look for 'acceptable' applications of biotechnology. Another recommendation was to let an intermediate, a relative outsider to both networks, who can skilfully judge propositions from either side on their acceptability for the other, act as a moderator of the discussion.

5. National Legal Provisions and Other Mechanisms for Public Information and Participation

On assignment of the Netherlands' Ministry of the Environment, MEBO Environmental Consultancy prepared an inventory[1] of the (legal) possibilities for public information and participation within the framework of national regulations on safety in biotechnology in European countries, including the views of several non-governmental organisations[2] (NGOs) on these possibilities. The inventory provided the background information for the *Seminar on Public Information and Participation*,[3] which was held on July 6th, 1994 in the Netherlands. The objective of the seminar was to exchange information of the different mechanisms and practices on public information and participation in European countries. In addition, it also aimed at gaining insight in how these mechanisms and practices are perceived by the NGOs.

COUNTRY	CONTAINED USE[1]			DELIBERATE RELEASE[2]		
	information provisions	participation provisions	public representation in advisory body	information provisions	participation provisions	public representation in advisory body
Austria	yes	yes	no	yes	yes	no
Belgium	yes	no	no	no	yes	no
Denmark	yes	yes	no	yes	yes	no
France	yes[4]	yes	no	yes	no	yes
Germany	yes	yes[5]	yes	yes	yes	yes
Ireland	yes	no	no	yes	no	no
Italy	no	no	no	no	no	no
the Netherlands	yes	yes[5]	no	yes	yes	no
Norway	yes	no	yes	yes	yes	no
Portugal	no	no	no	no	yes	no
Spain	yes	yes	no	no	yes	no
Sweden	yes	yes	no	yes	yes	no
Switzerland	no	no	no	yes	no	no
United Kingdom	no[3]	no	no	yes	yes	yes

1. *The contents of these provisions differ widely from country to country. The contents vary from having information available upon request to announcing the submission of notifications through newspapers and placing them on a public register. Only in Austria, Belgium, Denmark and the Netherlands it is mandatory to provide the public with information about these notifications. Moreover, except Belgium, Ireland, Portugal, Switzerland and the United Kingdom, most European countries have established legal provisions for public participation in the notification procedures. In some of the countries it is possible to submit comments to the Competent Authority (CA) and in other countries one may legally challenge, appeal or object a decision by the CA, often depending on the proposed risk classification of the notified contained use activity.*

2. *The provisions vary from having information publicly available through public registers to announcing applications in the proximity of the sites of release through posters at the town hall as in France, or through announcements in national newspapers and governmental publications as in Austria, Belgium, Denmark, the Netherlands and the United Kingdom. As regards public participation in the application procedures, all European countries, except Belgium, Ireland, Italy, Portugal and Switzerland have established provisions. The possibilities vary from submitting comments to legally challenging, appealing or objecting decisions made by the CA.*

3. *In case of first time use and risk categories 2, 3 and 4.*

4. *Consent cases are placed on public register.*

5. *In case of risk categories 2, 3 and 4.*

5.1 Perspectives on the United Kingdom

At the seminar the representative of the CA indicated that the approach to public information taken on contained use differed a little from the procedure for deliberate release, in recognition of the differences between the two types of activities. In particular, contained use work often represented an early research or developmental stage, when the future commercial values of a project was unclear. Flexible safeguards for intellectual property were therefore necessary. However, the systems for contained use and deliberate release were similar in that both were based on maximizing free access to information rather than active public involvement in case by case decision making.

The representative of an environmental NGO viewed that the system for access to information satisfied a basic 'right to know', although some other UK NGOs using the registers had felt that information had not been provided quickly enough. This was to be considered as a start up problem. However, the operation of the register had raised a number of other issues:

1.   Applicants may request to withhold commercially confidential information from the register. In at least one case, information withheld on these grounds had been central to understanding the risk assessment put forward by the company. However, only a few companies had sought to withhold substantial amounts of information.

2.   There is no formal system of consultation, and no requirement to take comments from the public or NGOs into account.

3.   The legal provision setting up the registers states that they should include "a summary of the reasons why the national biosafety advisory committee has advised that the consent should not be granted". It should also be able to give a few sentences of its reasoning on important aspects of any application, and why the balance of opinion came down in favour of granting a consent. A recent re-assessment of its advice to give a consent to a release involving a baculovirus modified to carry a scorpion gene did result in the register carrying a few lines explaining the basis of their judgement. This had set a helpful precedent and was a practice that should be continued.

4.   The monitoring data so far put on register were very brief, and were limited to data gained in response to formal monitoring requirements included in the consent. To give the public confidence that the assumptions made in risk assessments are being borne out in practice, the data that reach the register on the outcome of releases needed to be fuller.

5.   SNIFS (Summary Notification Information Formats that are exchanged between the CAs of EU member states) are not put on the UK register, and are marked for CA attention only. Many NGOs around Europe saw this as an unnecessary restriction on public information.

5.2 Perspectives on Germany

The Law on Genetic Engineering of 1990 provided for very extensive public participation in the authorization procedure for commercial genetic engineering installations and deliberate release operations. From the very outset, according to the representative of the CA at the seminar, the provisions governing public participation had been targeted by demands to amend the Law on Genetic Engineering against the background of a more general discussion on Germany as a location for biotechnology. The view that the consultation procedures, in their original form, had failed to meet the expectations placed on them, and would jeopardize the ability of the CAs responsible for release operations to function, prevailed. The Law amending the Law on Genetic Engineering of December 1993 therefore set about reducing the degree of public participation. The most significant amendment was that a public hearing no longer takes place in the context of the application procedure for releases.

The way in which the amendment of the regulations had been received depended on the perspective of those affected. Applicants had welcomed the reduction of public participation. For the present, the CA's ability to function seemed to be guaranteed. Without the relief provided by the amendment the CA would have had to prepare and hold hearing procedures to hear almost 50,000 objections per release case. On the whole the reaction of nature conservation associations and genetic engineering critics had been negative. As a consequence, the German Nature Conservation Circle had, at least temporarily, withdrawn its representative from the Central Commission for Biological Safety, the CA's advisory body. On the other hand, whereas the environmental groups lamented the abolition of the hearing procedures for release operations, at the same time they had referred to such hearings as token events, as a frustrating farce over whose disappearance there was no need to mourn.

As a response to the CA's contribution to the seminar, the representative of a local anti-genetic engineering group focused on their experience with the authorization procedure on a specific release experiment (before the amendment of the Law). The following issues were addressed:

1. The application forms could only be examined at local government offices, and it was not allowed to make copies. These conditions had not allowed NGOs to examine the risk evaluation in a thorough way as relevant scientific libraries were barely within reach of the release site in a rather remote area.
2. Objections could only be submitted by individuals, and not by NGOs, and these individuals had to show the likelihood of being directly affected by adverse effects on their own health or properties as a potential consequence of a specific release.
3. Objections against releases on the basis of social and political arguments, or criticizing the scientific methods and aims of a release were considered beyond the scope of the legislation. However, despite the legal scope of objections allowed to be taken into account by the CA in the decision-making procedure, NGOs should continue to use a broad spectrum of specific and general, scientific and ethical considerations.
4. The hearings had revealed the CA's inability to give a clear definition of the concept of 'environmental harm' and had shown a lack of basic biological knowledge on several occasions.

As one of the consequences of the abolishment of the public hearing provision, the NGOs should now focus their efforts on non-institutionalized forms of influencing public opinion towards deliberate releases of genetically engineered organisms.

5.3 Perspectives on Norway

Public information and consultation were key issues in raising awareness and promoting public acceptance of modern biotechnology, according to the representative of the Norwegian CA. These issues had to be seen in the larger context of general rules on access to information and participation which are applied in Norway.

Act No. 69 (19 June 1970) concerning Public Access to Documents in the (Public) Administration rules that documents in administrative cases are public. In principle, this meant that anyone can access any document issued or received by central and local government bodies. The main exceptions were documents drawn up for an agency's internal preparations of a case and information which was subject to a statutory obligation of secrecy, for example, confidential business information.

More specifically, the Genetechnology Act contains a specific rule concerning the kind of information that cannot be kept confidential. Public participation under the Genetechnology Act has also been made explicit. Further, it was pointed out that the Norwegian Genetechnology Act also regulates aspects such as ethical and social considerations and issues related to sustainability. How these provisions would be utilized in practice was as yet not clear. The following issues were raised in more detail by the representative of the CA:

1.   Public participation should be secured at the EU-level, as not only industry, but also NGOs should, as far as possible, be involved in discussions on new legislative or policy proposals.

2.   Public participation in Norway should be secured in case its national legislation had to be amended, due to changes in European Union legislation, since the Norwegian CA has to comply with its national legislation to consult the public before changing it.

3.   Despite that the final legal decision by the national CAs is taken after consultation of all EU member states, it should be possible for Norwegian citizens to maintain a right of appeal in case of placing GMO-products on the market. Within the Norwegian regulatory framework, this decision would be subject to appeal. From a Community perspective, this seems to be problematic considering the finality of the decision making process as foreseen by Article 21 in Directive 90/220/EEC.

However, no concrete solutions were proposed or suggested by the representative of the Norwegian CA.

5.4 Perspectives on Sweden

According to the representative of a Swedish nature protection organization, all Nordic countries have a similar tradition with respect to freedom of information. The Nordic rules are not limited to specific fields or to specific subject matters. They are in general considerably stronger and more far-reaching compared to those of other European countries. Sweden has a similar public consultation process on release applications as Norway. During these consultations in Sweden, many times discussions had taken place that had gone beyond a strictly technical evaluation of the risks involved in a specific release. The Swedish Law on Biotechnology also contains a provision to take ethical aspects of a GMO-release into account. Compared to the Norwegian law the Swedish formulation was viewed as much weaker. Like in Norway, it was as yet not clear how this provision will be utilized in practice.

1.   A commonality in the perception of both the representative of the Norwegian CA and the Swedish NGO was their fear that the Nordic approach to an open and democratic government would not be able to stand up against the way of

decision-making in the European Union in the light of its democratic deficit.
2. Most releases conducted in Sweden were very similar to those in other European countries. An example of a release experiment was presented, from which the information in the application had been classified as confidential in France, while the whole dossier had been made publicly available in Sweden. It was therefore a necessity to develop clear and common criteria as to what constitutes a valid claim for confidentiality, in order to harmonize public access to information at the European level.

5.5 Perspectives on the Netherlands

The Dutch Constitution provides that the government should perform its duties in open communication with the public. Derogations from this principle can only be made by way of parliamentary legislation and are laid down in the Government Information (Public Access) Act. Such derogations may be constituted by information that might damage the security of the State and confidential business information.

This act affects, for instance, the workings of the national advisory body to the CA as their meetings must be open to the public, and its papers must be disclosed, unless one of the aforementioned derogations is applicable. An important conclusion by the representative of the CA was that, as far as it concerns public information and participation, Dutch law did not treat GMOs as a special substance and in this respect the situation was very similar to the UK situation. Moreover, the CA also deployed some non-legal mechanisms for communicating with the public. The following examples were mentioned: The organization of seminars on specific issues for all parties interested, and the organization of so-called 'field trial days' for applicants, representatives of the CA, its advisory body and everyone who has submitted objections or taken legal actions against the Minister of Environment.

In her contribution the representative of an environmental NGO indicated that:
1. The organization had frequently pointed out procedural omissions in application procedures and appealed against permits issued by the CA. As a result, the permits were often rejected by the Council of State on formal grounds. However, more fundamental issues raised in the objections, like the validity of risk assessment and ethical concerns, had never been dealt with by the Council of State.
2. Further, an improvement of the science of risk assessment was seen as a prerequisite towards an agreement on safety measurements needed to minimize risks to the environment and the consumer.
3. The issue was raised that in the case of an approval to market a GMO-product by another EU member state, it was not clear where a Dutch NGO could submit objections or make an appeal. Therefore, the conclusion was drawn that, due to the relative openness of the Dutch system, it was nice to have discussions at the national level. However, the lack of transparency of the decision-making processes within the European Union undermined the potential usefulness of these discussions at the national level.
5. Finally, there was also a need for a more sensible discussion on the contribution of gene technology towards a sustainable future.

5.6 Perspectives on France

According to the representative of the CA, the question what kind of information is relevant to the public had been debated extensively. On the one hand, general information on environmental releases of genetically modified organisms did not allow to understand all the ins and outs of a release, which might cause indifference or dogmatic reactions by the public. On the other hand, precise information was difficult to apprehend by the general public and raised the issue of the confidentiality of the information submitted. Therefore, the legislation had specified which information was to be considered non-confidential. In addition, it had been decided, when possible, that information should be made publicly available in the proximity of the release site. For each release of transgenic plants, a sheet of information would be written and would contain a description of the non-confidential information. This information sheet would be sent to the Prefect of the Department (region) where the release will take place. An announcement at the town hall should indicate the existence of the information sheet. Every citizen may submit comments to the ministry responsible for the release authorization.

According to the representative of an environmental organization:

1.   The information sheets were only made publicly available after the CA had taken their decision to grant an authorization to release. On the other hand, he acknowledged that the CA receives the advice of its national biosafety advisory body (Commission du Génie Biomoleculaire, CGB), which has at least a channel through which the public could make its opinion known and through which they could eventually participate in the decision making process. The majority of the CGB-members, however, comes from the scientific community, especially from the domain of biomolecular engineering, and therefore implicitly tended to favour the release of genetically modified organisms.

2.   In addition, the quality of risk assessment was questioned as the scientific experts of the CGB mainly seemed to be concerned with the construction of the organism. Studies on the long term ecological impacts of large and commercial scale releases were ignored, partly because the scientific tools to conduct such studies did not yet exist.

3.   Further, the discussions within the CGB were not open to the public. It would however be interesting to know the reasons for rejecting an application, or the changes demanded by the CA in order to be able to authorize a release. This would enable the 'civil society' to understand the level of risk acceptable to the CGB in relation to interests of the release.

6. Outlooks at the Community Level

At the final session, Goffredo Del Bino from the EU Commission's DG XI, elucidated recent policy commitments[4] towards open dialogue, access to information and transparency undertaken by the Commission in 1992 and 1993. As regards access to environmental information at a Community-wide level the Council of Ministers adopted on 7 June 1990 Directive 90/313/EEC on the Freedom of Access to

Information on the Environment. This Directive places an obligation on all public authorities at national, regional or local level to ensure freedom of, access to, and dissemination of information relating to the environment. This means any available information in written, visual, oral or data base form, on the state of the environment and on activities or measures adversely affecting or likely to affect the environment as well as information on administrative and other measures taken. Under this Directive any person has a right of access to all information other than that protected under commercial and industrial confidentiality, without having to prove an interest. The authorities are obliged to respond within 2 months, and reasons must be given for a refusal to provide the information requested. To the opinion of Del Bino, this is quite a far-reaching piece of legislation in terms of access to information. However, there are no general Community provisions concerning public consultation or participation, as this could be considered an issue to be dealt with by Member States under the principle of subsidiarity. More specifically for biotechnology, the specific provisions on access to information of Directives 90/219/EEC and 90/220/EEC on the use and release of GMOs had to be seen as complementary to those of Directive 90/313/EEC. Del Bino indicated that the EU Commission has an open and positive attitude to public information and consultation.

In the plenary discussion after his contribution, a member of the European Parliament indicated to know many organizations and people requesting information on environmental issues from the EU Commission, who complain they were sabotaged in their efforts. The reply to this criticism was that the issues surrounding access to information just had started to evolve.

Ranking of countries according to their attitude to public involvement in decision making over the use of GMOs as derived by Sue Mayer, Greenpeace-UK, using information in the MEBO survey:

Country	Attitude to public participation
SWEDEN AUSTRIA DENMARK NORWAY THE NETHERLANDS	RECEPTIVE
GERMANY	INCREASING AMBIVALENCE
SPAIN UNITED KINGDOM BELGIUM FRANCE	GRUDGING ACCEPTANCE
IRELAND SWITZERLAND PORTUGAL ITALY	HOSTILE

In her contribution to the final session, Sue Mayer from Greenpeace-UK presented a ranking of countries as regards their attitude to public involvement (see above). The ranking was to be considered as a subjective assessment of whether they appear to welcome and make easy public involvement. The scale moves from the frankly hostile at the bottom, to grudging acceptance, to those countries at the top which take real steps to seek public opinion. Countries considered to be grudgingly accepting were those where the public could obtain information but this was not encouraged or made easy, countries considered to be hostile showed they had little intention of making information available.

At the end of the seminar, the question was raised how to bridge the gap between differences in world view. One of the participants phrased the issue as follows:

> One world view is that science has answers and the other is that it may not. What are the consequences? The problem we all will go away with is: Are we correct to cling to either one of these world views? Can we ever constructively discuss these things? Or does it come down to a straight fight and who wins public hearts and minds?

To Mayer's opinion, the controls which are exerted over what are legitimate areas for risk assessment poses another difficulty. Exclusion of the public through the construction of a purely technical agenda for the risk assessment was seen by most NGOs as missing the point. In their view, more fundamental questions have to be asked, like: Why is the risk being taken and in whose interest is society being asked to take this risk? What other ways are there of providing the claimed benefits that would not involve genetic transfer? Are the claimed benefits actually real for those who will bear the risks? Therefore, NGOs suggested that CAs and their advisory committees must enter into dialogue with the public about what constitutes harm, and how to deal with scientific uncertainty and ignorance. In addition, it was proposed not to commit to only one high risk technology, but to develop a diversity of approaches, including ecological agriculture. At the seminar itself, none of the CA-representatives reacted to these suggestions.

According to Mayer, what constitutes harm to nature is decided by advisory committees, whose members make judgements from their own world view with little or no opportunity for democratic review. This was illustrated by considering the UK's Guidelines on Fast Track Procedures for Certain Releases of GMOs, in which the UK's advisory biosafety committee had effectively decided upon a definition of harm which had never been subjected to external scrutiny. Genetic pollution was therefore being tacitly sanctioned, since the committee had decided that the transfer of some specified genes does not constitute (significant) harm. A different world view, which considers that any genetic pollution constitutes harm by introducing DNA which could not have been transferred by natural mechanisms, would have come to a different conclusion from a review of the same scientific data. In the plenary discussion after her contribution, one of the members of the UK advisory committee commented that information about the proposals for Fast Track Procedures had been sent out, but no response at all was received. This was perceived as very frustrating by the people involved in administration.

7. Some Personal Observations and Comments

As the seminar preceded the Xth Meeting of the national CAs for the implementation of Directives 90/219/EEC and 90/220/EEC, it would have been of relevance to the NGOs to have been informed whether the issues discussed at the seminar were on the agenda of that CA-meeting, or, as a consequence of the seminar, have been put on the agenda. However, these meetings are not open to the public and their minutes are not publicly disclosed. Further, after more than a year, to my knowledge, the initiative of the Dutch CA to start discussions between CAs and NGOs, through the organization of the seminar, has had no follow-up by the CA of another EU member state, and the results of the seminar have had hardly any effect on improving and harmonizing the legal provisions for public information and participation between European countries.

During the mid-1990s, the number of applications for approval to place GMOs on the market of the European Union was starting to be considerable. Several products based on genetically modified organisms have been given market clearance at that time. Until then, due to internal disagreement between the national CAs and the European Commission on monitoring and data requirements concerning risk assessment, including its scope, all decisions on the placing of GMO-products on the market have been established under Article 21 of Directive 90/220/EEC. Moreover, the issue of establishing unambiguous, scientific-technical criteria as to the concept of 'environmental harm' also needed to be resolved between the CAs and the European Commission. This indicates that in every case at least one member state did not wish consent to be given and that therefore in every case a vote on the matter had to be taken.

Hence, the conclusion is justified that different perspectives between and within European countries on the required quality of risk assessment in biotechnology do exist, which indicate that other than scientific-technical considerations are indeed, however very implicitly, exerting their influence on the outcome of the decision-making process on applications for the (commercial) release of genetically modified organisms. Again, these findings confirm the gap between the scientific *acceptability* of a (commercial) application of GMOs, which should be the same to every CA of a EU member state, and its *acceptance*, which appeared to differ among the CAs of the member states.

To my opinion, it is highly unlikely that the gap between *acceptability* and *acceptance* will be bridged in the nearby future, given the attitudes of the parties involved. Take for example the following exchange of views at the seminar between a representative of a consumer NGO and the chairman of a national biosafety advisory committee, who was genuinely wondering what the scope of the discussion was:

> It seems to me that the two directives have been set up to assess the possible harm to humans and the environment involved in releasing genetically modified organisms. What I hear from the NGOs is why don't we give them greater opportunity to discuss sociological issues. We as CAs want public participation in risk assessment, but this NGO attitude gets in the way. It is not the role of CAs to take sociological issues into consideration (..) One should separate the risk assessment of an individual release of a genetically modified organism and the sociological aspects, which should be part of a more general assessment

of the whole of the technology.

Although the representative of a consumer NGO showed some understanding for this viewpoint, he did not fully agree:

> I can understand that you as a scientific committee have to make a scientific evaluation of the risks. But you must understand the view of NGOs, too. To their opinion, the assessment of the risks cannot fully be separated from wider concerns. Why should we discuss the risks of an application we do not think useful at all?

At the same time, the European Commission (CEC 1993a), in recognition of its White Paper, has intensified its efforts to remain an attractive location for the biotechnology industry, and has considerably expanded research programmes within the area of Life Sciences and Technologies. Its expenditure of 1,572 million ECU signified an increase in budget of 741 million ECU compared to a previous similar programme. Three specific areas with respect to biotechnology research were identified, including "areas which are essential to the exploitation of the life sciences, but which may require special attention in respect of other factors such as socio-economic or ethical issues, would be addressed by activities, involving key players and users in a dialogue aimed at socially acceptable solutions and a well-informed public" (CEC 1993). Through these programmes and mechanisms, the European Commission expects to achieve a fuller realization of the Community's potential in biotechnology. Especially its perspective on the latter areas reveals that some of the key players, like consumer and environmental NGOs, remain to be viewed as of strategic importance to developments in European biotechnology.

Whether the follow-up activities as suggested at the seminar on public information and participation would be organized by the European commission or the national CAs, was unclear at the time of this writing. At the end of the seminar, it was recommended that issues such as scientific uncertainty in risk assessment and its scope, the kind of information that should be made publicly available and the kind of information that may be considered as confidential business information and the potential role of biotechnology to sustainable development, needed a more in-depth discussion. However, given the issues to be discussed between industry, CAs and NGOs, common sense suffices to foresee long and difficult debates between all parties concerned about developments in biotechnology, especially if one of the parties does not feel taken seriously.

Harmonization at the European level of the rules for public access to information, establishment of clearcut criteria as to what constitutes confidential business information, development of common methodologies to risk assessment, including data and monitoring requirements, and establishment as to what constitutes 'environmental harm' are a prerequisite to be able to judge from the viewpoint of scientific *acceptability* whether a certain GMO-application could be accepted.

However, to be able to judge from the viewpoint of public *acceptance*, fora at the national and European level are needed to discuss issues relating to sustainability and socio-economic and ethical concerns. It would be difficult to organize active consultation on every GMO-application, since the number coming forward is gradually increasing. My suggestion is to address this by public consultations on important applications to release, like applications involving a donor/host combination that has never been seen before, or applications involving significant scaling up from previous releases. A second possible approach, that might be able to deal with the full range of issues raised by GMOs, including impacts on the environment and on agriculture, is a national biotechnology advisory board, a body independent from the regulatory system, but with sufficient links to regulators to ensure that its views help to influence the future direction of the regulatory system, as well as to biotechnology research policy makers. It would be composed of representatives of NGOs, industry, and academic institutions, but the majority of members would have public interest affiliations.

Notes

1. Except the CAs from Greece and Luxembourg, all CAs from EU Member States, Austria, Norway, Sweden, and Switzerland have cooperated in preparing the overview.
2. The following NGOs have cooperated in preparing the overview and/or participated in the seminar: Natur og Ungdom (Friends of the Earth-Norway), Swedish Society for the Conservation of Nature, NOAH (Friends of the Earth-Denmark), BUND (Friends of the Earth-Germany), Arbeitskreis gegen Gentechnologie Göttingen (local group of the Gen-Ethic Network, Germany), Cork Environmental Alliance (Ireland), Greenpeace-United Kingdom, The Green Alliance (United Kingdom), World Wide Fund for Nature (United Kingdom), Stichting Consument & Biotechnologie (the Netherlands), Stichting Natuur & Milieu (the Netherlands), Vita Vitalis (Belgium), Greenpeace-France, Confédération Syndical du Cadre de Vie (France), Gruppo sulla Attenzione di Biotecnologia (Italy), Greenpeace-Switzerland, Friends of the Earth-Europe (Brussels).
3. The seminar preceded the Xth Meeting of the national CAs for the implementation of Directives 90/219/EEC and 90/220/EEC, 7-8 July 1994, Heemskerk, the Netherlands. Part of this process are three-monthly meetings for the exchange of views between the CAs. These meetings are often preceded by a seminar on a specific theme.
4. On 2 December 1992, a first Communication on Transparency was adopted indicating ways to improve access to information during the preparation of the legislative proposals, (OJ C 64, 05.03.1993). On the same date a further Communication was adopted concerning open dialogue with interest groups, proposing a code of conduct and a transparent list of the interest groups who are contacting the Commission (OJ C 64, 05.03.1993). The progress in implementation of these was reported in a further Communication adopted in June 1993 on Transparency in the Community (OJ C 166, 17.06.1993). On 5 May 1993, the Commission adopted a further Communication (COM(93) 191 final) in which it stated that in principle, open access to all Commission documents should be authorised, with only certain exceptions, aimed at protecting public and private interests (OJ C 156, 08.06.1993). The adoption by Council on 6 december 1993 of a Code of Conduct on Improved Access to Information, to be implemented jointly by the Council and the Commission. Under this Code of Conduct any individual has the right to ask for preparatory and working documents of the Commission before an official Commission decision is taken. The adoption on 2 February 1994 of a further Communication (C/94/125-2) outlining a range of measures to improve openness, dialogue and access to information.

References

Cantley, M.F. 1995. 'Popular attitudes and the public interest.' In: M. Fransman, G. Junne and A. Roobeek (eds.), *The Biotechnology Revolution*. Oxford UK & Cambridge USA: Blackwell.

[CEC] Commission of the European Community 1993a. *Biotechnology and the White Paper on Growth, Competitiveness and Employment; preparing the next stage*. Communication from the Commission to the Council, the European Parliament and the Economic and Social Committee.

————. 1993b. *The S&T content of the specific programmes implementing the 4th Framework Programme for Community research and technological development (1994-1998) and the Framework Programme for Community research and training for the European Atomic Energy Community (1994-1998)*. COM (93)459, Brussels, 6 October: Section Life Sciences and Technologies.

————. 1993c. *Summary Record of a Round Table on the Biotechnology Regulatory Framework*. EU Commission Secretary General, 4 October, SG (93) D/149516/D.

Dodet, B. 1994. 'Industrial perception of EC biotechnology regulations.' *Trends in Biotechnology* **12** (December), pp.473-476.

Free University of Amsterdam 1991. *Application of genetically modified organisms in the environment: Knowledge, involvement and considerations of NGOs*, Working Group Biology & Society, Ministry of Economic Affairs, August. (Toepassing van genetisch gemodificeerde organismen in het milieu: kennis, betrokkenheid en overwegingen van maatschappelijke organisaties, Werkgroep Biologie en Samenleving, Vrije Universiteit Amsterdam, Ministerie van Economische Zaken, augustus 1991).

Friends of the Earth Europe 1993. *Letter to the European Commission*. 20 August.

[OECD] Organization for Economic Cooperation and Development 1989. *Biotechnology: Economic and Wider Impacts*. Paris.

12

On How the People Can Become 'The Prince': Machiavellian Advice to NGOs on GMOs

Peter Wheale and Ruth McNally

1. Introduction

'The bio-industrial complex'[1] is a world-wide complex of scientific expertise, technological capabilities and transnational capital accumulation operating on a global scale which is underpinned by modern genetic engineering techniques (*micro*genetic engineering) and demands large-scale replacement technology, public funding and state regulation – see Wheale and McNally 1988 Part II, 1994; McNally and Wheale 1994, 1995a). In this paper we argue that if we want to question the technological design which shapes our social relationships and challenge the power structures of 'the bio-industrial complex', then it is not enough merely to appeal to *alternative* technologies and democratised societies, because that just makes life easier for 'power-holders' or controlling agents, 'the Princes' – in this instance, the biotechnology industry, government funding bodies and regulatory agencies which are integral to the 'bio-industrial complex'. No, we support Bruno Latour's (Latour 1988: 39) position that we must "get inside science and technology, that is, to penetrate where society and science are simultaneously defined through the same strategems." We believe that non-governmental organisations (NGOs) have the necessary dynamism and flexibility to transform the 'bio-industrial complex' and are therefore well placed to achieve this penetration. We appeal to NGOs, in the form of a letter after the style of that sent by Nicolo Machiavelli to the Magnificent Lorenzo De' Medici, to formulate strategies to liberate the European citizen from what we argue is 'authoritarian' (bio)technology.

In the essay that follows we proffer our advice, in Machiavellian guise, to NGOs on how they might best recognise opportunities and devise strategies for 're-engineering' the biotechnology project in Europe in line with democratic principles. After some reflections on democratic technology and pragmatic approaches to understanding the nature of reality, we advise NGOs concerning: the constancy of ideological positions; the introduction of a risk-benefit analysis in place of the risk analysis which is required by the deliberate release Directive 90/220/EEC; the concept of risk assessment as merely a technical exercise; the lack of resources for, and paucity of data on, risk assessment work; the importance of defining 'risk' and 'harm'; and the European Commission's implementation of 'harmonisation', 'transparency' and 'step-by-step' approaches to genetic engineering. Finally, we exhort NGOs to accept the role of liberating the people from 'authoritarian' biotechnology.

Letter from Peter Wheale and Ruth McNally to NGOs:

GENETIC engineering underpins a world-wide complex of scientific expertise, technological capabilities and transnational capital accumulation operating on a global scale. This complex constitutes what we call the 'bio-industrial complex' and it forms an integral part of the hyperindustrialisation which characterises the emerging post-modern order, a socio-technical order which is radically changing our relationships both on a micro-level – for example, the employer-employee relationship, the doctor-patient relationship, the agricultural supplier-farmer relationship, and the mother-baby relationship, and on a macro-level – the North-South relationship, and the technosphere-biosphere relationship. We believe these relationships and the technological design which shapes them are essentially authoritarian, that is, they are ILLEGITIMATELY hierarchical, and the power structures which support them should be challenged and the technology which shapes them should be democratised.

In the essay which follows we presume to proffer our advice to you, the non-governmental organisations (NGOs), in something of the style of Nicolo Machiavelli – the master strategist of REALPOLITIK, on how we believe you might best recognise opportunities and devise strategies for 're-engineering' the biotechnology project in Europe in line with democratic principles. We hope you will not consider it too presumptuous of us but as it is our sincere intention to be of service to you we are fully confident that you will be kind enough to accept it, seeing that we could not give you a more valuable gift than the means of being able in a very short space of time to grasp all that we, over so many years and at some discomfort, have learned and understood. We have not embellished this essay with superfluous decoration or overburdened it with extensive referencing, for our ambition has been that nothing should distinguish this essay save for its contents and the seriousness of its subject matter.

We consider that you have the necessary dynamism and flexibility through your informal networks to transform the 'bio-industrial complex'. It is because your role is to make controversies visible and to problematise social relations, including those of science and technology, that you are the best placed social agents to achieve this transformation and to mobilise public opinion. This is why we appeal to you to act as a Liberator – to liberate The People from authoritarian technology.

Peter Wheale & Ruth McNally
(Tilburg & London, 10th September 1995).

2. Concerning Democracy and Technology

> *A man who is made a prince by the favour of the people should work to retain their friendship; and this is easy for him because the people ask only not to be oppressed.* (Machiavelli 1970, *The Prince*, 'IX: The constitutional principality', p. 69)

Scientists have been conceived as citizens of *virtu*, self-rulers of a perfect moral commonwealth, and in this Republic of Science they were presumed apolitical, fraternal and disinterested (Gibbons and Wittrock 1985). Such a utopian conception of a scientific fraternity has long since been demythologised in favour of a more realistic conception of scientists as men and women who will act pragmatically and politically as they perceive the circumstances demand. Indeed, many scientists have welcomed the increased association between science, government and industry because such *corporatism* has aided them in obtaining the order of financial support necessary for the development of, so-called, 'big science'. Far from being disinterested, in the years following World War II the expansion of national government-funded scientific research (see, for example, Wheale et al. 1986, Chapter 4), and, more recently, European Commission-funded research and technological development programmes, has caused both science and technology policy in Europe to become highly politicised.

Biotechnology is given pride of place in the recommendations of the European Commission's White Paper on growth, competitiveness and employment (CEC 1994a), reflecting the belief of the European Commission that modern biotechnology is a field of human endeavour offering great potential for innovation and economic growth, amply justifying boldly corporatist strategies (see Wheale and McNally 1993). The European Commission (SEC 1991) takes the view that public authorities, using millions of ECU of EU tax payers' money, should help to stimulate competitiveness by providing financial support for basic and applied research and strengthening the related infrastructure by instituting a regulatory framework which facilitates the patenting of living organisms, stimulating technology transfer, and disseminating information designed to improve public understanding and consumer choice.

European biotechnology forms but a part of the hyperindustrialisation which characterises the emerging post-modern order. The 'bio-industrial complex' produces technology which reflects its power structure and is producing technologies which configure the user or consumer in particular ways and therefore have an important role in shaping our social relationships. Biotechnological design is essentially *authoritarian*, that is, it maintains *illegitimately* hierarchical social relationships. A technology is democratic if it has been designed by 'contestable design criteria' (because the process of generating and refining design criteria can never be finalised) to reflect democratic structures and if it has been chosen with democratic participation and oversight (Sclove 1995: 32-33).

If we wish to question these existing relationships we must change the technological design of the processes and products of the biotechnology industries and in doing this we pose a *democratic* challenge to the power structures of 'the bio-industrial complex'. Richard Sclove (1995) provides a pragmatic programme for institutionalising the core activities of democratic technological politics. He suggests how the microlevel steps: of awareness and mobilisation, social readiness to participate in core activities, including the initiation of democratic research and development design and integrative and constructive technology assessment (CTA), eventually leads to macrolevel structural transformation (see Figure 1). In Figure 1, the broken arrow indicates that the eventual macrolevel structural transformation, brought about in part by grass-roots efforts, would have a positive, facilitating, feedback effect on the core steps.

If European citizens are to acquire 'technological citizenship' with rights to information, participation and consent (particularly to avoidable risks incurred through the employment of technology), then, just as Rousseau's concept of citizenship in *The Social Contract* carries with it certain obligations to participate in the democratic process, so Frankenfeld (1992) argues, that these rights should be symmetrical with certain social duties, such as the duty to be informed and have autonomous thought, and to exercise technological civic literacy and technological civic virtue. We would not advocate that any miscreant should be 'forced to be free', as Rousseau suggested, but many scholars argue that if we had this 'external autonomy' (primarily, the right to informed consent) then, 'internal autonomy' (the ability to reflect rationally and to have moral responsibility) is likely to follow. To fully understand any activity it is essential to participate in it in order to learn the 'rules' which 'rest on a social context of common activity' (Winch 1958: 84). Moral understanding, according to Dahl (1985: 51), involves having an adequate understanding of the objectives of the governing system and only in a democratic system do people have the opportunity to develop their moral competence.

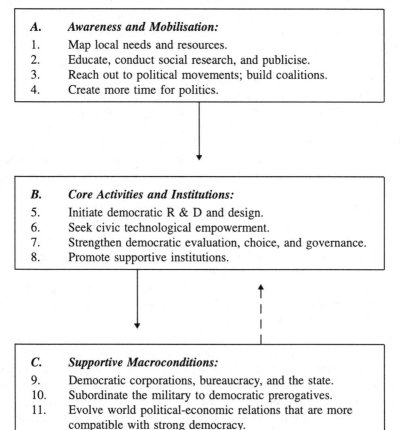

Figure 1: Institutionalizing a democratic politics of technology
(Source: R.E. Sclove 1995. *Democracy and Technology*. New York & London: Guilford Press, p.206)

Ultimately, it is not possible to *demonstrate* the superiority of the democratic system of governance over the authoritarian. The pragmatist's justification of tolerance, free inquiry, and the quest for undistorted communication can only take the form, as Richard Rorty (1985) argues,

> of a comparison between societies which exemplify these habits and those which do not, leading up to the suggestion that nobody who has experienced both would prefer the latter. It is exemplified by Winston Churchill's defense of democracy as the worst form of government imaginable, except for all the others which have been tried so far. Such justification is not by reference to a criterion, but by reference to various detailed practical advantages (Rorty 1985: 11-12).

This is the political and moral argument which we wish to put before you but we turn now to address the implied epistemological and metaphilosophical questions which are prone to confuse us and confound our purpose.

3. On Approaches to Understanding the Nature of Reality and What Our Strategy Towards Them Should Be

> *Our community – the community of the liberal intellectuals of the secular modern West – wants to be able to give a post factum account of any change of view. We want to be able, so to speak, to justify ourselves to our earlier selves . This preference is not built into us by human nature, it is just the way we live now* (Rorty 1985: 13).

The consequence of epistemological relativism is that all knowledge claims in science, ethics and aesthetics are *normatively* grounded. As the norms upon which the rationalised knowledge claims are 'constructed' are each different and derive from different 'value spheres' or fields of activity, this has given rise to notions of differentiated 'discourses', 'communication systems' or 'fields of argumentation' (for a recent taxonomic evaluation of the erosion of these, see Von Schomberg 1995: 15-16, and in this volume: Chapter 10). German scholars, in particular, Kant, and Max Weber and, more recently, Habermas and Luhmann, have been preoccupied with relativism and, in the latter two cases, even disturbed by the 'lonely provincialism' of our knowledge claims. However, any approach which characterises the different actors, social movements, interest groups or expert systems as organic wholes, operating within a single episteme, 'value sphere' or paradigm is not a reasonable characterisation of them but a caricaturisation.[2] It is a reification of the plasticity of discourse.

> To say that they have 'institutionalised norms' is only to say, with Foucault, that knowledge is never separable from power – that one is likely to suffer if one does not hold certain beliefs at certain times and places. But such institutional backups for beliefs take the form of bureaucrats and policemen, not of 'rules of language' and 'criteria of rationality'. To think otherwise is the Cartesian fallacy of seeing axioms where there are only shared habits, of viewing statements which summarize such practices as if they reported constraints enforcing such practices (Rorty 1985: 9).

From the pragmatists' perspective, however, the relativism of our knowledge claims is of enormous strategic value in discursive practices. First of all, the recognition that knowledge lacks an ahistorical and universal grounding means that all knowledge can be treated sceptically and is therefore more easily challenged. The idea that knowledge is contingent and revisable, that there is no 'totalising self-referential critique', no way of ultimately 'distinguishing between theory and ideology' or between 'true consensus' and 'false consensus' (Habermas 1987), is undermining the legitimacy of traditional scientific authority, and this is reflected in the public's increasingly critical attitude to 'expert systems' (see Wheale and McNally 1994). When there is a loss of faith in the epistemology which underpins *all* science-based expert systems, then the public can no longer trust any expert system to appraise the dangers and risks of technology because the theory underpinning the identification and measurement of these is underdetermined, that is, ultimately unknowable.

Secondly, without an ahistorical point of reference, 'only the dialogue is relevant', and as both constructivism and empiricism do contribute to *our* understanding of the world, to neglect the use of either one of these dimensions of our understanding of 'reality' is to self-impose a discursive constraint upon ourselves which will unnecessarily hamper our strategic objectives. In the realm of *realpolitik* we therefore believe it is strategically necessary for non-governmental organisations (NGOs) to use both the constructivist and the empiricist approaches in their discursive practices. In the field of genetically manipulated organisms (GMOs) it is important to recognise that the concept of 'risk' is a social construct and that decisions on what is an 'acceptable risk' are political. Nonetheless, there are also vital empirical inputs to such constructions and these empirical inputs, as well as their incumbent value-judgements, should be contested.

4. Concerning the Constancy of Ideological Positions

The question is no longer to free truth from the system of power – it would be a chimera since truth itself is power – but to separate the power of truth from the hegemonic forms (social, economic, cultural) inside which it circulates today. In brief, the political question is no longer that of mistake, illusion, alienated consciousness or ideology, it is that of truth itself (Foucault 1970: 26).

Just as the objects of knowledge – genetically engineered organisms, for example – are hybrids, so too are the *subjects* of knowledge; the subject of knowledge is a discursive construct. "Vision is no longer solely a matter of how the world impinges upon us but also the power to see, and hence the power to construct realities" (Prins 1993: 5). To this perspective of the partial, incongruent, fragmented subject we must add the notion of strategy. The contradictory ways in which the same subjects construct the same objects can be better understood by appreciating their strategic objectives, rather than by seeking to identify a unifying *grundnorm*, 'value sphere' or paradigm. And as Latour (1988: 30) observes: "'Science', 'technology' and 'economics' are three different faulty labels applied to only one serious strategic problem".

Although all discourses are necessarily ethnocentric, that is, culture-specific, their 'rules' do not constitute 'epistemic traps' – impenetrable incommensurate rationalities – because the culture which produces them is *our own* Western culture. And it is precisely because there is therefore an essentially shared rationality that interest groups can be strategically versatile in their constructions of contested objects, even constructing the same object in contradictory ways in different social arenas. This point can be illustrated by the contrary constructions of genetically engineered organisms used by industrialists in the fields of patenting and regulation. For the purposes of patentability, genetically engineered organisms are constructed as being unique and original; whereas, for the purposes of regulation they are constructed as being part of a continuum with naturally occurring organisms.

The European Commission may wish to present itself as politically neutral, rather in the mould of Max Weber's idealised bureaucracy of the rational-economic order, but it cannot escape the range of socio-economic and political pressures to which it is inevitably subject. Of course, the extent to which alternative knowledge claims – 'artefacts', to use Niklas Luhmann's (1986) term – are input into the 'communication system' of the European Commission varies depending partly on the differential resource mobilisation ability of different actors. NGOs with alternative or 'counter culture' knowledge claims are at a disadvantage, from a resource mobilisation point of view, as compared with the 'bio-industrial complex'. Nevertheless, as we have argued elsewhere (Wheale and McNally 1994; McNally and Wheale 1994, 1995a, 1995b), the reflexivity created by the communications of so-called 'new social movements' responding to the high-consequence risks of modernity has a dynamic function in the process of the institutional transformation of modernity to a post-modern order.

Our advice to NGOs is not to strive to be consistent – to eschew constancy – since consistency is an impediment not borne by your adversaries. Just as industry simultaneously argues in the legislative arena that genetically engineered organisms are merely part of a continuum with 'nature', whilst in the patenting debate that they are 'inventions', so too should NGOs be flexible in their approaches, adopting, and subtly adapting, their arguments instrumentally to suit the purposes of the debate. Do not be bullied into constancy by your critics since this will hamper your endeavours. And remember, the notion of a 'grand narrative' is untenable. The Western tradition that typically assumed "not to have property in the self is not to be a subject, and so not to have agency" (Haraway 1991: 135) must be abandoned. Do not fear being a 'cyborg' – a hybrid subject – and the hydra-like qualities it endows you with will confound your enemies.

5. Concerning Risks and Benefits

Science and technology are Janus-faced, simultaneously generating catastrophic as well as utopian scenarios (Wheale and McNally 1988: xv).

From time to time there has been pressure for the introduction of a risk-benefit analysis in place of the risk analysis which is required by the deliberate release Directive 90/220/EEC. For example, in 1989, when the European Parliament expressed its Opinion on the draft Directive, it proposed that there should be an evaluation of the social costs *and benefits* of any proposed deliberate release (European Parliament 1989, Amendment No. 38). The official response of the European Commission to the Opinion of the Parliament on the proposed Amendment was as follows:

> The Commission considers that only the environmental risk assessment of a deliberate release falls within the scope of this Directive and it is therefore not appropriate to introduce other considerations such as social costs and benefits (CEC 1989: 4).

From a strategic perspective, we advise NGOs that an assessment of the risks alone is easier to challenge than an assessment which includes both risks and benefits. The reason for this is that just as risks are socially constructed, so too are social benefits. Whereas a risk analysis can be challenged on the basis of demonstrable risks, when a risk-benefit analysis is undertaken, such risks may be legitimated on the basis of potential benefits. Thus to challenge a risk-benefit analysis requires not only the demonstration of unacceptable risks, but also the refutation of the claims that the benefits are realisable and/or that they justify the taking of such risks. Given that the proposed benefits of genetic engineering are often expressed in terms of feeding the hungry or helping the sick, challenging such benefits is strategically problematic. Therefore, we advise that the present situation – risk analysis rather than risk-benefit analysis – is more favourable to NGOs.

Despite the clear pronunciation of the European Commission cited above, NGOs must be vigilant in ensuring that proposed benefits are not being used either covertly or overtly to justify the taking of risks. NGOs must scrutinise the opinions of national Competent Authorities on notification dossiers submitted under Directive 90/220/EEC to ensure that this rationalisation is not being practised. One example of such a rationalisation is to be found in the comments of the Netherlands Competent Authority on the genetically engineered viral vaccine against fox rabies, Raboral V-RG (see McNally 1995a, 1995b, and Chapter 7 in this book), which states that the risks of this vaccine are very small compared to the beneficial effects (see CEC 1993). Such a line of argumentation is not legitimate under Directive 90/220/EEC and further such instances should be challenged.

We also advise NGOs to scrutinise EU product legislation which is supposed to comply with Article 10.2 of Directive 90/220/EEC. This Article specifies that the provisions of Directive 90/220/EEC do not apply to the placing on the market of products containing or consisting of genetically engineered organisms covered by other Community legislation which provides for a specific environmental risk assessment similar to that laid down in the Directive. NGOs should argue that in order to comply with Directive 90/220/EEC such legislation, which includes Council Regulation 2309/93 relating to medicinal products for human and veterinary use, should evaluate environmental risk *independently* of proposed benefits. The Competent Authorities must evaluate genetically engineered organisms as living organisms with the potential to cause environmental harm, and not be concerned with their efficacy as products; they should not bow to pressure to relax environmental considerations for reasons of utility.

6. Concerning the Politics of the Debate on Risk Assessment

As we design technological systems, we are in fact designing sets of social relationships and as we question those social relationships and attempt to design systems differently, we are then beginning to challenge, in a partial way, power structures in society (Cooley 1980: 523).

There is a valid criticism that the concept of risk assessment in the context of the release of genetically engineered organisms and as embodied in the legislative apparatus is limited to a technical exercise which presumes that such releases will occur. That this would seem to be the case is indicated by an examination of the EU Directive on the deliberate release of genetically engineered organisms (90/220/EEC) where one finds that no class of organism – not even those based on known human pathogens or crop pests – is specifically prohibited from being released. In other words, from a legislative perspective, every genetically engineered organism is 'innocent until proven guilty', and the function of the data in the technical risk assessment dossier required by the release authorities is to attest to that innocence. Indeed, it might be argued that at the product stage, environmental risk assessment of genetically engineered organisms under the release Directive is more of a measure for the completion of the internal market – a means of generalising the authorisation of release activities – than a mechanism for prohibiting those activities which could harm human health and the environment. Moreover, it is also true that large areas of public concern over the risks of the uses of genetic engineering and genetically engineered organisms – including whether such practices should take place at all – lie outside of the scope of risk assessment as required by the legislative framework under the Directive.

The economic role of legislated risk assessment of environmental releases and its function in the completion of the internal market together with its failure to address larger conceptions of risk pose a dilemma for some NGOs. The dilemma is over whether or not to engage in debate over the assessment of risks of the release of specific genetically engineered organisms and over modifications of the legislative structure itself. For to do so, some NGOs argue (mistakenly in our view), would be to endorse the regulatory framework and its narrow conception of risk; it would be to accept the agenda that the legislative framework embodies, namely that environmental releases will take place and that all that is required to manage risk is the measurement of certain physical variables.

However, in our opinion there are at least two important reasons why NGOs must participate in the debate. Firstly, the releases are already taking place and will continue to do so; rather than being perceived as an expression of disapproval, were the NGOs to stand on the sidelines it would merely allow the authorisations and releases to proceed without hindrance. Secondly, whilst it is sometimes argued that the risk assessments required under the Directive are *only* technical, this is not quite accurate; they are not *even* technical: the quality of data used in many cases is poor and would not withstand independent scientific scrutiny. This is partly because the legislative framework prescribes no protocols for measuring risk and requires no minimum standard of data in the risk assessment dossiers submitted to the regulatory authorities for consent to release or to place a product for release on the market. Annexes II and IIA of the adapted deliberate release Directive 90/220/EEC are simply lists of criteria about which the Directive states: "Not all points will apply to every case. It is to be expected that individual notifications will address only the particular subset of considerations which is appropriate to individual situations" (Commission Directive 94/15/EC: 21). In other words, in the first instance choice of which risks are assessed in the notifications lies with the party who wishes to release a genetically engineered organism, rather than with the regulatory authorities.

So what should NGOs do? Drawing on firstly the resources and secondly the discourses of the European Commission itself, there appears to be a number of strategies open to NGOs, and these will be described in the following sections.

7. Concerning Resources and Disinterested Risk Assessment

Many complex technologies pose substantial hazards and risks to individuals, communities, regions, or even to the entire planet. To impose such risks on people without even their tacit consent is undeniably an act of tyranny (Zimmerman 1995: 92).

With regard to resources, it is certainly true that there is a lack of risk assessment data and that risk assessment research is costly, and it is also true that most NGOs do not individually have the resources to undertake scientific work on risk assessment. However, the dearth of risk assessment data is also an obstacle for the regulatory authorities. In recognition of the paucity of available data the European Commission has allocated funds for risk assessment research under the Research and Technological Development (RTD) Programmes. For example, the budget line entitled 'Prenormative Research: Biosafety', in the Biotechnology Programme of the Fourth Framework RTD Programme has as its objective the gathering of data of utility to regulatory authorities when carrying out risk assessment under Community legislation.[3]

In practice, it is not uncommon for the public resources for risk assessment research under the various EC/EU Biotechnology Programmes[4] to be allocated to those who have produced genetically engineered organisms intended for release into the environment. These resources are used by the producers to conduct research activities which generate data which are then put into the technical dossiers which are submitted to the regulatory authorities for approval under the deliberate release Directive. It is unrealistic to expect those parties who have a vested interest in *not* discovering risks to undertake such research impartially. Thus, this practice is objectionable because it is liable to produce results which are unrepresentative of the risks due to lack of disinterestedness of the parties which conduct the research. This opens up two approaches for NGOs. Firstly, to argue that the scarce resources earmarked for gathering data to assist the regulatory authorities charged with the task of risk assessment would be better spent if there was a clear separation of interests (division of powers) between those who research the risks of a given genetically engineered organism and those who create it. In other words, to lobby that public resources to assess the risks of a genetically engineered organism should not be allocated to the producer of the genetically engineered organism. Secondly, and allied to the first approach, NGOs should identify competent researchers, for example in university ecology departments, and encourage them to submit proposals under the Biotechnology Programme to undertake risk research on genetically engineered organisms. The advantage of this would not only be its potential to generate a bank of disinterested data on risk, but also the development of protocols for the scientific evaluation of risk research.

8. Concerning the Nature of Harm and Risk

In order for NGOs to have a strategic approach to risk assessment, it is necessary for them to adopt definitions of both 'environmental risk' and 'harm'. Our advice is that they should adopt the definitions below, the strategic advantage of which will be elucidated in the sections which follow.

'Environmental risk' is the likelihood that environmental harm will arise. The environment consists of land, air and water, together with the living organisms, including humans, which are supported by those media. 'Harm', in relation to living organisms, is damage to their health or other interference with the ecological systems of which those organisms form part. In the case of humans, harm also means offence to their senses and damage to their property.

Environmental risk can be represented as follows (see Wheale and McNally 1993):

$$R = m(H/C)$$

where: R = environmental risk   m = coefficient of mutation
         H = index of harm   C = containment (= 1/probability of release or escape)

The environmental risk of a genetically engineered organism is the product of its harmfulness and the probability that it will escape from containment. Containment is determined by containment measures – biological, physical and procedural – which contain the organism. An organism with a high harm index released in the open field would pose a high environmental risk; whereas a relatively harmless organism under isolation containment would pose a low environmental risk. The risk of a given genetically engineered organism can be reduced by making it less harmful and/or by increasing the containment conditions under which it is used.

The above equation permits risk to be quantified. In the sections below we give advice on the construction of a numerical index of harm and a numerical grid of containment. Using these two indices the risk of using or releasing a given genetically engineered organism can be constructed numerically. A maximum value for acceptable risk can be established, above which no consents should be given.

We recognise that the numerical values of harm, containment and risk are necessarily arbitrary but they have the following merits. Firstly, they represent a scale of risk – some risks do appear to be greater than others. Secondly, such a framework would render the process of risk assessment more transparent and it is our view that a transparent framework of risk assessment would be to the strategic advantage of NGOs since challenges under such a framework would be easier to mount than under the present system in which the methods used for determining acceptable risk are unarticulated.[5]

9. Concerning 'Harmonisation'

'Harmonisation', 'transparency' and 'step-by-step' are three much-used terms in the European Commission's discourse on the ideal legislative framework for genetically engineered organisms, but at present these terms are largely rhetorical. In this section which examines 'harmonisation' and in the following two sections on 'transparency' and 'step-by-step' we elucidate the extent to which the current legislative framework falls short of these ideals and the way in which the mobilisation of these terms could be a very fruitful strategy for NGOs.

We conceptualise contained use and deliberate release as being along a continuum of containment, ranging from high containment measures designed to prevent escapes, measures designed to minimise escape, measures which are simply good microbiological practice, through to controlled release and finally to open field release.

Council Directives on both contained use (90/219/EEC; see also Commission Directive 1994b) and the deliberate release (90/220/EEC; see also Commission Directive 1994a) of genetically engineered organisms are concerned with controlling the use of genetically engineered organisms, and part, at least, of their *raison d'être* is environmental protection. The jurisdictional difference between the two Directives merely reflects the *intentions* of the notifier; from an environmental and human health perspective it does not matter whether a given genetically engineered organism is present in the environment as a result of a deliberate release or an accidental escape. In the case of viruses, which are both products (vaccines and pesticides) and tools (vectors) of genetic engineering, the dichotomy between contained use and deliberate release is particularly false given that it is virtually impossible to contain them. From an environmental perspective *one* Directive would suffice, namely, a Directive to control the release – whether accidental or deliberate – of genetically engineered organisms into the environment. Yet at present, not only is this continuum artificially bisected on the basis of bureaucratic, rather than environmental, logic, but the two Directives are themselves not in harmony, as is described below.

Whilst the contained use Directive classifies genetically engineered micro-organisms into two groups (Article 4) and identifies three containment categories (Annex IV) (plus 'good microbiological practice'), the deliberate release Directive classifies genetically engineered organisms into two different groups (Annex IIA and Annex IIB) and does not distinguish between different types of releases, for example, it does not differentiate open field releases from restricted field releases.

Annex II of the contained use Directive characterises Group I organisms which may be used with minimum containment. Minimum containment measures under the contained use Directive represent a higher level of containment than any release would provide. Yet the deliberate release Directive does not set any equivalent characterisation of what constitutes a 'safe' organism for environmental release.

Another inconsistency is that Category 1 containment measures for micro-organisms in Group II of the contained use Directive for modified micro-organisms (CEC 90/219/EEC) is only intended to *minimise* and therefore not *prevent* release (see CEC 90/219/EEC Annex IV). Group I micro-organisms are even less contained than those in Group II because they are only required to be contained by good microbiological practice. The contained use Directive thus recognises the probability that such genetically engineered organisms will escape into the environment (since the measures are only intended to *minimise* their escape), therefore it logically follows that there should be a requirement for an environmental risk assessment for work carried out with Group I organisms or under containment Category 1 conditions of the contained use Directive.

A further example of the lack of harmonisation concerns work with genetically engineered organisms which are believed to be harmful. Whilst the contained use Directive gives very strict guidance with respect to how dangerous pathogens are to be handled, the deliberate release Directive makes no distinction between these and any other organism (see also Wheale and McNally 1993: 265-66).

Our advice to NGOs is to pursue a strategy of lobbying for harmonisation between these two Directives. NGOs should argue for a harmonisation that dove-tails the two Directives in order that the same level of environmental protection is given to the same organism under both Directives.

10. How 'Transparency' May Be Achieved by the Construction of an Index of Harm and a Grid of Containment

The European biotechnology industry argues that it would like the legislative framework for the control of genetically engineered organisms to be transparent and objective, and the European Commission would like to comply with the industry's demands. NGOs should assist them in this process by suggesting how this might be achieved.

The first step must be to construct an index of 'harm'. What should be demanded is the classification of a representative range of non-genetically engineered organisms on a scale from 1 (the least harmful) to, say, 10 (the most harmful) with respect to their potential to cause harm. This taxonomy would then serve as a reference index for the classification of genetically engineered organisms. This is not to suggest that the potential harm of a given genetically engineered organism would be presumed to be identical to the host organism from which it is derived. Rather, what would be required would be the demonstration, through risk assessment research, that it is no more harmful than the organisms with which it is classified.

The next step should be the precise definition of categories of containment and release. From an environmental perspective, as we have argued above, it matters not whether a given genetically engineered organism at large in the environment arrived there as a result of an accidental escape or of a deliberate release. Contained use and deliberate release should be conceptualised as a continuum with the most stringent containment provisions at one end and open field releases at the other. A number of containment categories (we suggest six, see next section) should be fully charac-terised with respect to physical and procedural measures, and these categories should be harmonised across both the deliberate release and the contained use Directives.

The above numerical indices should then be used in calculating the risk of a work proposal – 'contained use' or 'deliberate release' – involving a genetically engineered organism as follows. The engineered organism should be allocated an index of harm. A particular physical/procedural containment category should be selected and the probability that the genetically engineered organism will escape from the containment category should then be calculated on the basis of the potential of the organism for reproduction, dispersal and survival under these containment conditions. The index of harm and the probability of escape should then be multiplied together, in accordance with the equation in section 8, to calculate the level of risk of the proposed work. For example, if it were proposed to use a genetically engineered organism with the highest degree of harmfulness, 10, in a containment facility from which it was estimated it had the probability of escaping of 0.1 (probability is measured on a scale from 0 to 1), then the risk of such a proposal would be calculated by multiplying 0.1 by 10 (i.e., 0.1 x 10 = 1), giving an estimated risk of 1.

This framework not only provides a mechanism for calculating relative risk, it also provides a means for estimating what is an acceptable risk. Using the above example, a probability of escape of 0.1 would mean that 10 per cent of such organisms would be likely to escape. An escape rate of 10 per cent of an extremely harmful organism (harm index 10) is unacceptable, and therefore a risk assessment of 1 is too high. We advise a risk assessment of 0.01 should be the threshold value, above which consent to undertake the work should not be given. To have any hope of proceeding, the proposer in the example would either have to make the genetically engineered organism less harmful or reduce the probability of escape by increasing the level of containment to the point where its calculated risk would be rendered below or equal to the minimum limit. Should the proposer achieve this level of safety – the 'acceptable risk' – then consent to the release should be given.

We advise NGOs to further their aim of protecting health and environment from unintended harm by pressuring the European Commission to implement the rhetoric on transparency and objectivity by adopting a framework for risk assessment, such as we describe above, to underpin the legislative framework for the environmental control of genetically engineered organisms.

11. Concerning 'Step-by-step'

In the sections above we have described a strategy which uses the 'bio-industrial complex's' rhetoric on 'harmonisation' and 'transparency', in other words, we advocate open and publicly visible procedures for the regulation and control of genetically engineered organisms. In this section, we advise how the NGOs should also co-opt the 'bio-industrial complex's' rhetorical principle of a 'step-by-step' progression of proposals for the release of genetically engineered organisms into the environment.

We have already argued that containment is a key component in the limitation of environmental risk. We have provided elsewhere (see McNally and Wheale 1989) details of a practical approach to the implementation of the 'step-by-step' principle, as advocated in the OECD report on safety considerations for recombinant DNA work (1986) and in the report of the Royal Commission on Environmental Pollution (RCEP 1989) in the UK.

The principle of 'step-by-step' is that the taking of each progressive step towards open field releases is dependent upon the evaluation of the earlier 'steps' in terms of protection of human health and the environment. However, for such a concept to be meaningful, it is necessary for the 'steps' to be defined, to be made 'transparent'. Only then will it be apparent whether the rhetoric on 'step-by-step' is being matched by the practices. In order to apply the 'step-by-step' principle we have constructed six discrete levels of containment/release. The containment/release levels equate to the contained use Directive's containment categories 3, 2, 1 and good microbiological practice, plus restricted field trials and open field trials. The transition from one containment level to the next represents a reduction in the containment of the genetically engineered organism and thus each such transition equates with at least one 'step'. In accordance with the 'step-by-step' principle the transition from one containment level to the next – each step – involves an increase in risk and should be conditioned upon having progressed through the previous steps, and each such step should be the subject of a new risk assessment.

12. Exhortation to NGOs to Liberate the People from Technological Authoritarianism

To comprehend fully the nature of the people, one must be a prince, and to comprehend fully the nature of princes one must be an ordinary citizen (Machiavelli 1516, Letter to Lorenzo De' Medici, in: Machiavelli 1970: 30).

After deliberating on all the things discussed above, we asked ourselves whether in the present-day Western world the times were propitious for recognising a new Prince – 'the People'. We believe that so many things conspire to favour democratically controlled technology rather than technological authoritarianism that we cannot imagine there was ever a time more suitable than the present. The creation of intellectual property rights in living organisms, the commodification of the biosphere and the imperialist project in 'gene hunting' demand the continuing engagement of the 'new social movements' in this endeavour. The fact that 'new social movements' – feminism, environmentalism, animal welfarism, conservationism, egalitarianism – have emerged as such a potent force in our *Liberal Democracies* is itself evidence which points to the desire of citizens to participate in shaping the sociotechnical order (see also McNally and Wheale 1995b).

We have referred above to evidence that the rules, roles, relationships, and expectations generated by the 'bio-industrial complex' are susceptible to substantial revision. In this essay we have presumed to proffer some Machiavellian advice to you, the NGOs, on how we believe you might best recognise opportunities and devise strategies for the 're-engineering' of the European biotechnology project in line with democratic principles. By operating strategically, and utilising both constructivist and empiricist discourses, we believe you will continue to create authentic opportunities for expanding the 'spheres of impact', as Frankenfeld (1992) describes technological fields, in which the European (technological) citizens can participate in decision-making, enabling them to renegotiate 'the social contracts', which, as Zimmerman (1995: 97) asserts, each major technology embodies.

It is you, the 'nomads of the present', as Alberto Melucci (1989) calls you, with your myriad of informal networks, dynamism and instability who possess the flexibility through the reflexive process – the dialogical exchange of communications in which the objects of knowledge are mutually subjectively reflected upon, to transform the 'bio-industrial complex'. It is you which are most able to make controversies visible to the public and problematise the social relations of science and technology. We have suggested strategies by which, incrementally, at least, this transition can be brought about in modern biotechnology. We therefore appeal to you, the NGOs, as key agents of social change, to consciously take on the role of Liberator of The People: to liberate us, the New Europeans, from authoritarian technology and help us democratise our technological design, choice and governance. Let us finalise our appeal by quoting Machiavelli's own exhortation to Lorenzo De' Medici for liberation from barbarism:

> *Let your illustrious House undertake this task, therefore, with the courage and hope which belong to just enterprises* (Machiavelli 1970, *The Prince*: 138).

Acknowledgement

Dr. Peter Wheale wishes to express his gratitude to the Netherlands Organization for Scientific Research (NWO) for funding his Visiting Fellowship at Tilburg University during which time this paper was researched and written.

Notes

1.   We consider that the social and technical components of the 'bio-industrial complex' are not self regulating or tied to each other in an 'organic' way; and conflicts and schisms within it are commonplace, for example, over plant breeders' rights and patents. We prefer the concept 'bio-industrial complex' to the metaphor 'system', as in 'sociotechnical system', because the term 'complex', unlike 'system', does *not* imply consensus, 'closure' or stabilisation. For a recent critique of the 'sociotechnical system' as a metaphor and its application in social studies of technology (SST) by social constructivists, see Hård (1993).

2.   A recent example of such a caricaturisation is Frank Laird's (1993) construction of 'direct' (agency) and 'pluralist' (structuralist) paradigms as *empirically* derived. These two paradigms are then juxtaposed and their respective democratic merits *prescriptively* compared and contrasted. Our general criticism of this conceptual approach is that, in practice, collective action is not a unitary empirical phenomenon (see also Melucci 1989). Spontaneous associations and identity construction are in constant flux.

3.   The European Commission states its objectives for funding research on biosafety under the Biotechnology Programme of the Fourth Framework as follows:

> In order to ensure the safe applications of biotechnology, particularly in relation to the commercialization of new varieties of crops, or other organisms acquiring novel genetic traits, thorough knowledge is needed of their behaviour in, and interactions with different components of the ecosystem. Research will be approached at two (preferably combined) levels. First at the basic level of molecular ecology and molecular interactions, and second, at the level of prenormative research, which gathers data of particular usefulness for regulatory authorities when carrying out risk-assessment under Community legislation (CEC 1994b: 49).

4.   For example, the Biotechnology Action Programme (BAP), the Programme for Biotechnology Research for Innovation, Development and Growth in Europe (BRIDGE), and the Biotechnology Programmes.

5.   We originally proposed such a method to the European Commission in our interim report to DG XI on the implementation of Annex II of the proposed Directive 90/220/EEC to live viral vaccines. We are pleased to see that some elements of such an approach have been adopted. The European Commission's Ad hoc Working Party on Environmental Risk-assessments for Medicinal Products Consisting of or Containing Genetically Modified Organisms (CEC 1994c) now recommends that the level of risk is assessed by combining the estimate of the magnitude of harm if the hazard were to be realised with the likelihood or frequency of such harm being caused; although accepting that it is 'difficult' to 'multiply' qualitative statements such as 'high' and 'low' and that therefore there must be scope for flexible, 'case-by-case evaluation' (CEC 1994c: 6).

References

[CEC] Commission of the European Community 1989. *Communication from the Commission to the Parliament on the Council's common position concerning the amended proposal for a Council directive on the deliberate release to the environment of genetically modified organisms* (SEC (89)2091 final - SYN 131, 6th December). Brussels: CEC.

————. 1993. *Comments on the notifications C/B/92/B28 & C/F/93/03-02* (XI/A/021/93, June). Brussels: CEC.

————. 1994a. *Growth, Competitiveness & Employment: The Challenges and Ways Forward into the 21st Century.* Brussels: CEC.

————. 1994b. *Biotechnology 1994-1998: Workprogramme.* Brussels: CEC.

————. 1994c. *European Commission Ad hoc Working Party on Environmental Risk-assessments for Medicinal Products Consisting of or Containing Genetically Modified Organisms* (III/5507/94 Draft 2). Brussels: CEC.

Commission Directive 94/15/EC 1994a. 'Commission Directive 94/15/EC of 15 April 1994 adapting to technical progress for the first time Council Directive 90/220/EEC on the deliberate release into the environment of genetically modified organisms.' *Official Journal of the European Communities* (No. L, 103), pp.20-27.

Commission Directive 94/51/EC 1994b. 'Commission Directive 94/51/EC of 7 November 1994 adapting to technical progress Council Directive 90/219/EEC on the contained use of genetically modified microorganisms.' *Official Journal of the European Communities* (No. L, 279), pp.29-30.

Cooley, M. 1980. 'Computerisation – Taylor's latest disguise.' *Economic and Industrial Democracy* **1**, pp.523-39.

Council Directive 90/219/EEC 1990. 'Council Directive of 23 April 1990 on the contained used of genetically modified micro-organisms.' *Official Journal of the European Communities* (No. L, 117), pp.1-14.

Council Directive 90/220/EEC 1990. 'Council Directive of 23 April 1990 on the deliberate release into the environment of genetically modified organisms.' *Official Journal of the European Communities* (No. L, 117), pp.15-27.

Council of Ministers 1994. 'Common Position (EC) No 4/94 adopted by the Council on 7 February 1994 with a view to adopting European Parliament and Council Directive 94/.../EC of ... on the legal protection of biotechnological inventions (94/C 101/104).' *Official Journal of the European Communities* (No C 101, 9 April), pp.65-75.

Dahl, R. 1985. *Controlling Nuclear Weapons.* Syracuse, N.Y.: Syracuse University Press.

European Parliament 1989. 'Opinion of the European Parliament (on the Proposal for a directive COM(88)160 final -SYN 131).' *Official Journal of the European Communities* (No. C, 158), pp.222-226.

Foucault, M. 1970. 'La crise dans la tete.' In: P. Rabinow (ed.), *The Foucault Reader* (1986), Harmondsworth: Penguin.

Frankenfeld, P.J. 1992. 'Technological citizenship: A normative framework for risk studies.' *Science, Technology and Human Values* **17**, pp.459-84.

Gibbons, M. and Wittrock, B. (eds.) 1985. *Science as a Commodity.* Harlow: Longman.

Habermas, J. 1987. 'Questions and counterquestions.' In: R.J. Bernstein (ed.), *Habermas and Modernity.* Cambridge: Polity Press, pp.192-216.

Haraway, D.J. 1991. *Simians, Cyborgs, and Women.* London: Free Association Books.

Hård, M. 1993. 'Beyond Harmony and Consensus: A Social Conflict Approach to Technology.' *Science, Technology and Human Values* **18** (4), pp.408-32.

Laird, F.N. 1993. 'Participatory analysis, democracy, and technological decision making.' *Science, Technology and Human Values* **18** (3), pp.341-61.

Latour, B. 1988. 'The Prince for machines as well as for machinations.' In: B. Elliot (ed.), *Technology and Social Change.* Edinburgh: Edinburgh University Press, pp.20-43.

Luhmann, N. 1986. 'The autopoiesis of social systems.' In: F. Geyer and J. van der Zouen (eds.),

Sociocybernetic Paradoxes: Observation, Control and Evolution of Self-Steering Systems.
London: Sage.

McNally, R. 1995a. 'Genetic madness: The European rabies eradication programme.' *The Ecologist* **24** (no.6, Nov/Dec), pp.207-212.

————. 1995b. 'Mad dogs or jackasses: The European rabies eradication programme.' In: P.R. Wheale and R. McNally (eds.), *Animal Genetic Engineering: Of Pigs, Oncomice and Men.* London: Pluto Press, pp.109-124.

McNally, R. and Wheale, P.R. 1989. *The Environmental Consequences of Genetically Engineered Live Viral Vaccines.* Report to CEC DG XI, Contract Number B6614/89/91.

————. 1994. 'Environmental and medical bioethics in late modernity: Giddens, genetic engineering and the post-modern state.' In: R. Attfield and A. Belsey (eds.), *Philosophy and the Natural Environment.* Cambridge: Cambridge University Press, pp.211-226.

————. 1995a. 'Genetic engineering, bioethics and radicalised modernity.' In: R. von Schomberg (ed.), *Contested Technology: Ethics, Risk and Public Debate.* Tilburg: International Centre for Human and Public Affairs, pp.29-50.

————. 1995b. 'Bio-patenting and innovation: A new industrial divide?' In: O. Morrissey (ed.), *Biotechnological Innovation, Societal Responses and Policy Implications*, Proceedings of a Workshop hosted by the Centre for European Social Research, University College Cork, 6-7th April, supported by CEC DG XII, pp.7-17.

Machiavelli, N. 1970. *The Prince.* B. Radice and R. Baldick (eds.), translated with an introduction by G. Bull, Harmonsworth: Penguin Books.

Melucci, A. 1989. *Nomads of the Present: Social Movements and Individual Needs in Contemporary Society.* Victoria: Hutchinson.

[OECD] Organisation for Economic Cooperation and Development 1986. *Recombinant DNA Safety Considerations.* Paris: OECD.

Prins, B. 1993. 'The ethics of hybrid subjects: Feminist constructivism according to Donna Haraway.' *European Theoretical Perspectives on New Technology: Feminism, Constructivism and Utility*, Proceedings of CRICT Workshop, 16-17th September 1993, Uxbridge: Brunel University.

[RCEP] Royal Commission on Environmental Pollution 1989. *The Release of Genetically Engineered Organisms to the Environment.* London: HMSO.

Rorty, R. 1985. 'Solidarity or Objectivity?' In: J. Rajchman and C. West (eds.), *Post-Analytic Philosophy.* New York: Columbia University Press, pp.3-19.

SEC 1991. *Promoting the Competitive Environment for the Industrial Activities Based on Biotechnology Within the Community* (629 Final). Brussels: European Commission.

Schomberg, R. von 1995. 'The erosion of our value spheres: The ways in which society copes with scientific, moral and ethical uncertainty.' In: R. von Schomberg (ed.), *Contested Technology: Ethics, Risk and Public Debate* Tilburg: Int. Centre for Human and Public Affairs, pp.13-28.

Sclove, R.E. 1995. *Democracy and Technology.* New York & London: The Guilford Press.

Wheale, P.R. et al. 1986. *People, Science and Technology.* Hemel Hempstead: Wheatsheaf.

Wheale, P.R. and McNally, R. 1988. *Genetic Engineering: Catastrophe or Utopia?* Hemel Hempstead and New York: Wheatsheaf & Simon Schuster.

Wheale, P.R. and McNally, R. (eds.) 1990. *The Bio-Revolution: Cornucopia or Pandora's Box?* London: Pluto.

Wheale, P.R. and McNally, R. 1993. 'Biotechnology policy in Europe: A critical evaluation.' *Science and Public Policy* **20** (no.4, August), pp.261-79.

————. 1994. 'What bugs genetic engineers about bioethics.' In: A. Dyson and J. Harris (eds.), *Ethics and Biotechnology.* London: Routledge, pp.179-201.

Wheale, P.R. and McNally, R. (eds.) 1995. *Animal Genetic Engineering: Of Pigs, Oncomice and Men.* London: Pluto.

Winch, P. 1958. *The Idea of a Social Science.* London: Routledge & Kegan Paul.

Zimmerman, A.D. 1995. 'Towards a more democratic ethic of technological governance.' *Science, Technology and Human Values* **20** (1), pp.86-107.

13

Lacking Scientific Knowledge or Lacking the Wisdom and Culture of Not-Knowing

Christine von Weizsäcker

1. A Short Introduction to "Not-Knowing"

Socrates, as reported in Plato's *Apologia*, defended himself during his trial and said, that he knew himself to be a "Not-Knower". In the Greek text there is a fine and remarkable difference between the two words he uses for "knowing". The first word describes the type of knowing that is the precondition for being a not-knower: ξύνοιδω (freely translated: I am connected when seeing). It can mean that Socrates is with himself when seeing and knowing. It can mean that he looks for togetherness, cohesion and context. Both translations and interpretations are linked and probably lead to the same result. If I stay in my right body and my right mind when I observe, I am bound to acknowledge my limitations in time and space and I realize that I am a Not-Knower. If I try to see and know togetherness, cohesion and context, then I respect and appreciate the otherness of others and I realize that I am a Not-Knower.

Socrates very confidently and proudly confessed himself to be a Not-Knower. Not-Knowing is the precondition and the result of his years of investigation, research, questioning, discourse and learning. Sustaining the attitude of Not-Knowing can lead into a sustainable pathway of discourse and learning.

Attention has to be drawn, however, to the other and admittedly sad element of Socrates' story: To be a Not-Knower does not necessarily enhance the chances for getting a regular and well-paid job with high social standing. It does not necessarily lead to products that can be profitably sold on the market. And it may cause personal trouble ranging from marital difficulties to political persecution.

The question of the interrelationship between "knowing" and "not-knowing" fascinated many European philosophers. Kant expressed it as follows: "The subjective preconditions of potential knowledge are the preconditions of objective knowledge" (Kant 1781: A90/B122). I take this as an invitation to reflect upon the role of Western or Northern experts. Are they the only relevant constituency of knowledge? Do they have the monopoly of the "correct" subjective preconditions of potential knowledge? If not, do we lack facts or focus? Do we need more factors or more actors? And here the philosophy of science has direct links to politics: Whose knowledge is considered relevant? Who decides on technological pathways? The sociological question of "Why do people act as they do?" and the philosophical question of "What is the issue at stake?" have to be supplemented by the political question "Who are the subjects of knowledge, decision, action and responsibility?"

The "view from nowhere" (Nagel 1986) of the lonely subject, the natural scientist, is an appropriate description of a special and exclusive experience. As an unquestioned generalized world view, however, it is anthropologically unrealistic. If the natural scientists pose as bodiless and timeless disinterested outside observers of unquestionable facts they often successfully hide the important fact that natural scientists are a potent political pressure group. Their interests, points of view and policies are not in themselves an indisputable law of nature. Other people have equal claims to aims, passions, knowledge, discourse, action and learning. A researcher who clearly and openly states his interests and point of view gets on equal footing with other kinds of people and their other kinds of knowledge. This may deflate the personal hubris of the researcher. Deflation, however has some advantages. It allows more versatility and it makes for good company.

Niels Bohr, the great atomic physicist and philosopher, invited researchers to take this step. He drew attention to the necessary complementarity of perception: "From these circumstances follows not only the relative meaning of every concept, or rather of every word, the meaning depending upon our arbitrary choice of viewpoint, but also we must, in general, be prepared to accept the fact that a complete elucidation of one and the same object may require diverse viewpoints, which defy a unique description" (Bohr 1961: 96). The realization of the interrelationship of complementary terms, according to Bohr, "depends upon the unity of our consciousness" (Bohr 1961: 99). Here again "consciousness" (literally translated: knowing together) is linked to the insight into the structural limitation of our knowledge.

Exclusive and assured knowledge is the result of forcefully cutting off contexts, embeddedness and specificity of time and place, i.e. historicity and locality. This type of knowledge is by necessity an instrument of power, control and manipulation. It invites domination and extraction of resources. Power and domination are facts of life, but not the only ones. They need to be complemented, provided with the missing links and put in place by the wisdom and culture of not-knowing. It may well be that dialogue and cooperation between people of diverse talents is the anthropologically soundest perspective for science and politics. It could easily go hand in hand with an appreciation for the "subjective qualities" of non-human contributors to the web of nature. Anyway, it would be the "not-knowers' policy" for dealing with risks.

The present debate on risk assessment in biotechnology should be more than a humble funding plea for a few more research projects in technology assessment. It is evident that such research is overdue, utterly necessary and highly relevant, both on the scientific and on the political level. But such research is not enough for tackling the underlying controversies. The task consists in finding a philosophy and a policy for science and technology that fit each other and that are worthy of and compatible with democracy. The precautionary principle is an adequate starting point in this search. It also implies a contextual approach, cognostic knowledge and co-responsibility (Weizsäcker 1995a). Cognostic knowledge means knowledge that is at home with the fact that other beings are also subjects of knowledge and therefore appreciates diversity and reciprocity.

It is very understandable that the vicissitudes of the environmental crisis provoke an increasing demand for safety. What sort of safety is it going to be? Professional experts are peddling safety as a commodity which they can exclusively provide due to their superior and exclusive knowledge. This is the type of safety that is compatible with concepts of expertocratic global management. It replaces the complex process of citizen's decisions with complicated attempts at scientific prognosis. It implicitly defines people as stupid bundles of insatiable needs which have to be lured, pacified, channelled, catered for and petrified into predictable units.

If this concept of safety is challenged by opposing arguments a second line of defence for expertocracy is installed. Since reality is chaotic and – strictly speaking – unpredictable, the "why", "what" and "who" of decisions does not matter. Everything goes. And it goes best for those already in power.

Hopefully there is a third choice besides expertocracy and "chaotic" legitimation of the status quo. How about the "not-knowers' policy"? It is the policy of differentiated and complementary knowledge, of structural damage-limitation and of cooperation. It's strength lies in the multidimensional debate, the safety of diversity and in creative legal frameworks. It is based on a structure of polycentric empowerment, participation and cooperation? The most urgent task in implementing the "not-knowers' policy" is to safeguard or recreate the endangered infrastructure for democratic responsibility and multi-facetted learning.

Whilst following the Biotechnology Debate in Germany, in Austria, in the European Union and at the level of the United Nations during the past ten years, I attempted to identify and started to analyze conflicting basic assumptions underlying the political debate on biosafety issues.

2. Prognosis or Decision?

Prognosis is an attempt to use the analysis of past events for predicting the future. These predictions have the character of "probabilities of expectation". Scientific prognosis at its best not only explicitly states the underlying theories but also clearly states its assumptions about the expected framework of future external preconditions. It clearly states its contexts and its decontextualizations. Such clear and humble prognosis lies at the root of scientific successes and has well earned its high public recognition.

In highly dynamic, highly complex and long-term areas of research, however, it becomes more and more difficult to adhere to the decent scientific procedure of explicitly stating the stable framework of expected external preconditions (see Popper 1965; Hahn 1976; Bruckmann 1977; Beck 1986). Consequently, it becomes more and more difficult to distinguish scientific prognosis from more or less educated guesses, from prophecy and from scientific wishful thinking. The development of modern science and technology is highly dynamic and it dynamizes the social and natural environment. Releases of genetically engineered organisms influence very complex ecosystems. The expected effects of these releases are potentially and probably far-reaching in time and space. It so happens that modern so-called key-technologies left the home-area of scientific prognosis with its firm rules of experimental restriction and scientific competition. They are defined and socially constructed so as to gain the privilege of monopolizing the search for solutions. They are publicly funded prophesies and claims. The question remains open, however, whether the claims will be borne out by reality and whether the prophesies will turn out to be self-fulfilling or self-abolishing. A cautionary remark: The political and economic mechanisms by which the public and the stock market may be successfully persuaded are not necessarily persuasive to the natural world. In the past, environmental impacts already challenged many unsuitable technological ventures. But what is the price for abolishing an unsuccessful prophecy? The higher the bet, the bigger the loss!

The choice of direction and focus of science and technology is obviously not governed by eternal laws of nature out of human reach. Their direction and focus is not an adequate object of science itself. It depends on political decisions. The liberty of pursuing one's scientific questions – which is a very important political liberty worth defending – must not be confused with an automatic public obligation to further and fund certain pursuits of a certain group of citizens. The direction and focus of public funding is a matter for the public to decide. Public participation, not the deregulation of public participation, is a fair and adequate response to the structural problem of science and technology which leaves its humble home-area of reproducibility and enters into the arena of historical uniqueness. If scientific risk assessment is used as a political "end of the pipe solution" leaving the preceding funding and focusing procedures for science in inaccessible mists of policy-mythology then this very risk assessment has gained a false importance. Public participation in risk assessment procedures – even if it were attained – is not enough. Scientific and technological pathways have their share of decision-making "from cradle to grave". If the public is affected by these decisions the public has to participate in the decisions at all these stages.

3. Hypotheticality versus Error-Friendliness

There are certain mega-technologies that do not allow the normal scientific experimental procedure based on trial and error. Prof. Wolf Häfele, one of the fathers of the fast breeder in Germany, gave an outspoken and clear analysis of this structure in the context of nuclear power. He classified nuclear power as a technological venture which enters into the domain of "hypotheticality" (Häfele 1974: 401). What does that mean? It means that this technology leaves the domain of classical experiments with their spatial and temporal containment. Häfele calls it a tech-nological adventure of "the order of magnitude of the history of mankind" (Häfele 1974: 401). By the way he – unlike other people who reacted to this insight – confessed faith in this adventure.

It could well be that modern biotechnology also leads us into another adventure of the order of magnitude of the history of mankind. It certainly shows some elements of hypotheticality:

1.　　Its scientific and technological impacts and hazards can perpetrate themselves both spatially and temporally, potentially through the entire biosphere. Releases of genetically manipulated organisms are irreversible and cannot be recalled (Wills 1994). Releases are not scientific experiments in the classical sense.

2.　　The choice of this technological pathway increasingly acquires the character of a self-fulfilling prophecy, of belief and make-believe. Prophesies can however turn out to be catastrophically self-abolishing.

3.   The impetus of research and development focused on so-called key technologies has an unfair disregard for other technological options.

4.   Modern biotechnology is expensive. This implies a concentration of
investment and of power. There is a very powerful constellation of biotechnological stakeholders in research, industry and governments. There are marked
similarities to the alliance supporting nuclear power. It is powerful enough to
bulldoze down the normal rules of a fair market: The new quality of the
conflict is reflected in the difficulties of the debates on "patents on life", on
the general labelling of genetically engineered food, on legislation that will
make full risk insurance obligatory and on a Biosafety Protocol within the
framework of the UN Convention on Biological Diversity. In the hypothetical
world of modern biotechnology the public fears to be on a racetrack where it
is permitted to bribe the jockey, to dope the horse and to change the rules
during the race.

If these observations are correct, the repeated demand to confess one's basic faith in
the potential of this new technology becomes less of an absurdity. It becomes an icon
of the technological realities of today.

How does an "experiment of the order of magnitude of the history of mankind"
comply with some cultural inventions we are proud of? How does it comply with
democracy, with the protection of minorities, with equality of opportunity and
freedom of choice?

I do not see any international forum in which there is an adequately comprehensive,
sufficiently long-term and decently serious exchange of views and negotiations on
this technological mega-adventure involving the present generation of humanity, let
alone the future ones. I do, however, see many instances of experts condemning the
public to mutism, confusion and resignation.

What are the arguments against a technological pathway of the hypothetical kind?
Why should we weaken or abolish such an impressive option? It has to do with the
fact that the future is open. It has to do with the fact that we learn from mistakes. It
has to do with the fact that some options have such a size and scope that they
exclude other options. It has to do with the fact that it is more rational, nicer, more
comfortable and certainly more sustainable to learn from small mistakes instead of
learning from mistakes of the order of magnitude of the history of mankind.
Hypotheticality is the arena for autocratic planners. What is the arena in which not-
knowers can feel at home?

Debates on "Chances and Risks" often do not reflect on the two basic assumptions
implied in these very terms. The first assumption is "We know our expectations but
the future itself is open and unpredictable", and the second is "A strictly impartial
evaluation of events is not possible". For an open future we need strategies suitable
for coping with uncertainties. We need a framework of cooperative options and of
learning. Selective ad-hoc perfectionism is a shortsighted strategy. It is like
pretending to know who is going to be the world champion without knowing the type
of game the future will bring. Let me quote an old evolutionary law formulated by
Ronald Fisher in 1930: "The rate of increase in fitness of any organism at any time
is equal to its genetic variance in fitness at that time" (Fisher 1930: 35). In other

words, streamlining evolution is hampering evolution.

I coined the term 'error-friendliness' (Weizsäcker and Weizsäcker 1984; Weizsäcker and Weizsäcker 1987; Weizsäcker 1990; Weizsäcker 1995b) to describe a unique combination of qualities in living organisms. Firstly, living organisms are error-tolerant. There are many diverse contributions to this error-tolerance: e.g. repair mechanisms for genes, redundancy and compartmentalization of cells and cell subunits, wound healing and parental protection for the next generation. Living organisms are, however, not the natural phenomena with a maximum of robustness and tolerance against outside interference. They are vulnerable, they are error-prone. And here lies the second contribution to error-friendliness. This may consist of a passive error-permissiveness, it may be active, playful error-production. Amongst the many mechanisms involved in this are e.g. genetic mutations and the behavioural tendency of higher organisms to actively search for surprises, in short: curiosity. The balanced and cooperative combination of error-tolerance with error-proneness is what I called error-friendliness. Error-friendliness combines exposure with tolerance. It is the suitable framework within which errors can turn into learning, into new successes and again into new survivable and productive errors. Error-friendliness is complementary to Darwinian fitness. The aspects of fitness and error-friendliness are reciprocally exclusive viewpoints which cannot be taken simultaneously. Fitness is a term derived from looking into the past. It represents the successes of past history. Error-friendliness points to the future. It is, if I may say so, the successful biological betting system and the successful infrastructure for learning. Error-friendliness guards the structural preconditions of mutually supportive safety and innovation.

The literature about fitness is abundant and present in most readers minds. This is not always true for the creative contribution of errors. The importance of errors needs to be stressed in the face of a prevailing blunt perfectionism which does not know the basic difference between past and future events. Lewis Thomas formulated some very articulate reminders: "Biology needs a better word than "error" for the driving force in evolution. Or maybe, "error" will do after all, when you remember that it came from an old root meaning to wander about, looking for something" (Thomas 1979: 30). "Mistakes are at the very base of human thought, embedded there, feeding the structure like root nodules. If we were not provided with the knack of being wrong, we could never get anything useful done" (Thomas 1979: 37).

Error-friendliness reflects the conditions under which mistakes can be a new beginning and do not only mean an ending. It represents the wholesome framework, the creative limits and the supportive infrastructure for such errors.

Together fitness and error-friendliness are the two legs on which the co-evolution of ecosystems walked. Coevolution is at its best within a framework of: (1) *high diversity*, (2) *a rate of change below the critical relative speed of innovation* (Weizsäcker 1993a: 44) and (3) *the maintenance of barriers*.

Modern mega-technologies tend to monopolize the privilege of daring, erring and learning for a select group of specialists. If all technological accidents keep being blamed on the weakness, stupidity or criminality of the human factor there seems to be something fundamentally wrong with the anthropological assumptions of the planners. If ecosystems keep coming up with major unforeseen effects, there seems to be something fundamentally wrong with the biological assumptions of the planners. A little exercise in not-knowing would certainly be helpful in overcoming blind spots and in widening the horizon.

With the introduction of deliberate releases of GMOs we are faced with a dilemma between diversity and safety to which there is no easy solution. The massive and rapid introduction of GMOs performed deliberately and systematically calls for careful central control. Central control paying due respect to the justified demand for a high level of protection (e.g. Article 100a of the Treaty of the European Union) can realistically be only achieved for a few organisms. The high costs and the long time involved can only be repaid through massive and international releases. The releases of a small number of costly products in need of a huge market will inevitably lead to market concentration and a severe loss of genetic and cultural diversity in its wake.

It is very inviting for our heavily indebted governments to believe in the proclaimed "end of all biosafety problems", to join the international rat-race for deregulation and thus cut down on the expenditures with which they subsidize their high national safety standards. Disregard, however, does not get you off the horns of a dilemma.

An international legally binding biosafety protocol is one important step governments can take to get out of the tragic trap of endless deregulation, voluntary arrangements or non-regulation. On 16th November 1995, at the end of its second meeting which took place in Jakarta, the Conference of Parties to the UN Convention on Biological Diversity decided on a mandate to negotiate an international legally binding Biosafety Protocol[1] (UNEP/CBD/COP/2/CW/L.22 1995).

Biosafety regulations alone, however, are not sufficient to harmonize innovation and safety in this technological venture. The very structure of genetic engineering may prove to be far from error-friendly. It advocates itself with, yet again, an increase in the rate of change in the agricultural sector which may surpass the critical relative speed of innovation and consequently lead to a massive loss of biological and cultural complexity and diversity. Genetic engineering advocates itself with the construction of organisms optimized in accordance with narrow, short-term criteria – thus cutting down on diversity. It advocates itself with the removal of biochemical barriers between species. It advocates itself with a world-wide distribution of its products thereby speeding up the destructive trends of modern agricultural monocultures. These aims fundamentally contradict the framework of an error-friendly co-evolution. This clearly points to the risk that, in the long run, the real diasters in the field of agriculture and ecology will not lie in some rare far-fetched side-events but in the very successes of mainstream genetic engineering.

4. "Engineering of Public Acceptance" versus "Risk Limitation"

The debate on chances and risks of a single technological bet is often accompanied by a certain form of political negotiation called "promotion of public acceptance". Acceptance promotion is based on a purely strategic assessment and is meant to keep environmental stakeholders from initiating surprising public sanctions against government or industry policies. It is meant to justify decisive bets on the future without questioning or changing the reigning criteria and standards of the decision-makers within the scientific community, governments or industry. Invitations for discourse issued to environmental stakeholders under the regime of "acceptance promotion" are invitations to limit the range of questioning and to comply with the narrow frame of reference. There are other – less cynical – forms of political negotiation. They concentrate on "risk limitation" based on the precautionary principle, or on "global regionality for the environment". The latter tries to combine global cooperation against ecologically destructive global structures with differentiated and diverse solutions at local and regional levels (Scheidewind and Lunau 1994). It combines the urgent task of a precautionary approach to global and invasive mega-technologies with a special attention to the whole range of participative, culturally and environmentally embedded, locally specific technological and social options. Megatechnologies which can be globally applied and managed by a small group of experts do not rely on the differentiated creativity and cooperation of other people. This seems to have an emotional, aesthetic and political attraction for some people, but not for others. Only "not-knowers" are at ease with the knowledge and creativity of others. "Not-knowers" enjoy science and technology. But they oppose a science and technology that destroys the cultural basis of "not-knowing", i.e. that violates the respect for the knowledge and creativity of others. Intercultural dialogue strongly depends on "not-knowing".

During the past years, the important international negotiations on technology and on the environment often did neither meet the analytical standards of a debate appropriate for such far-reaching issues, nor the requirements of an adequate democratic decision-making (Weizsäcker 1995c). The Uruguay Round of the General Agreement on Tariffs and Trade (GATT) and its Trade Related Intellectual Property Rights, for example, radically redefined the cultural, social and legal character of animals, plants and microorganisms. The decision-makers, however, did not invite public discussion or seek democratic legitimation. Public inattention seems to be a fully acceptable sort of public acceptance.

And what happens at the UN-level? At the Earth Summit (UNCED) in Rio the Biodiversity Convention and Agenda 21 were agreed upon and are now being implemented. Chapter 16 of Agenda 21 has the title "Environmentally sound management of biotechnology". In the introduction the following sentence can be found: "Biotechnology, an emerging knowledge-intensive field, is a set of enabling techniques for bringing about specific man-made changes in deoxyribonucleic acid (DNA) or genetic material, in plants, animals and microbial systems, leading to useful products and technologies." So, the chapter starts with the prophecy that this technology will prove "environmentally sound" and "enabling" and that its products will be "useful". The introduction goes on to name the aims of the UN-agenda in the field of biotechnology. Amongst these are: "To engender public trust and confidence" and "to promote the development of sustainable applications and to establish appropriate enabling mechanisms".[2] (Agenda 21, 1992: Chapter 16) It is quite frightening how fast we are approaching the ballyhoo of technology acceptance and how fast the words of the debate on environment and development get worn and torn in the public relations of genetic engineering (Weizsäcker 1995d). More money is spent on doctoring public acceptance than on technology impact assessment[3,4] (UNIDO paper for CSD 1995, EU Document No.6277/94). This is contrary to the not-knowers' curiosity and respect for the knowledge of others.

5. Technology-Centred Risk Assessment versus Problem-Oriented Comparison of Different Technological Options

Biotechnology assessment which compares risks and chances is closely related to economic cost-benefit analysis. It shares some of the weaknesses of the economic model. The first one is the limited range of time and of parameters: consumers' and producers' choices follow short-term optimizations. The second one is the structural disadvantage of the consumer or citizen: Producers have a better infrastructure of communication, of public relations and of technology assessment. Dominant branches of high science and high technology tend to monopolize the power to define rationality and progress. They adhere to the somewhat mythical assumptions that those persons and tools causing damage are always best suited to assess and to mend that damage. Technology-centred risk assessment is inimical to the inclusion of social, cultural and ethical criteria or domesticates these criteria into servicing technological aims.

Moreover, technology-centred risk assessment undermines the separation of political powers (Weizsäcker 1993a: 48), which successfully shaped our political structures. If a small group of experts advises parliaments and influences legislation, if the same group of experts is drafting government policies and if the same group, again, is called to the law courts to give independent evidence, the separation and mutual control of legislation, government and jurisdiction cannot function properly. Problem-oriented comparison of different technological options is a way out. The German Bundestag had Parliamentary Enquiries of both types: technology-centred and problem-oriented ones. They lend themselves to the analysis of the differences. Problem-oriented comparison certainly widens the range of relevant expertise. Since interdisciplinarity forces experts to translate their findings for each other it also gives the public a better chance to understand the issues at stake.

This is a good basis for the triple task of assessing and comparing the qualities of different technologies (Weizsäcker 1995e). The word 'technology' comes from the old Greek language. It is defined as a means to an end. The quality of a technology clearly depends on its adequacy to meet certain ends. Technology is not "good" because it is complicated. It is not "good" because it requires expensive instruments and/or long training for the technicians. "High-tech" according to this basic definition means having a high standard in meeting the ends of the users.

There are three contributions necessary in the making of such "high-tech": The first contribution comes from people who carefully find out what they really want, who discuss their hopes, values, ends and aims, and who identify, describe, negotiate and reconcile conflicting aims (Burns and Ueberhorst 1988; Weizsäcker 1993b). In modern economic language this is called the demand side.

The second contribution to technology comes from the technologists, tool-makers, inventors and producers of means.

The third contribution comes from technology assessment. Technological inventions have to be measured. Do they fit the ends of their users? Do they allow or destroy the rich diversity of values, aims and hopes? Do they protect the freedom of choice?

Do they comply with the common values shared by a given community or society? A technology may all of a sudden become counterproductive, i.e. it may counteract its very ends. A technological pathway which results in many long-term effects may be entered bearing in mind a single short-term effect only. A technology may not allow the freedom and fair chance of non-consumption. And worst of all, a technology may grow into a mythological, state-financed end in itself and it may shun comparison with other measures and technologies.

Creativity and innovation is usually only attributed to the second of the three contributions listed above. Social recognition and a favourable structural framework are therefore nearly exclusively granted to the "tool-makers".

Our Western dominant culture has huge innovative potentials in providing means and tools. It has frightening structural weaknesses in sovereign citizens' decisions on ends. It does not adequately match efforts in technology with efforts in comparative technology assessment. This disproportion needs redressing. If no such efforts are made, our society could be rightly called a "technologically paradoxical society", i.e. a society which takes special pride in its high technological standards and at the same time is inimical to the very concept of technology.

Not-knowers, on the one hand, take less pride in controlling unquestioned "tools as such". On the other hand, they take more pleasure in asking people. The art of not-knowing may be needed to dissolve the technological paradox into a meaningful discourse on technology. The identification of gaps in scientific knowledge would be part of the pleasure of such a discourse. This would be a happy ending to the strange stagnation in scientific curiosity surrounding mainstream biotechnology assessment, in which many scientists fight for narrowing down the scope of risk assessment and for reducing the number of sanctioned questions permissible in the context of releases of GMOs.

Notes

1. Draft decision submitted by the Chairman on Agenda Item 4.4: Consideration of the Need for and Modalities of a Protocol for the Safe Transfer, Handling and Use of Living Modified Organisms. UNEP/CBD/COP/2/CW/L.22, p.3.

2. Chapter 16 of Agenda 21 was on the agenda during the 3rd Session of the UN-Commission on Sustainable Development in New York in April 1995.

3. Report of the United Nations Industrial Development Organization (UNIDO) prepared for the discussion on Chapter 16 of Agenda 21: Suwana-adth, Malee and Campbell, Virginia (Technology Promotion Section, Technology Service and Investment and Technology Promotion Division of UNIDO) January 1995. *Financing Biotechnology for Sustainable Development*, pp.10-11.

4. Draft Proposal on a "Special Programme for Biosciences and -technologies" submitted by the EU Commission to the President of the Council of the European Union on March 30, 1994. Document of the Council of the European Union No.6277/94. Figures quoted on page 30 of Drucksache 431/94 of the Report of the German Government to the Bundesrat (Federal Council).

References

Beck, Ulrich 1986. *Risikogesellschaft. Auf dem Weg in eine andere Moderne*. Frankfurt.

Bohr, Niels 1961. *Atomic Theory and the Description of Nature, Four Essays*. Cambridge.

Bruckmann, G. (ed.) 1977. *Langfristige Prognosen. Möglichkeiten und Methoden der Langfristprognostic komplexer Systeme*. Würzburg.

Burns, Tom R. and Ueberhorst, Reinhard 1988. *Creative Democracy – Systematic Conflict Resolution and Policymaking in a World of High Science and Technology*. New York: Greenwood Press.

Draft decision submitted by the Chairman on Agenda Item 4.4: Consideration of the Need for and Modalities of a Protocol for the Safe Transfer, Handling and Use of Living Modified Organisms. UNEP/CBD/COP/2/CW/L.22, p.3.

Fisher, Ronald 1930. *The Genetical Theory of Natural Selection*. Oxford: Oxford University Press.

Häfele, Wolf 1974. 'Hypotheticality and the New Challenges: The Pathfinder Role of Nuclear Energy.' *Minerva* **XII**, p.401.

Hahn, H. 1976. *The Next 200 Years*. New York.

Kant, I. 1781. *Kritik der reinen Vernunft*. A90/B122.

Nagel, T. 1986. *The View from Nowhere*. Oxford: University Press.

Popper, K.R. 1965. 'Prognose und Prophetie in den Sozialwissenschaften.' In: E. Topitsch (ed.), *Logik der Sozialwissenschaften*. Köln.

Schneidewind, Uwe and Lunau, York 1994. 'Von Akzeptanzsicherung über Gefährdungsbegrenzung zu "Globalregionalität für die Umwelt".' *GAIA* **3** (6), pp.311-314.

Thomas, Lewis 1979. *The Medusa and the Snail. More Notes of a Biology Watcher*. New York: The Viking Press.

Weizsäcker, Christine von 1990. 'Fehlerfreundlichkeit: Ein Kriterium zukünftiger Technikentwicklung.' In: Roland Schaeffer (ed.), *Ist die technisch-wissenschaftliche Zukunft demokratisch beherrschbar? Beiträge zum Kongreβ der Heinrich-Böll-Stiftung*. Bonn/Frankfurt: Heinrich-Böll-Stiftung e.V., pp.197-202.

———. 1993a. 'Einführungsvortrag.' In: *Bericht der parlamentarischen Enquête-Kommission betreffend "Technikfolgenabschätzung am Beispiel der Gentechnologie" – Gutachten und Stellungnahmen*. Band 3, Wien: Österreichischer Nationalrat.

———. 1993b. 'Competing Notions of Biodiversity.' In: Wolfgang Sachs (ed.), *Global Ecology. A New Arena of Political Conflict*. London, pp.129-130.

———. 1995a. 'Biodiversity – Extractive versus cognostic knowledge.' In: *Research for Development. Sarec 20 Years*. Stockholm: Sarec, pp.91-103.

———. 1995b. 'Error-friendliness and the Evolutionary Impact of Deliberate Releases of GMOs.' In: Vandana Shiva and Ingunn Moser (eds.), *Biopolitics. A Feminist and Ecological Reader on Biotechnology*. London: Zed Books, pp.112-120.

———. 1995c. 'Anmerkungen zum Spannungsbogen Demokratie und Umwelt.' In: *Entsorgte Demokratie. Zum Abbau demokratischer Strukturen im Umweltbereich. Tagungsdokumentation*. Werkstattreihe Nr. 90 des Öko-Instituts. Freiburg/Darmstadt, pp.6-14.

———. 1995d. 'Gentechnik und Artenvielfalt. Eine schwierige Beziehung, die als ideale Partnerschaft gelten möchte.' In: Jürgen Wolters (ARA), *Leben und Leben lassen. Biodiversität – Ökonomie, Natur- und Kulturschutz im Widerstreit*. Gießen, pp.53-59.

———. 1995e. 'Options for Diverse and Viable Technologies, Structures and Lifestyles.' Paper presented at the Seminar on "Genetic Engineering: Science, Ecology and Policy", 10th April 1995 at the Permanent Mission of Malaysia to the UN in New York. Penang: Third World Network, pp.2-5.

Weizsäcker, Christine von and Weizsäcker, Ernst Ulrich von 1984. 'Fehlerfreundlichkeit.' In: Klaus Kornwachs (ed.), *Offenheit-Zeitlichkeit-Komplexität: Zur Theorie d. offenen Systeme*. Frankfurt/New York, pp.167-201.

Weizsäcker, Ernst von and Weizsäcker, Christine von 1987. 'How to Live with Errors? On the Evolutionary Power of Errors.' *World Futures: The Journal of General Evolution* **23** (3),

Christine von Weizsäcker

Ervin Laszlo (ed.), New York/London/Paris, pp.225-235.

Wills, Peter R. 1994. 'The ecological hazards of transgenic varieties – Scrambling Nature's Algorithm.' Paper presented at the International Conference on Redefining the Life Sciences, Penang, Malaysia, 7-10 July 1994. Forthcoming publication by Third World Network, Penang.

14

Risk Communication and the Ethos of Democracy[1]

Christoph Rehmann-Sutter and Adrian Vatter

1. Introduction

The moral challenge of environmental risks combined with the application of modern technology is the imposition of physical dangers to others. In fact technology itself and its forms of application have several other ethical aspects beside their environmental risks: exclusion of alternative economic or technological strategies, discrimination and power between human groups, use and impoverishment of ecosystems etc. Some of these other aspects may also lead to political conflicts. The risk aspect represents therefore only a section of the moral challenges of technology. However, it is no doubt the leading dimension in political regulation issues of technology implementations. We want to find out, why this is so, with what kind of problems a society is confronted when decisions should be collective decisions, why and in what respect only democratic decisions can be morally motivated.

The history of technology in the second half of the 20th century is not only a history of inventions and of a tremendous acceleration of innovation, but also a history of disasters. Technology revealed itself in its intrinsic multidimensionality: technology is not only the art of reaching goals with efficient means, but also a substantial change in concrete reality. The 'means' are real things in the real world of things and share their fate. They interact and are altered during these interactions, there is corrosion and ageing of materials, there is the unpredictable human factor able to change the real effects of the technology, and there is the location of things in dynamic ecosystems, interacting with them in a complex and often uncontrollable way. The list of disasters caused by technology is long and growing. Only a small selection got symbolic appreciation as icons of technical fallibility: 'Seveso', 'Bhopal', 'Chernobyl' etc. They were singular events with a clear source of harm. Others, like the destruction of the ozone layer, the global warming and the extinction of species are cumulative effects of myriads of small technical interventions, each of them sometimes as harmless as going shopping by car.

'Learning from disaster' (Jasanoff 1994) – the task for policy with reference to societal use and control of technology could not be described any better. There are two learning strategies, which could be named 'shallow' and 'deep'. The first is more or less what has been realized already. Josée van Eijndhoven analyzed the historical development in European risk regulation since the beginning of the series of technical catastrophes in the seventies. She finds that politics have *reacted* each time after severe mishaps. "Disaster policy is adapted stepwise", and: "The implication of this history is that new accidents are needed to push disaster management forward" (van Eindhoven 1994: 128). Such a strategy is an overtly inadequate way to deal with the deep rooted inherent and not accidental problems of ecological risks of modern technology. It is rather symbolic and minimalistic. The cynical consequence is the need of new disasters in order to prevent ecological risks.

If politics should emancipate from its reactive condition and become prospective, many efforts are needed. We suggest in this article that one of them should be a new and fundamental reflection on the potentialities of politics itself. We try to contribute to this discussion with some terminological clarifications (2 and 3), with an ethical analysis of the task of informed consent in small and larger groups concerning risk impositions (4), and with a (not comprehensive) inventory of public participation issues (5). Risk communication, provided it is adequately conceptualized, might be a means by which the ethical debate about biotechnology could cope with its political impact.

This paper highlights some basic ideas of a current research project – in which both authors are involved – on possibilities for a democratic handling of ecological risks.[2] We address the question of risk assessment in relation to release experiments of genetically modified organisms, dealing with it as a paradigm for environmentally relevant technology.

2. Risks, Risk Assessments and the Assessment of Risk Assessment

There is no generally accepted definition of the concept of 'risk'. For political and ethical discussions a strict coupling of risks to human actions and decisions is convenient. Starting with Rescher's formula of a risk as "the chancing of negative effects – of some loss or harm" (Rescher 1983: 5), we can introduce the criterium of accountability to human actions or decisions and refer to:

> *Risk*: The chancing of negatively valued effects (loss or harm) due to human decisions.

The consequence of this restricted usage is that with the concept of 'risk' those negative environmental changes which are in principle accountable to human responsibility may be isolated. These are handled as the moral or political issue of risks. What *nature* 'does' is no issue for morals or politics. If a risk issue emerges, it will focus on the question, how human actions and decisions should *respond* to natural dangers. Hurricanes are dangers, not risks. But the decision to settle in a place frequently afflicted by hurricanes involves the taking of a risk.

A standard example for decisions involving risk is playing roulette. A player gives a stake and holds the risk of not getting it back again, while hoping to earn higher winnings with luck. In spite of the not neglectable complexities of the stakeholders situation on the existential dimension, roulette is in one respect a simple situation: in the perspective of the deciding subject there is only one stakeholder and only one person affected by the potential loss or the potential winning. The stakeholder as well as the person affected are identical with the actor. Ecological risks of technological setups are not in the same way undertaken by deciding stakeholders. Either the persons affected by potential harm are not the same individuals as the deciding actors, or else they include also other persons, beside the actor(s). It is, as though a roulette player would mix his fortune with that of his neighbours but would make the playing decisions all by himself. Ecological games consist in giving stakes exceeding the fortune of the player and including the fortune of others. There are three groups of people concerned in a different way: the actors (i.e. the persons deciding), the stakeholders (i.e. the persons potentially affected by some loss or harm), and the beneficiaries (i.e. the persons enjoying advantages from the existence of the setup). These three groups may fall asunder. In order not to hide this *nonidentity* of the actor group with the group(s) of the positively and/or negatively influenced persons we stress a distinction within the terminus of risk: if the possible effects of the undertaking of the risk affect the actors themselves, we speak of *undertaken risks*. This is the ordinary roulette situation. But if the possible effects of the undertaking of the risk affect (also) others, not (only) the actors themselves, we speak of *imposed risks*. This is the case in the ordinary ecological situation. In the case of imposed risks the constellation of actors and affected is such that we may not say, the affected persons "undertake" the risk, even though they are involved.

Possible effects affect:

| actors themselves | ————————▸ | *undertaken risks* |
| *(also) others* | ————————▸ | *imposed risks* |

But what is the sense of the term 'risk' in the case of imposed risks, where the affected persons do not 'undertake' any risk at all, as we have said? Nondeciding but affected persons experience these so-called risks as *dangers*. Playing on streets is really dangerous for children. To simply say that it is risky for them, would hide that they are not responsible for the danger they are confronted with. There is a sharp difference between natural dangers and those dangers out of actions of others: the latter can be perceived as *injustice*, while the former are not accountable within the sphere of morality (Shklar 1990). 'Natural' events are *per definitionem* events not accountable to human decisions. So, the terms 'risk' and 'danger' are bound to a certain perspective: risks involve the actor perspective, whereas dangers involve the perspective of the affected. Imposed risks are perceived as dangers by the affected. But when we classify these dangers as risk impositions by others we are introducing the question of justice; we are questioning these decisions of others. They could be unjustified encroachments.

To summarize: the moral challenge of environmental risks connected with the application of modern technology in an anthropocentric view is the imposition of physical dangers to life, health and freedom of others. The actors are either *not* affected by the hazard or they are *not the only* persons affected. This circumstance of decisions in the field of environmental risks is responsible for introducing these decisions into the sphere of politics (Winner 1986). The rationale of classical decision theory – as mainly a theory of decisions under uncertainty affecting only the actors themselves (Arrow 1970; Luce and Raiffa 1967) – cannot be applied directly to resolve situations where actors are affecting the interests of other competent beings.

This has also direct implications for the validity of so-called risk assessment procedures: they can only accomplish what is promised in their name, if they are oriented on the appropriate risk concept. Risk impositions cannot be assessed with the same rationality as risk undertakings. The criterium for legitimate risk impositions can*not* be a reasonable calculation of probabilities, potential losses, chances, costs and winnings.

The broadest of all possible definitions of Risk Communication (RC) is given by the US National Research Council (1989):

> *Risk communication*: An interactive process of exchange of information and opinion among individuals, groups, and institutions; often involves multiple messages about the nature of risk or expressing concerns, opinions, or reactions to risk messages or to legal and institutional arrangements for management (Wiedemann 1993: 22).

In the situation of conflict the term RC with all its hopeful connotations can also be utilized to confirm convenient ideologies. It can function as an instrument to spread the previously identifiable responsibility among a passive public without changing anything in the decision procedures except the way of communication.

In this essay, focusing on ethical aspects of RC in the context of risk assessment, we want to use the term in a more restricted way:

> *Risk communication*: The collective assessment of technological (or ecological) risks and the collective assessment of risk assessment.

In this formula communication is considered on two levels: (i) The communication about the risks, about its components, context and significance, and (ii) the communication about the perception, description and evaluation of the risks. Communicative quality can be advanced on both levels: on the level of the perception of a socially embedded risk and on the level of reflection about that socially undertaken perception. And on both levels communication may also fail.

Our perspective on that complex phenomenon of risk assessment is conflict-oriented. We want to understand, why technological interventions are nuclei for social conflicts, and what the structure of this type of conflict is. These issues have to be treated in order to discuss the question, what would be the task of improvements of the communicative methodologies actually being practiced in industrialized modern societies.

On the way to a clearer vision of tenable RC procedures we cannot avoid normative discussions. We want to find a 'good' communicative practice. The word 'good' in this claim is not only extrinsically good, with respect to its functionality: A 'good' communicative practice is not synonymous with an efficient communication, but has to be an *intrinsically* good communication. What is the meaning of that claim?

3. The Structure of Environmental Risks

It is no novelty for the discourse of philosophical ethics to discuss risk impositions. The fact that the attempts to preserve life, well-being and wealth may impose risks to other individuals is reflected in the core of political philosophy at least since enlightenment. Thomas Hobbes (1985: 185 and ch. 17) described the natural state, where no legal order existed, as a "war of every man against every man", and the passage from the natural to the contractual state was a desirable step of general risk-reduction. It was this general expectation of lowering the risks to which everybody is imposed that legitimated the subordination under the political sovereign and the corresponding renunciation of power. However, are those risk impositions related to classical modern political theory really comparable to the risk of technology we have to cope with today?

There are some important and quite overt differences. Perhaps the main point is what may be called a diffusion of accountability. Hobbesian risk is e.g. the risk of being robbed or being killed by some other actor, i.e. the risk of being the victim of some direct action of other individuals or groups of individuals. Once the event has taken place, there will be culprits and complainants. The actors are potentially identifiable (even if in reality the police has not found every gangster yet) and the victims are potentially identifiable (even if in reality not every victim will sue the culprits). As Daniel Schulthess (1994) has suggested, the structure of ecological and technological risks differs from the structure of classical situations precisely in not having identifiable and isolable culprits and/or in not producing active complainants (see Figure 1).

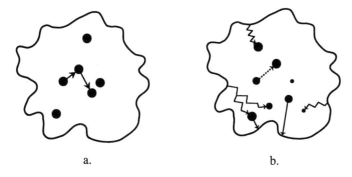

a.   b.

Figure 1: The effects of risk
a. The situation with direct and imputable injuries between human individuals.
b. The 'ecological' situation with indirect and not imputable injuries by chains of effects in the environment. (The dotted arrow signifies 'direct' elements in ecological risk situations. The small spot represents a new individual, e.g. a child.)

The release of recombinant organisms into the environment is an excellent example to illustrate this difference. The direct action itself, i.e. the introduction of genetically modified organisms (e.g. of a pest resistant potato plant) is mostly not directly harmful to any other subject – except if the organisms are explicitly designed to harm (e.g. in biological warfare). In this case we consider the peaceful application of engineered organisms not designed to induce diseases, but constructed to do 'good'.

The environmental risks to be assessed in these cases are consisting of possible side effects or higher order effects (effects of effects) of the technical intervention. Eventually there may even be combinations with future environmental changes or with the effects of other (gene-)technical interventions in the same environment. One can imagine, at least theoretically, that such chains of effects could inflict harm to humans in a nearer or farer future. The exchange of the new genetic material with other loci of the chromosome, with genetic material of other species, perhaps other engineered organisms, could lead to new behaviour features of organisms we are not able to foresee now. The same DNA in organisms with other genetic backgrounds, where it could get to by horizontal transfer mechanisms, could have very different phenotypic effects. It might further destabilize the process equilibria of our already destabilized ecosystems, even of those ecosystems supporting a good human survival. For a detailed account of hypothetical scenarios of the undesired we refer to special literature.[3]

The special feature of the risk situation in decisions about releases of genetically modified organisms into the environment is, that neither the pathways leading to unfavorable effects nor the probabilities of such effects are really known. The risks are only assessable on a rather speculative level. The decisions concern unknown risks. This makes the issue more complex, as not only the acceptability of some risk in relation to some benefit has to be assessed, but also the nature and quality of the risk itself. Both assessments take place under uncertainty. On the political level there are conflicts between interest groups (companies) who are taking the missing knowledge about risks as a sign for their irrelevance, and environmentalists who are alerted by the mere fact that knowledge is missing (Rehmann-Sutter 1992). This may not be a unique specialty of genetic engineering, but in this case it is a novel technology enjoying high public concern. The fact that we decide with the aid of insufficient knowledge is becoming obvious and unneglectable.

In summary, the *direct* ('Hobbesian') risk is the probability to be affected by a direct action of other human beings (or groups) lessening one's freedom or life-chances. The remedy is a limitation of unhindered freedom of all actors down to a degree where the freedom of one is not the destruction of the freedom of the other. Or with Kant's renowned formula: "Law ("Recht") is the idea of the conditions under which the ability of choice ("Willkür") of the one can be combined with the ability of choice of the others, following a general rule of freedom" (Kant 1922: 34). This sort of regulation, however, cannot eliminate all problems with the legitimacy of classical risks. In singular cases it may be unclear where the limit is, for it was conceptualized at a very high level of abstraction. There are cases where the boundary has to be infringed because even higher values are in danger.

In contrast, the paradigmatic case of *indirect* (ecological/technological) risk represents the probability that effects of technical interventions into the environment, maybe even in combination with the effects of other technical interventions or environmental changes, will indirectly lessen the freedom or life-chances of human (and non-human) individuals in the present or the nearer or farer future. 'Effects' may in both cases include side-effects and higher order effects. The remedy in this case may only be a sort of prudence of the present actor community. The question is, how decision-procedures may institutionalize this prudence.

4. Action Competence: The Objective of Risk Communication

4.1 Consent and rationality in the medical discourse

There is a renowned field of ethical reflection in medicine about the acceptability of risks of technical intervention into the life of others. Since this field has generated some clarities about the participation of patients in decision procedures, it was suggested by Christine von Weizsäcker (1991), Günter Ropohl (1994: 118) and others to compare the situation of environmental hazards with the risk of medical therapies.

Perhaps the analysis of this less complex situation may help us with the objective of RC. We have to be cautious, however, not to overdraw the analogy.

Medical interventions are actions involving others. In medical treatments there is at least one medical expert – the physician – and an individual who receives treatment. The latter is physically involved. Every treatment is bearing some risk – at least the risk not to be successful. Especially new and experimental treatments may contain risks to induce harm as a side-effect. And every decision about treatment is value-laden: it involves judgements about the best interests of the patient. The patient desires that after a medical treatment things should be better. "Better", however, is a subjective assessment of a rather complex situation of life. What seems "better for the patient" may differ with a changing perspective. As medical ethicists emphasize, there may be moral tensions bctween the principles of autonomy and beneficence in cases where individuals decide against their own best interests (Beauchamp and Childress 1989: 209 ff.).

The solution medical ethics proposes for this type of problem is discussed under the title of "free and informed consent". The argument in favour of it is strong and may be summarized as follows: the moral community is composed of individuals capable of responsible decisions. The main criterium for belonging to the moral community is that an individual is respecting the others as members, too; as being capable of responsible decisions. Only free decisions may be responsible decisions. Decisions under coercion or under deception are not responsible in that moral sense. Consequently, the disregard of the freedom of others in an action involving them is blameworthy, because it is excluding a violator – a person who decides alone in cases where others are involved also – from the moral community.

On the other side this argument prescribes the respect of the consent (or dissent) of the involved patient. In order for a consent to be real and reliable it has to be given in a state of freedom (no coercion) and in the possession of all relevant and true information (no deception). H. Tristram Engelhardt sums the moral principle of autonomy up as follows:

> Authority for actions involving others in a secular pluralist society is derived from the free consent of those involved. As a consequence,
> i. Without such consent there is no authority.
> ii. Actions against such authority are blameworthy in the sense of placing a violator outside the moral community in general, and making licit (but not obligatory) retaliatory, defensive, or punitive force by members of any particular moral community (Engelhardt 1986: 85 f.).

Consent is the origin of moral authority of an action involving others. For this reason recent ethical guidelines regard the capacity to give free and informed consent as the main criterium to select potential subjects for medical research. With regard to research involving persons with mental or behavioral disorders the current CIOMS/WHO guidelines state that:

> Such persons will not be subjects of research that might equally well be carried out on persons in full possession of their mental faculties (CIOMS/WHO 1993: 22 – guideline 6).

The research involving children is similarly restricted. (CIOMS/WHO 1993: 20 – guideline 5). The community is clearly expressing the will to protect feeble individuals from unconsented-to force and risk.

The underlying rationale of this search for a free and informed consent of the patients and research subjects is not to prevent conflicts or disagreeable public discussions but an ethical principle: the respect of *self-determination* or *autonomy* of human persons.

We believe this is not the end of the explanation. Further questions arise: Why can a free and informed consent of the involved subjects give moral authority to the action? This question is perhaps a more precise version of the other difficult question for the *meaning* of the terms 'self-determination' and 'autonomy'. Engelhardt gives only a negative answer to this:

> Justification of the principle: the principle of autonomy expresses the fact that authority for resolving moral disputes in a secular, pluralist society can be derived only from the agreement of the participants in the disputes, since it cannot be derived from rational argument or common belief. Therefore, consent is the origin of authority (...) (Engelhardt 1986: 86, cf. ch. 2).

Consent seems to be the last criterium at disposition, after the other candidates – "rational arguments" or "common beliefs" – are disqualified and proved not to be a basis for a peaceful settlement of conflicts in a secular, pluralist society. Engelhardt is seeking for a criterium that could be accepted by all parties – and he proposes nothing more than the *acceptance* of all parties.

Despite of its indisputable logical stringency this explanation is very abstract. And it contains no reflection on the limits of its individualistic (or atomistic) premise.[4] But it does not seem too difficult to find a positive answer, as soon as we omit the atomistic premise according to which individuals are a sort of monades capable of producing responsible decisions after being fed with information.

We may consider the physician-patient-dyad as a (small) group undertaking collective actions. The dyad is assembled of individuals both able to act individually. The physician may undertake her decisions without release of information; the patient may only deal with the physician strategically in order to make her do what he wishes. In these cases of acute alienation the group does not appear as an acting subject. If the needs of the patient, his values and attitudes to life, disease and death are mediated with the knowledge and skill of the physician as well as with her values and attitudes to life, disease and death, the group may get closer to a decision which will be *more* than a mere (mechanical) superposition of the individual desires. Communication may lead to or at least approach a real community, a common responsibility. We can say that a communicating group may be *enabled to act*. The single actors help each other to *find their real will* or their "true self" (Meyers 1987). The responsibility may be shared. Both participate in a process leading to the decision. Freedom is not independence but *self-identification* in communication with the other persons involved.

Without further details or improvement of this philosophy of group communication, we merely claim that it is not completely false. We can see a stimulating conse- quence: group communication and consent is not a burdensome removal of an obstacle for free action. Quite on the contrary, there is freedom to gain what could not be won with other strategies: the *action competence of the group* – or the action competence of the individuals-as-members-of-the-group. This is a somewhat deepened interpretation of the principle of consent. Let's go back now to the ecological risk situation.

4.2 The community of affected beings

The decision to realize or not to realize a project is only an exponent of a complex evaluation and definition of a situation. This includes a clarification of the needs and the expectable contribution of a certain technical intervention to the affected beings in comparison to alternative strategies available. It also includes an assessment of the relevance of the needs. The proposed technology is promising a direct response to and an assessment of the relation of the responded-to needs to the 'real world' problems. This again includes an evaluation of the security measures, of the quality of risk research, of the quality of the total knowledge available about the systems concerned. Furthermore it includes the knowledge of who might be affected by harm or loss and by what kind of harm or loss. It finally includes an estimation of the urgency of the intervention. There are lots of other relevant elements of the situation. As stated in Rehmann-Sutter (1993), we only know about what type of action we are deciding, when we know the relevant aspects of the situation, i.e., all relevant circumstances of the decision. Without these, a decision cannot be responsible, i.e., cannot 'respond' to the situation. And if this knowledge about the circumstances is missing, the lack of knowledge itself is one of the relevant circumstances. In the case of the release, for example, of something as harmless as a pest resistant potato crop, there is dissent about several of these issues. The fact of dissent among experts is itself one of the relevant circumstances for the decision-making. One option is always, to make further investigations and seek clarification. This does not mean, not to make a decision, but take the liberty to ask questions and decide at the right moment.

The bare amount of questions involved in a serious clarification by a larger group of a situation enables a decision to get better. Only the smaller part of the questions are technical questions and need scientific experts to respond. For the other issues the solutions are improved by a multitude of different views and angles.

Considering at a general level, we recognize the first of several differences to the consent in medical ethics: not all potentially affected persons may ever be included in any communicative process as they are still children, not even born or not identified as belonging to the group of affected persons (i). We do not know, how far the chain of effects of the decision concerned will propagate, or if we do, the persons are not all in the status of active participants in rational discourses at the present time. A second difference shows up when the symmetry of being a moral agent and being a morally considerate being is questioned: Not all potentially affected beings are human persons, nevertheless they deserve moral consideration (ii). Thus the lives of animals, plants, and the viability of different species are changed, impoverished or eliminated with certain technical interventions i.e. their possible hazardous consequences.[5] These beings are members of the community affected by the decision concerned. In nearly every case the community of involved beings is far more extended than in the physician-patient-dyad (iii). Communication is not merely a dialogue but a multicentered discourse. In medical action there is one clear and unquestioned goal motivating all parties: the healing (Budd and Sharma 1994) (iv). In technological action there is no agreement in the goals. Some see technology as a means to make profit and/or to secure places of employment, others as the destiny of *homo sapiens*, others as a means to improve the quality of life on this planet, still others as an instrument to stabilize social hierarchies, etc. The goals are not always obvious, sometimes not even known to the actors themselves.

All the differences mentioned above are accompanied by important parallels to the medical situation: The decisions involve value judgements (v). The scientifically decidable questions are only one part of the issue. Scientific questions are restricted to the explication of the expected effects of the diverse open options. The other part consists of the determination of the relative weight of the different factors involved, the relative value of the different expectable gains and losses, and always an evaluation of the (moral) weight of probabilities. As Nicholas Rescher showed clearly, even the simplest risk-evaluation procedures are value-laden.[6] These observations are confirmed by experiences made in public participation experiments (see Nelkin and Pollak 1980; Renn and Webler 1992; Renn 1993). For the same reason as in medicine, generalizable value accounts cannot be presupposed in the resolution of conflicts about values in risk assessments (vi). The societies are pluralist and secular and contain different ideas even about rationality (Rehmann-Sutter 1995). The moral authority of a decision about technological risks can only be derived from an agreement of the participants (vii). Something like free and informed consent has to be the origin of authority. This agreement of the participants has to be generated in communicative procedures which have to interrelate the different interests and different backgrounds (viii). The consent has to be significant, not only a formal or superficial consent. The group has to reach a state of action competence as a group.

These reflections lead to an outline of a *vision of democracy* in the age of ecology: The self-determination (or autonomy) of those persons affected by decisions.[7] The concept of democracy needs an interpretation for each changing condition. The democratic principle may be expressed in general terms as 'rule by the people'. The context of specific practical problems of the communities of these people should be our guideline for a distinct political philosophy of democracy. This will play a leading part in the ongoing learning process, actualizing the ethos of democracy within a changing milieu of practical problems. Our formulation tries to express this democratic ethos in a way that a modification of the existing political rule systems may be discussed. It is taking into account that – whilst the world is changing rapidly – democracy must also change, not so much its fundamental ethos but its concrete formulation.

The suggested formulation has two stings: "Self-determination (or autonomy)...": a group of people is self-determining or autonomous if the group is involved in a communicative practice, so that the individuals may determine their real will according their true self as members of the group, and that the group is competent to act responsibly (1); "... of those persons being affected by decisions": the group considered is not always coextensive with the group of citizens of a given legal system or the members of an association (2). The state is a special case where decisions about legal rules have to be made. The group of the affected persons by a decision about legal rules are the citizens within that legal system. We use the concept of 'politics' in a wider sense including not only the legal boundaries of the life situation of persons, but also extralegal boundaries such as technology and its effects (see Winner 1986). Therefore, the extension of the group concerned is variable. Who belongs to that group depends on the decision at stake. Sometimes it will overlap traditional political frontiers and transcend the border of the future. It may itself be an issue to bargain, who belongs to the group of those affected.

Clearly, there are tensions between the ideal of consent and the real circumstances of decisions about technological risks which we have mentioned as the four main differences to the medical situation. Real communicative procedures cannot omit compromises.

5. Public Participation Issues

Starting from the specific qualities of technological risks, the following aims at discussing questions concerning concrete proposals for a participative risk communication. Each will open a new set of questions. We do not pretend to answer them here.

5.1 Democracy of the affected:
Qualified rights of participation for those highly affected

In concrete situations, where decisions about technological implementations involving environmental risks have to be made, conflicts about the decision itself are easily transformed into the question of *who* should decide. The strongest legitimation to challenge established settings of institutional power is based on the existence of vital threats. A risk imposition cannot have moral authority if those highly affected by the risks were not allowed to participate in the deciding procedure. This claim of those highly affected by threats is directed not only against autocratic decisions of power holders (e.g. companies), but also against the imposition by a less negatively or even positively affected majority in democratic procedures. It seems useful to allocate certain privileges to the highly affected due to their higher degree of exposure – instead of merely offering a large field of participation possibilities. Ideally the unanimity-rule should be applied, i.e. all those highly likely to be affected have to agree without exception. This would fulfill the idea of democracy and informed consent by providing total self-determination of each and everyone in a perfect way. However, this rule is hardly practicable since not all negatively affected persons are known and present; because it enables all those – who might be affected in a negative way – to prevent a decision by exercising their veto and due to the high cost of transaction. Consequently, the unanimity-rule would lead to the prevention of all solutions related to locally negative effects. This again would cause resistance by the opposition and would itself be considered unfair, as the result of the decision would automatically be obvious from the start and therefore prevent any contribution to solving a conflict. However, the basic idea of allocating specific decision-making rights to those highly affected should nevertheless be observed. Basically, the following should be aimed at: the higher and more likely a fundamental threat, the more qualified i.e. the larger the majority must be. This principle seems plausible and should be acceptable by all those involved.

Simple majority decisions by all those involved (e.g. national plebiscites) are insufficient with regard to the principle of fairness[8] which requires the same chances of influence for all those involved and provides all actors with a fair chance to decide a plebiscite. The realization of this principle requires an institutional strengthening of those specifically affected by risks involving vital threats (concerning fundamental rights) because they are numerically in a weaker position, without, however, allocating them an exclusive right of decision.

Uebersax (1991: 191 f.) makes the following proposition: if those likely to be primarily affected by risks refuse the technological project, their veto should only be overruled in a subsequent national referendum by a qualified majority, for example of 2/3rds.

As we can see in the case of the release of recombinant organisms, one central difficulty is that each realized partition of citizens into a group of highly affected persons and into a group of involved but not highly affected persons is quite arbitrary. The ecosystems are not confined and we do not know which negative ecological effects we have to calculate. But this theoretical uncertainty could perhaps be tolerated in favour of an improvement of the decision quality. That arbitrarily constituted group of those highly affected by risks could be regarded as *representative* of those highly affected in reality. They would still have a politically discernable voice.

In our formulation of the democratic principle we have used the term 'affected by decisions'. It is evident that this means a larger group than the term 'affected by risks'. Real procedures will have to live with a certain amount of arbitrariness in the social definition of these groups. For, if each decision was preceded by a *de novo* partition of the population into these two groups, a decision might never be made.

5.2 Direct and understandable information

"Risk communicators should avoid technical and bureaucratic language, and, instead, address people's concern directly. They should provide the public with information that can be related to personal experiences and that fosters individual learning" (Kenney and Winterfeldt 1986: 424).

The participation interest may be increased by an open, direct and pro-lay communication policy. The quality of the information-feedback from the participation is directly dependent on whether the planning commission informs early, understandably and directly. However, it seems that there is a particular lack where risk conflicts are concerned: "Perhaps most pressing is the need for improving the presentation of risk information. It does not make much sense to tell lay people that the risk of contracting cancer from radionuclide emissions from a coal fired power plant is 10^{-7} per year for the maximum exposed individual. They are likely to respond: But is it dangerous to live near the plant?" (Kenney and Winterfeldt 1986: 422).

This example shows that the issue of understandability is twofold. On one side there is a *problem of terminology* and specialized scientific language, and on the other side there is a *problem of relevance*. The first is much easier to resolve. One could explain for example: If you are living beside that power plant for a 100 years, meeting the conditions of maximum exposition, one person out of 100.000 may get cancer as an effect of the radionuclide emission. This is the meaning of the probability of "10^{-7} per year". The second problem is not resolvable at all by the aid of translating strategies. If I had to live near that power plant, the question of existential significance is not answered by a complete information at the scientific level. I would have to integrate this condition in my personal value system, into my landscape of expectations and plans. Here the following questions may arise: How difficult would it be to make that power plant even safer? Why are these measures not undertaken? How important is the existence of that source of danger? What alternatives of problem resolution could be developed (solar energy, production with a lower energy input, etc.)?

5.3 Open conflict settlement

The demand for open planning processes meets several institutional and psychological obstacles. One point is that only the minor part of technological projects are held by public institutions. Decisions of private companies within a system of free market cannot be public in an early state of planning for reasons of competition. And the decision-making processes of companies are only rarely democratic even within the company. Companies are aiming at efficiency in competition not at public justice. So, the public may only participate indirectly: the framework of legal constraints (safety prescriptions), the behaviour of buying and consumption and in the formation of the 'image' of the company in the public. Formalized participation processes may particularly take place on the first of these topics, on the level of the legal framework.

However, even in public administrations a better participation is not easy to realize. It changes the social roles of the office-holders as they have to share power and – perhaps most importantly – the processes become much more complicated. While open debates may increase the number of conflicts and the number of involved actors they also provide advantages. Perhaps there is neither a net loss of efficiency nor a net increase of conflicts. Basically it shows that it is easier to reconcile conflicts at an early stage of the planning; that their simultaneous settlement opens more reconciliation opportunities and that the prevention of subsequent resistance to the execution of the project is easier. The confidence required and a fundamental consensus despite opposing interests may be established, when good experiences are accumulated with innovative communicative settings.

5.4 Early and repeated participation of the population

Participation and information with reference to risk topics are necessary and sensible throughout the process of decision-making, since the practical solution is pre-determined at a very early stage of the definition of the problem, thus causing factual constraints which are hardly negotiable at a later stage (Zillessen et al. 1993). The population should therefore already participate in the fundamental decision-making and not only at the occasion of the detailed planning of technological risk sources. However, there is a very low interest of public participation during the early stage of the determination of the aims, since the motivating personal concern is missing. At the occasion of complex risk conflicts a further difficulty occurs: "The timing of risk communication entails a difficult trade-off between the social imperative to inform without delay and the need for full scientific information and analysis. Improved understanding is needed as to effective ways to communicate in a timely manner while minimizing potential errors or subsequent conflicting information" (Kasperson 1986: 280).

An early and continuous participation is most likely realized by the so-called iterative planning process (Veuve 1987). Iterative procedures, where – with the participation of independent actors – each planning step may be repeatedly run through and changed with regard to its content even in the early stages of the goal-determination, offer the advantage that the results of the first run may be taken into consideration at the occasion of the following. The introduction of the iterative process together with the inclusion of external actors increase the chances to win additional support, to increase the detection of external restrictions and tune them to one's own goals, to promote education processes on all sides by feedback-loops and mechanisms, to prevent later opposition and problems of execution by introducing the conflict negotiation in the early stages.

5.5 Competence of the participants

A central problem of the decision-making regarding the regulation of technological risks is the fact that the assessment of the need and the related risks of a major technological project requires a high knowledge of the particular subject. An insufficient information of those concerned may cause inconsistent and improper decisions with high subsequent costs (Renn et al. 1992). Sufficient competence and technical information at the earliest possible stage of the procedure are therefore central requirements of a competent participation of the population (Renn et al. 1995).

If competence is regarded as the knowledge necessary to make consistent and proper decisions, an extended concept of relevant knowledge is needed. The scientific and technical information is only one component. The other is the knowledge only available in the perspective of those affected by the effects of a decision. There is a type of knowledge we may call "Betroffenenkompetenz", i.e. the competence of the specifically affected. They have access to knowledge about the local problems, the local history and the local culture, and are therefore able to evaluate the consequences within this local frame.

Consequently, concrete measures must be taken, in order to diminish the lack of information and the missing specific knowledge of the "population involved in the procedure". This again involves a two-way communication between the administrators of the scientific/technical knowledge and the administrators of the specific knowledge of those affected. The partners have to render *each other* competent.

Experience shows that even those likely to be affected in a negative way are capable of participating in the decision-making without detrimentally influencing the rationale of the particular subject (Seiler and Webler 1995). Competence in this context means that the final decision is based on the highest level of knowledge, on rational criteria of the evidence-examination, and that the awareness of the consequences of the different options has been adequately taken into consideration (Renn et al. 1992: 19).

5.6 Representation of long-term interests

For an important part of the population the subjective concern and the short-term consequences of a planning decision are decisive for their active participation. Conventional procedures of citizen-participation may therefore often lead to an increase in the imbalance between the direct object-related and non-related interests, thus causing an additional neglect of general and long-term interests.

Owing to often long-term and unintentional consequences of technological risks, it is necessary to find detailed procedures in order to take into consideration the interest of those affected who may not participate themselves or who are not capable to take part in the conflict: "In essence, participation (should be) a struggle by the 'have-nots' to wrest away power from the 'haves'" (Kasperson 1986: 276). At the same time compensating measures are the centre of attention, protecting the rights of environment and posterity, especially those of future generations (Saladin and Zenger 1988). These demands may be met by establishing deputy-roles. In cases where a conflict between the interests of the presently living humans and those of future generations as well as non-human beings may not be prevented, the deputies have to take care that the conflicts are handled knowingly. The difficulties in identifying the true interests of the represented parties are uncontested and one has to be aware of them. However, they are not important enough to overrule deputies of the natural environment and of future generations.

5.7 Transformation of zero-sum- into positive-sum-conflicts

Seemingly insoluble risk conflicts often arise because those negatively affected assume that the opposite side is taking advantage at their expense. Participation procedures help to transform zero-sum- into positive-sum-conflicts. This means a change of conflict-positions into a situation where it is not one actor winning at the expense of another, but where all actors profit from an additional advantage (win-win-situations). This, however, is only possible if there are different solutions available which should theoretically be realised. Zero-sum-conflicts may not always be avoided. However, they are partly changeable into positive-sum-conflicts by:

1. Leaving the scope of the decision-making open as long as possible, until a clearing of the interests may be achieved. If the decisions are made at the beginning of a negotiation process, certain conflicts may not be recognized at this stage and those involved are often not yet aware of the dimension of their scope of action. An optimum balance of interests is therefore hardly possible since factual necessities and positions of prestige are created by the early decision-making.

2. Avoiding a segmentation of the decision into many single decisions as the latter endangers a more complex meeting of the interests (Hoffmann-Riem and Schmid-Assmann 1991: Bd.1, 67 ff.); and widening the object of the negotiation ("overall solution" as opposed to "segmentation") as this allows to link different matters under certain circumstances so that every party may definitely win with a general solution (Susskind 1987: 117 ff.). The more controversial the topics to be negotiated are, the sooner the actors may

optimize their interests by forming a complex basis for negotiation. In situations of distributive negotiation one side may only win at the expense of another – the classic "zero-sum-system". On the basis of an integrative negotiation, however, all parties involved profit from advantages by negotiating objects which they assess differently – the classic "win-win-situation".

3.   Looking for compensating solutions, which increases both the number of compensation possibilities (locally, objectively, symbolically) and the number of actors that can be reconciled (Kunreuther et al. 1984; Lake 1980; O'Hare et al. 1983: 67 ff.). At the same time it is necessary to clearly point out that with compensation solutions there is always a danger of the opportunism with reference to sitings, i.e. actors (e.g. communities and regions) receive financial compensation for taking over problems caused by the collective. Especially economically weak regions are victim of such a practice; these financial compensations, however, often do not correspond with the needs of the affected (Morell and Magorian 1982: 175). Compensations in the field of the protection of the environment, for example, seem to be far more sensible than financial ones (Fietkau 1991: 9).

6. Conclusion

On the one hand there is unanimity among many parties involved with regard to the fact that innovative attempts in *communicative methodology* are urgent and helpful to cope with the impacts of technological innovations. On the other hand, however, there is a very diverse understanding of what these impacts are and what should be the corresponding aim of communicative improvements. The content of the problem to which RC should be a response is highly dependent on the position of the actor within the texture of sociotechnical systems. An actor-perspective is seldom a neutral or impartial perspective. This is already given with the perception of the problems to which RC is designed to be concerned with. For industrial observers RC is primarily an inevitable means to improve the efficiency of cooperation with the public. For government representatives RC may contribute to make their decision-making procedures more credible. For critics RC is paired with the hope for more influence. Each perspective suggests its own criteria to evaluate real communicative processes or propositions for RC procedures. RC *per se* is too broad a concept to contain illuminative hints for deciding which perspective is more relevant than others and which criterium should have priority. In the last resort every exchange of information about and in connection with risks has to be described as RC.

The concept of free and informed consent is both intelligible and perplexing. The comparison of the situation in experimental medicine with the situation of environmental hazards due to technological implementations confirms that the concept of consent is not free of presuppositions. A consent can only come about if the persons concerned are existent at the time of the decision. A consent is only possible in cases, where those beings affected and morally significant are also rational and intelligent subjects, and therefore are able to give or withhold a consent.

And thirdly, the crowd of the beings affected has to become an integrated group capable to act. Otherwise the answer to a question for consent is only a heterogeneous cluster of divergent echoes. The community of the concerned needs a unified voice to respond. All of these presuppositions are not automatically fulfilled in cases of environmental risks. The aim of political decision-making procedures is therefore twofold: firstly to find institutional solutions to the manifold problems of the necessary – though difficult to obtain – free and informed consent of the community of those affected. The solutions have to be realizable and good enough in order for moral authority of decisions to be derived. Secondly, to generate a transparency of the unsurmountable imperfection of real procedures with regard to the mentioned theoretical demands.

In any case, risk communication involves *innovative politics*. Or, as Ulrich Beck (1993) stated, even the invention of politics in the realm of technology assessment. Politics only merits its name, if its objective is *to realize freedom* of the citizens – realize in the dual sense of both conceiving the idea and implementing it. This introduction of a part of Hannah Arendt's political philosophy[9] into the realm of ecological risk leads to a non-atomistic concept of freedom in the "risk society". We have introduced it with the terms of "action competence of the group" and "self-identification in communication". Politics is not restricted to be an arithmetic combination of the single wills of the actors to an identifiable group will, but includes rendering possible processes of mutual education and a corresponding development of the will of the single communicators. We need Politics, not only politics.

Notes

1. We thank Ad van Dommelen for helpful comments and Sandra S. Sager for lingual advice.
2. The full title of the project funded by the Foundation *Mensch Gesellschaft Umwelt* (MGU) of the Kanton Basel Landschaft is: 'Demokratische Möglichkeiten zur Festlegung und Umsetzung von Maßstäben zur Beurteilung der Tragbarkeit von Risiken (sog. Schutzziele)'.
3. Cf. Schell 1994, Ginzburg 1991, Levin/Strauss 1991, Altmann 1993, Rehmann-Sutter 1992, Jäger and Tappeser in this volume.
4. The critique of social atomism is one of the central elements in the current feminist debate in philosophical ethics and constitutes also a main issue in communitarianism. See the excellent analysis by Wolgast (1987). How concrete relationships could be reflected in ethical evaluations is asked in the renowned essay by Benhabib (1987). A communitarian account gives Sullivan (1986).
5. For discussions of this topic see the collection of important texts in Armstrong and Botzler (1993) and Desjardins (1993).
6. "It is a fundamental and far-reaching fact of risk analysis that the different parameters of negativity are not necessarily commensurable. (...) Negativities cannot be adequately evaluated by a single number" (Rescher 1983: 21). "The 'person' at issue with evaluation can be either an individual agent himself, or a collective unit. In the former case, the issue is one of an individuals' own value system – a matter of personal orientation. In the latter case we confront the processes of group decision-making at issue in the political process. Either way, the element of subjectivity – of evaluative reaction – is ineliminably involved in the assessment of negativities" (Rescher 1983: 27). Other points where value judgements

are involved include the range of the considered effects, the question if very small probabilities can be neglected ('effective zerohood'), the weight of expected-value calculation in singular cases, the limit of absolute inacceptability and the selection of decision strategies in situations of uncertainties about probabilities and/or negativities (median comparison, maximin preference, maximax preference).

8.   A similar answer to the question about the idea of democracy gives Hansjörg Seiler (1994: 238-253): Democracy as an emanation of the right to self-determination of the affected citizens.

9.   Renn et al. (1995) consider the keeping/respecting of the fairness principle a central requirement for a successful risk communication procedure.

10.   "Auf die Frage nach dem Sinn von Politik gibt es eine einfache und in sich schlüssige Antwort, daß man meinen möchte, weitere Antworten erübrigten sich ganz und gar. Die Antwort lautet: Der Sinn von Politik ist Freiheit" (Arendt 1993: 28).

References

Altmann, Michael (coord.) 1993. 'Gene technology and biodiversity.' (multi-author review), *Experientia* **49**, pp.187-234.

Arendt, Hannah 1993. *Was ist Politik?* (ed. Ursula Ludz), München: Piper.

Armstrong, Susan J. and Botzler, Richard G. 1993. *Environmental Ethics. Divergence and Convergence.* New York etc.: Mc Graw-Hill.

Arrow, Kenneth J. 1970. *Essays in the Theory of Risk-Bearing.* Amsterdam/London: North-Holland.

Beck, Ulrich 1993. *Die Erfindung des Politischen. Zu einer Theorie reflexiver Modernisierung.* Frankfurt a.M.: Suhrkamp.

Benhabib, Seyla 1987. 'The Generalized and The Concrete Other.' In: Feder Kittay, Eva and Meyers, Diana T. (eds.), *Women and Moral Theory.* Savage: Rowman & Littlefield, pp.154-177.

Budd, Susan and Sharma, Ursula (eds.) 1994. *The Healing Bond. The Patient-practitioner Relationship and Therapeutic Responsibility.* London/New York: Routledge.

[CIOMS/WHO] Council for International Organizations of Medical Sciences in collaboration with the World Health Organization 1993. *International Ethical Guidelines for Biomedical Research Involving Human Subjects.* Geneva.

Desjardins, Joseph R. 1993. *Environmental Ethics. An Introduction to Environmental Philosophy.* Belmont, CA: Wadsworth.

Eindhoven, Josée van 1994. 'Disaster prevention in Europe.' In: Jasanoff, Sheila (ed.), *Learning from Disaster. Risk Management after Bhopal.* Philadelphia: Univ. of Pennsylvania Pr., pp.113-132.

Engelhardt, H. Tristram, Jr. 1986. *The Foundations of Bioethics.* New York/Oxford: Oxford University Press.

Fietkau, Hans-Joachim 1991. *Psychologische Ansätze zu Mediationsverfahren im Umweltschutz, FS II: 91-302.* Wissenschaftszentrum Berlin.

Ginzburg, Lev R. (ed.) 1991. *Assessing Ecological Risks of Biotechnology.* Boston etc.: Butterworth-Heinemann.

Hobbes, Thomas 1985. *Leviathan* (ed. C.B. Macpherson), London: Penguin.

Hoffmann-Riem, Wolfgang and Schmid-Assmann, Eberhard (eds.). 1991. *Konfliktbewältigung durch Verhandlungen. Informelle und mittlerunterstützte Verhandlungen in Verwaltungsverfahren.* Band 1, Baden-Baden: Nomos Verlagsgesellschaft, p. 67 ff.

Jasanoff. Sheila (ed.). 1994. *Learning from Disaster. Risk Management after Bhopal.* Philadelphia: Univ. of Pennsylvania Pr.

Kant, Immanuel 1922. *Metaphysik der Sitten* (ed. K. Vorländer), Hamburg: Meiner, 4th ed.

Kasperson, Roger E. 1986. 'Six Propositions on Public Participation and Their Relevance for Risk

Communication.' *Risk Analysis* **6** (3), pp.275-290.

Kenney, Ralph L. and von Winterfeldt, Detlef. 1986. 'Improving Risk Communication.' *Risk Analysis* **6** (4), pp.420-429.

Kunreuther, H., Kleindorfer, P. and Yaksick, R. 1984. *Compensation as a Tool for Improving Risk Communication.* Philadelphia.

Lake, L. (ed.) 1980. *Environmental Mediation: The Search for Consensus.* Boulder, Colorado.

Levin, Morris and Strauss, H. (ed.) 1991. *Risk Assessment in Genetic Engineering.* New York: McGraw Hill.

Luce, R. Duncan and Raiffa, Howard 1967. *Games and Decisions.* (7th pr.), New York etc.: Wiley.

Meyers, Diana T. 1987. 'The Socialized Individual and Individual Autonomy.' In: Eva Feder Kittay and Diana T. Meyers (eds.), *Women and Moral Theory.* Savage: Rowman & Littlefield.

Morell, David and Magorian, Christophe 1982. *Siting Hazardous Waste Facilities: Local Opposition and the Myth of Preemption.* Cambridge: Ballinger.

National Research Council 1989. *Improving risk communication.* Washington: National Academy Press.

Nelkin, Dorothy and Pollak, Michael 1980. 'Problems and Procedures in the Regulation of Technological Risk.' In: Richard C. Schwing and Walter A. Albers, Jr. (eds.), *Societal Risk Assessment. How Safe is Safe Enough?* New York/London: Plenum Press, pp.233-253.

O'Hare, M., Bacow, L. and Sanderson, D. 1983. *Facility Siting and Public Opposition.* New York.

Rehmann-Sutter, Christoph 1992. 'Gefährlichkeit unbekannter Gefahren – rekombinante Pflanzen im Freiland? Eine Kontroverse mit Barbara Weber und Ingo Potrykus.' *Folia Bioethica* No. 11, Geneva: SSEB-SGBE.

————. 1993. 'Nature in the laboratory – Nature as a laboratory. Considerations about the ethics of release experiments.' *Experientia* **49**, pp.190-200.

————. 1995. 'Welche Biologie ist empirisch?' In: Wolfgang Polasek (ed.), *Möglichkeiten und Grenzen der empirischen Wissenschaften. Interdisziplinäre Ringvorlesung MGU.* Liestal: Verlag des Kantons Basel-Landschaft, pp.88-100.

Renn, Ortwin 1993. 'Technik und gesellschaftliche Akzeptanz: Herausforderungen der Technikfolgenabschätzung', *GAIA* **2**, pp.67-83.

Renn, Ortwin and Webler, Thomas 1993. 'Anticipating Conflicts: Public Participation in Managing the Solid Waste Crisis.' *GAIA* **1**, pp.84-94.

Renn, Ortwin, Webler, Thomas and Tuler, Seth 1992. *Vorbeugendes Konfliktmanagement für risikobezogene Entscheidungen, Eine Studie zur Vorbereitung von Konfliktmanagment zur Sondermüllbeseitigung*, Erster Entwurf. Worcester.

Renn, Ortwin, Webler, Thomas and Wiedemann, Peter. 1995. *Fairness and Competence in Citizen Participation: Evaluating Models for Environmental Discourse.* Boston.

Rescher, Nicholas 1983. *Risk. A Philosophical Introduction to the Theory of Risk Evaluation and Management.* Lanham: University Press of America.

Saladin, Peter and Zenger, C.A. 1988. *Rechte zukünftiger Generationen.* Basel und Frankfurt a.M.

Schell, Thomas von 1994. *Die Freisetzung gentechnisch veränderter Mikroorganismen.* Tübingen: Attempto.

Schulthess, Daniel 1994. 'Contraintes globales et responsabilité individuelle.' In: *Analyse et maîtrise des valeurs naturelles: Actes du Colloque transfrontalier d'Arc-et-Senans (septembre 1993).* Besançon: Université de Franche-Comté, pp.243-246.

Seiler, Hansjörg 1994. *Gewaltenteilung. Allgemeine Grundlagen und schweizerische Ausgestaltung.* Bern: Stämpfli, pp.238-253.

Seiler, Hansjörg and Webler, Thomas 1995. 'Prozedurale Demokratie – Ein Beitrag zur schweizerischen Demokratiereform.' *Zeitschrift für Schweizerisches Recht* **114** (2), pp.171-199.

Shklar, Judith N. 1990. *Faces of Injustice.* New Haven and London: Yale University Press.

Sullivan, William M. 1986. *Reconstructing Public Philosophy.* Berkeley etc.: Univ. of California Press.

Susskind, Lawrence and Cruikshank, Jeffrey 1987. *Breaking the Impasse. Consensual Approaches to Resolving Public Disputes.* New York: Basic Books.

Uebersax, Peter. 1991. *Betroffenheit als Anknüpfung für Partizipation. Herleitung eines Modells der Betroffenenbeteiligung mit besonderer Behandlung des Aspekts örtlicher Betroffenheit.* Basel/Frankfurt a.M.

Veuve, Leopold 1987. *Plan directeur cantonal et participation.* Fribourg, Université de Fribourg.

Weizsäcker, Christine von 1991. Oral communication at the *Ethics Panel of the Forum Engelberg 1991 on 'The Genetic Revolution – Impacts on Biology and Society'.*

Wiedemann, Peter M. 1993. *Introduction Risk Perception and Risk Commmunication.* Jülich: Forschungszentrum Jülich GmbH (Arbeiten zur Risiko-Kommunikation, Heft 38).

Winner, Langdon 1986. 'Techne and Politeia.' In his: *The Whale and the Reactor. A Search for Limits in an Age of High Technology.* Chicago/London: Univ. of Chicago Press, pp.40-58.

Wolgast, Elizabeth 1987. *The Grammar of Justice.* Ithaca/London: Cornell Univ. Press.

Zillessen, Horst, Dienel, Peter C. and Strubelt, Wendelin (eds.) 1993. *Die Modernisierung der Demokratie.* Opladen: Westdeutscher Verlag.

15

Public Acceptance and Risks of Biotechnology

Darryl Macer

1. Bioethics and Risk Assessment

An important part of bioethics is risk assessment, the analysis and prediction of risks. Bioethics combines risk assessment, the concept of avoiding harm, with an assessment of benefits, the concept of doing good or beneficence. There are various risks of genetic engineering, for example the risk of unintentionally changing the genes of an organism, the risk of harming that organism, the risk of changing the ecosystem in which it is involved, and the risk of harming the ecosystem, and the risk of change, or harm, to any other organism of that species or others, including human beings (who may even be the target of change). The concept of risk in biotechnology involves both the potential to change something and the potential to harm. The extent to which a change is judged to be a subjective harm depends on human values, whether nature should be "intransient" or modified. This relates to the fears that technology is unnatural.

The risk to change organisms or ecosystems, which may not involve "harm", the standard meaning of risk, makes genetic engineering more complex. Many want to protect nature, not because of its value or property, but simply because it is there. The concepts and images that the words "life" and "nature" imply are similar in different countries (Macer 1994a). Related to this is the concept of biodiversity, which is now legally recognised as a good in the Biological Diversity Convention, primarily because of economic potential, but it is also protected because of aesthetic value. Biodiversity is a word used to picture the great diversity of living organisms on the planet. Just as the individual processes of life are dynamic, so is the composite of the lifeforms. The idea of dynamism also implies a balance, and this extends the framework that risk must be pictured in.

Rather than calling the ideas of benefit, risk, autonomy and justice, etc., bioethical principles, we could call them ideals (Macer 1994a). These ideals all need to be balanced, and the balance varies more within any culture than between any two. Ideals need to be included, together in a balancing act that fits reality. Surveys combined with observations of policy and behaviour in different countries allow us to look at how these principles and ideals are balanced. An examination of history also shows how the balancing act has varied in different times and places. In another paper I have discussed what is ethical biotechnology (Macer 1995).

Bioethics considers the ethical issues raised in biology and medicine, and especially those raised by human activity in society and the environment using biotechnology (Macer 1990, 1994a). Bioethics is a concept of "love", balancing benefits and risks of choices and decisions. It considers all living organisms and the environment, from individual creatures to the level of the biosphere in complexity. All living organisms are biological beings, and share a common and intertwined biological heritage.

1.1 Bioethics in history

The word "bioethics" comes to us only from 1970, yet the ideas and concepts the word encompasses come from human heritage thousands of years old. This heritage can be seen in all cultures, religions, and in ancient writings from around the world. The relationships between human beings within their society, within the biological community, with nature, and God, are seen in prehistory. Therefore we cannot precisely define the origins of bioethics. Human civilization has been tied to agriculture for many millennia, and the concept of bioethics first emerged in the relationships that people had with nature, a nature which could be cultivated to provide for human needs. For example, the decision to burn a forest and plant a crop is a bioethical decision. There is risk in the decision to burn or not to burn, and initially the judgement would be based on practical outcomes. If one area of forest was burnt and the land planted for several years with crops which then later failed, if the population density was low enough the group could move on to burn the next area of forest, and farm that. A gradual circle could be established, if the forest fires were contained. The risk of ecological damage is offset by the risk of lack of food, or by desire for a particular way of life. The decisions of how to use land, and nature, part of environmental bioethics, are not new. Neither is medical decision making, and the questions of abortion and euthanasia are evident in archeology and written records for millennia as well.

In the conclusion of an earlier book, *Shaping Genes* (1990), I said that we have much to learn from the issues raised by genetic technology, not just on the nature of our genes and the effects they have on us and other organisms, but also on the nature of our thinking about what is important in life. When we consider genetic engineering we can also consider the factors which affect our decision to use a given technology, some of which may have been taken for granted in the use of more traditional forms of agriculture or industry.

There are also lessons to be learnt about concepts of risk assessment, because genetic engineering is a technology associated, and perceived to be associated, with both benefits and risks (Macer 1992a, 1994a). One class of risks associated with genetic engineering is that of relatively high probability but low consequence. For example, the transfer of a gene for insect resistance to a neighbouring wild species of plant is likely if huge areas of land are being farmed. However, it would have little consequence to the farm or agriculture. We also have the risk of insecticide resistant insects, to which better strategies can be used to lower risk. Strategies to lower chances of resistance to *Bacillus thuringiensis* insecticidal protein include the patchwork farming of treated and untreated fields; methods to reduce the amount of untreated fields (that may suffer more insect attack) by computer simulation have been devised (Alstad and Andow 1995).

Another class of risks would be low probability, but high consequence, for example gene transfer to human beings that affected health; or escape of a vaccine-producing animal from a battery farm that contained infectious fatal virus. In the past we have seen numerous examples of new organisms and biological control agents, which have shown us that the most common result is that the agent does not work; however, a reasonable number does work (e.g. 10-20%). The risk comes from the few that have unexpected undesirable effects in an ecosystem, which is more common for introduced agricultural production species than for the biocontrol agents. The reason that biocontrol agents have been less risky is that better assessment of the benefits and risks has occurred, compared to earlier centuries of often blind introduction of new organisms.

Genetic engineering has been a catalyst for thinking about risk assessment and bioethics since its invention in 1974. However, the issues raised are not fundamentally different from those of the past (Macer 1993) and I would reject the use of the word "Genethics" which has been a recently coined term (e.g. Suzuki and Knudtson 1993). For example, to choose what plant species would be suitable as an agricultural crop, to select it, and to cross it, has been done for millennia and has seen the adoption of a hybrid of three species, wheat, as a staple of one part of the world. The speed at which change in characters can be brought about is faster with genetic engineering than traditional breeding. However, it does not have such a unique power of change as the special term, "Genethics" would imply. The greatest ecological change in the world is the age old agent of change, to deliberately set fires. The most powerful force underlying this would arguably be the often unforeseen consequences of a growing population of human beings.

1.2 Descriptive and prescriptive bioethics

There are two basic ways to approach bioethics, one being descriptive and the other being prescriptive. One describes how people make decisions, and the other recommends the process that can be used to make decisions, and/or the range of decisions that can be made. Descriptive bioethics includes the use of observation, and surveys, to describe the choices that people make. To make good choices, and choices that we can live with, improving our life and society, is certainly a good thing. However, what is good for one person may not be good for the broader society. The global nature of agricultural economics and environmental impact means we have to think far beyond the small field trial of a genetically modified organism (GMO). The choices that need to be made in the modern biotechnological and genetic age also extend from before conception to after death – all of life.

Prescriptive bioethics calls for certain factors to be included in decision making, certain groups of people to be involved, and even for certain decisions to be made, or at least a range of socially tolerable decisions. When it comes to risk assessment, the same distinction applies. We can describe the ways risks are perceived, and we can also call for certain risks to be included in an assessment, and for certain weight to be given to these risks. Different groups of people and countries may call for different levels of risk assessment and of what constitutes a significant risk (von Schomberg 1995). The legal tolerance limits of acceptable risk and harm are already broadly outlined in international covenants, such as the Declaration of Human Rights, and in international treaties on environmental protection which include limits on the permitted damage to the common environment, such as the convention on ozone-damaging chemicals, and on deep sea dumping.

There are calls for global laws on genetic engineering to join this list of international laws, to strengthen the weak consensus found between international regulations on GMO release. Agriculture is dependent upon water, and environment more generally, which are sometimes shared resources between different countries. Most maritime nations have declared 200 mile limits within which they claim prior rights to exploit marine resources, and the many examples of over-fished species illustrate the need for international fishing strategies, and also makes us especially cautious about the use of genetic engineering in marine aquaculture. Even on land, weeds and pest animals may spread rapidly in many cases.

Surveys are useful for descriptive bioethics. In fact, they are one of the most reliable methods if performed and analysed carefully. However, their role in prescriptive bioethics depends upon a number of factors: does the group surveyed represent the population, should the opinions of that group make decisions, can we trust that group whether it is the public, product consumers, scientists, politicians or farmers? Also, there are some principles which may be commonly perceived to be good, but are commonly ignored in daily life, for example, equal human rights, looking after the poor, and respect for the environment. Even the interpretation of surveys is clouded by the fact that leading questions can be used by surveyors who want to make different points.

To examine whether global guidelines are useful, and representative of descriptive bioethics, we can attempt to look at basic universal ideas that people use in deciding these issues (Macer 1992a, 1994a). Differences and similarities in risk perception are seen within any group of people within every society. Data from opinion surveys and observation suggests that the diversity of thinking within any one group is much greater than that between any two groups. In other words, in every group we may find the complete range of opinions from yes to no, and the reasoning behind these decisions. The diversity of comments is therefore a microcosm of the total picture. Furthermore, the social environment that people grow up in, and the education strategies in different countries, are becoming more similar – making the shared environment more similar. This suggests that a universal approach to regulation which is consistent with people's values is even more representative now than it was a century ago.

2. Descriptive Bioethics and Perceptions of Risk

There are several ways to observe or describe bioethics. Observations of culture and society are useful, but to avoid the dangers of mixing the descriptive and prescriptive elements of bioethics through the biased interpretation of subjective experiences, random surveys allow somewhat more quantification. World-wide there have been quite a number of surveys focusing on biotechnology (Zechendorf 1994). There are some consistent national tendencies over the degree of risks that people perceive from biotechnology even in Europe (Eurobarometer 1991, 1993), so it is interesting to ask the questions among more diverse countries. In 1993 an International Bioethics Survey was performed across ten Asian-Pacific countries of the world (Macer 1994a).

The degree to which actions of individuals, and also society, can be both described and predicted by surveys can only be determined after surveys are conducted. A written survey allows more thinking on issues than an interview. Also multiple choice answers can be leading, hence the use of many open response questions. The use of surveys is only one part of the overall approach we can use to look at cultures; the data from surveys must be explained by any description of the real world.

Another part of the data that we can use for evaluating public perceptions is the use of the products. We can perceive current practices in agricultural biotechnology by the preferences of farmers, consumers and what sort of products companies produce. Analysis of the factors relevant to these groups that are behind their perceptions is important. For example, the consumption of products of new biotechnology can best be seen from the results of the sales of these products in supermarkets and their acceptance by the farmers who first use them. However, the factors involved in their decisions require surveys to evaluate, for example, why they choose to use them instead of alternatives, and why people choose not to use them.

2.1 Survey strategies

There are various survey strategies. The first type is the use of fixed response questions, to choose from set answers, and this has been done in the USA (OTA 1987; Hoban and Kendall 1992), and in Canada for the Canadian Institute of Biotechnology (Decima 1993). There have also been comparative studies of scientists in the USA and in Europe, looking at their perceptions of the public image of genetic engineering (Rabino 1991, 1992). The Eurobarometer is a regular public survey in Europe, including different questions each time, and is conducted in all 12 countries of the European Community. In 1991 Eurobarometer 35.1 looked at biotechnology and genetic engineering, and in 1993 Eurobarometer 39.1 repeated the same questions. The Eurobarometer poll is limited because of the relatively small number of questions and the set format of the questions. But it is the most comprehensive in terms of sample response, randomness, size, and number of countries. There is some diversity within Europe, in biotechnology policy, public acceptance, and regulations.

Recent survey strategies in Europe attempt to look at reasoning more than just statistics (Hamstra 1991, 1993), which may shed more light on the factors which will affect policy development. There has been attention on qualitative survey approaches to look at factors used in decision-making, which can be useful to identify the range of factors that people use. Ideally they need to be combined with some quantitative measurement to discover which are the most common issues. However, by finding all the issues that people can think of, one can trace out key issues which are behind concerns. There is also a question of which group within society is involved in policy and opinion-making. Martin and Tait (1992), conducted surveys of selected groups of the UK public. They conclude that groups with an interest in biotechnology have probably already formed attitudes to it, which are unlikely to significantly change. They looked at industry, environmental groups, and local communities, which are major players in the development of policy at both national and local levels. They also suggest that people with the least polarised attitudes are most open to multiple information sources.

In New Zealand there was a study using both set and open questions in 1990 (Couchman and Fink-Jensen 1990). In Japan there have been several studies, the most comprehensive of these being a study that I did in 1991, among public, academics, scientists, and high school teachers, in which I also reviewed all the previous studies in Japan (Macer 1992a). From the results of open questions, it was found that some arguments that are often used in biotechnology debates, such as eugenic fears or environmental risk, are not the most common concerns voiced by people in open questions. The more common concerns are interference with nature or general broad fear. The use of open comments also found a great diversity and depth of comments among the public, with as much diversity as those expressed by scientists. The survey found that many people perceive both benefit and risk simultaneously and that they are attempting to balance these, which suggests that factors which alter this balance will change the depth of net support or rejection of a technology. Also I found that educated people show as much concern, in fact biology teachers considered there was more risk from genetic engineering than the general public (Macer 1992b, 1994b). The risk perceptions among scientists had some tendency to be more concrete than in the public, but all groups expressed a considerable variety of concerns.

2.2 International Bioethics Survey

The International Bioethics Survey was performed in 1993 in ten countries of the world, in English in Australia (A), Hong Kong (HK), India (IN), Israel (IS), New Zealand (NZ), The Philippines (P) and Singapore (S); in Japanese in Japan (J); in Russian in Russia (R); and in Thai in Thailand (T) (details and collaborators are in Macer 1994a). Public and student questionnaires were identical. The teacher's survey included some of the same questions, but half of the questions were about teaching and curriculum in bioethics and genetics (Macer 1994a). The randomly distributed surveys to public and teachers were sent with stamped return envelopes, and people were asked to respond within each country with no reminders.

The International Bioethics Survey focused on agricultural biotechnology, and medical genetics, with some other questions looking at environmental attitudes and attitudes to disease. The questionnaires included about 150 questions in total, with 35 open-ended questions. The open questions were designed not to be leading, to look at how people make decisions – and the ideas in each comment were assigned to different categories depending on the question, and these categories were compared among all the samples. In total nearly 6000 questionnaires were returned from 10 countries during 1993 (Macer 1994a). General information gathered in the surveys including sex, age, marital status, children, education, religion, importance of religion, race, income and rural/urban locality, and some data are in Table 1.

Results of the other questions, further background, and more examples of open comments have been published (Macer 1994a). In this paper the word "significant" implies a statistical significance of $P<0.05$. The funding for these surveys came principally from the Eubios Ethics Institute, with some assistance from the ELSI (Ethical, Legal, and Social Impact issues) group of the Japanese Ministry of Education, Science and Culture Human Genome Project, and the University of

Tsukuba. The high school samples in Japan are supported by the Ministry of Education, and are part of a longer term project to develop high school materials to teach about bioethical issues in the biology and social studies classes.

Table 1: Awareness of biotechnology and genetic engineering[*]

[percentages of total respondents]	Public								Medical or biology students								High School Teachers					
	NZ	A	J	J91	IN	T	R	IS	NZ	A	J	IN	T	P	S	HK	NZb	NZs	Ab	As	Jb	Js
N (returned questionnaires)	329	201	352	551	568	689	446	50	96	110	435	325	232	164	250	104	206	96	251	114	560	383
Response rate (%)	22	13	23	26	57	36	43	<20	60	70	66	65	50	70	80	52	61	28	47	21	37	26
Sex Male	41	45	52	53	61	48	36	38	41	50	67	53	42	46	23	45	64	62	48	63	88	92
Female	59	55	48	47	39	52	64	62	59	50	33	47	58	54	77	55	36	38	52	37	12	8
Urban	77	71	73	-	78	54	90+	80	85	89	49	85	58	87	96	88	31	73	75	79	63	66
Age (years)																						
Mean age	47.4	45.2	41.7	39.8	30.6	37.2	36.3	33.4	20.8	18.1	21.1	21.8	21.3	21.1	19.3	21.0	40.8	42.5	41.8	42.0	40.7	40.0
Marital status																						
Single	25	26	29	29	53	38	33	34	95	98	99	97	99	99	99	100	9	6	13	16	22	24
Married	59	62	66	66	45	59	54	62	3	0	1	2	0.4	1	0.4	0	83	86	79	70	77	74
Other	16	12	5	5	2	3	13	4	2	2	0	1	1	0	1	0	8	8	8	14	1	2
Children																						
No child	33	39	40	35	55	22	41	48	97	100	100	98	96	100	99	100	22	15	24	24	30	28
Education																						
High school	43	36	37	37	4	2	13	16	29	94	54	7	4	0	23	71	1	0	1	1	0	0
2 year college/technical	18	15	19	22	6	3	18	20	48	4	6	13	18	0	77	3	1	2	0.4	1	0.2	1
graduate degree	25	28	31	31	35	37	39	39	20	2	38	27	60	50	0	6	64	58	59	57	78	82
postgraduate degree	9	16	10	7	52	59	28	25	3	0	0	51	13	47	0	8	30	37	39	41	21	17
other	5	5	3	3	7	1	4	0	0	0	2	2	5	3	0	4	4	3	0.4	0	0.8	0.3
How important is religion?																						
Very important	27	23	10	-	40	46	10	38	28	19	5	36	54	89	32	21	20	17	42	47	7	10
Some important	26	27	33	-	27	44	38	16	20	41	16	24	38	11	41	40	17	29	23	26	25	37
Not too important	27	24	40	-	15	8	28	34	18	20	34	18	7	0	22	26	33	32	19	10	45	36
Not at all important	20	26	17	-	18	2	24	12	34	20	45	22	0.4	0	5	13	30	22	16	17	23	17
Awareness of Pesticides																						
Not heard of	2	5	3	4	5	0	2	4	2	5	5	6	0	1	7	13	0	0	0	0	0.4	0.3
Heard of	48	47	61	58	44	34	54	60	60	56	73	41	59	76	67	78	5	6	5	10	24	40
Could explain to a friend	50	48	36	38	51	66	44	36	38	39	22	53	41	23	26	9	95	94	95	90	76	60
Awareness of Biotechnology																						
Not heard of	23	19	6	3	10	2	8	18	13	25	5	7	6	13	0.4	8	0	6	0	8	1	1
Heard of	62	56	65	65	53	57	62	62	54	54	69	53	71	68	45	74	12	51	11	38	11	50
Could explain to a friend	15	25	29	32	37	41	30	20	33	21	26	40	23	19	55	18	88	43	89	54	88	49
Awareness of genetic engineering																						
Not heard of	9	9	9	6	17	13	14	8	0	3	8	10	17	4	1	7	0	4	0	1	1	15
Heard of	62	49	74	68	46	58	60	82	26	43	67	40	63	60	51	79	7	41	9	43	25	67
Could explain to a friend	29	42	17	26	37	29	26	10	74	54	25	50	20	36	48	14	93	55	91	56	74	18

[*]
1. J91 from Japan 1991 survey (Macer 1992a, 1992b).
2. A = Australia, HK = Hong Kong, IN = India, IS = Israel, NZ = New Zealand, P = The Philippines, S = Singapore; in Japanese in J = Japan, in Russian in R = Russia, and in Thai in T = Thailand. Details and collaborators are in Macer (1994a).
3. The teachers: b = biology teachers; s = social studies teachers.

2.3 Knowledge of science and risk perception

One of the factors that may relate to risk perception is knowledge of science, and the claim that increased knowledge is correlated to decreased perception of risk has been suggested in some other studies (OTA 1987) and is a commonly held view in academia and industry. In this 1993 study most respondents answered that they had some interest in science and technology, with few saying they did not. Another measure may be the response rate, which was generally between 20-30%, significantly higher than commercial mail box response. The 1991 Japan surveys suggest that knowledge of science is not so closely correlated with response rate (Macer 1992a, 1994a). An indirect measure of the depth of knowledge were the comments that were given in response to open questions.

The results of the awareness question for pesticides, biotechnology and genetic engineering in the International Bioethics Survey are shown in Table 1. It is interesting that biotechnology was generally one of the most unfamiliar terms, next to gene therapy, except in Japan, where it was one of the most familiar, consistent with other surveys (Macer 1992a). The awareness of gene therapy was the lowest among the eight developments included. Genetic engineering was generally the least familiar among the other areas, with pesticides, in vitro fertilisation, computers and nuclear power being most familiar. Awareness was significantly related to educational attainment in most samples. The samples with the greatest awareness were generally biology teachers, next were medical students (New Zealand, Japan, Australia and the Philippines), followed by the other groups, social studies teachers, biology students and the public. For all developments and in all samples, there was a positive correlation between awareness and the expressed level of interest in science from the results of the earlier question.

Following questions, discussed below, asked them whether they thought each development would have a benefit or not, and their perceptions about the risks of technology by asking them how worried they were about each development. The areas of science and technology included: In vitro fertilisation, Computers, Biotechnology, Nuclear power, Agricultural Pesticides, Genetic engineering. The results for genetic engineering are shown in Table 2. For this question, the comments were assigned into categories, and the results are shown. Both benefits and risks were cited by many respondents.

There was more concern about genetic engineering and pesticides, despite the lower familiarity with biotechnology. The degree of concern depends upon what people know. People do show the ability to balance benefits and risks of science and technology, consistent with earlier surveys (Macer 1992a, 1994b).

2.4 Bioethical maturity

People do not have a simplistic view of the positive or negative face of science and technology, and can often perceive both benefits and risks. Overall we do find a positive view, but for different applications there are quite different opinions. This balancing of good and harm is necessary for bioethics, and I have called this one indicator of the bioethical maturity of a society (Macer 1992b, 1994b). The use of surveys can provide us with some indicators of the degree to which society can make well-thought out "mature" decisions, rather than impulsive "childish" decisions based on immediate gain.

The types of concern that were expressed over genetic engineering give us some picture of risk perception (see Table 2). What is a risk? The idea of interference with nature is an aesthetic, religious or moral concern. It presupposes that it is bad to change nature, and is related to the risk of playing God, that we are changing God-given nature or that we are exerting God-like powers in the modification of nature. Eugenic, ethical and social impact concerns are risks related to the most common category of general human misuse. These extend from the type of ethical concern that we should not modify animals, a type of interfering with nature concern, through to the concern that we should not violate human rights, which is more universally accepted in law as a risk. More vague concerns of risk are seen in the categories of fear, and danger. The concerns of insufficient controls, it is a waste of resources, or conversely that we can control technology so we don't need to worry, are more concrete. Ecological and health concerns are also more concrete.

Table 2: Perceptions of benefit (Q6) or risk (Q7), and open comments about genetic engineering

[percentages of total respondents]	Public								Medical or biology students									High school teachers					
	NZ	A	J	IN	T	R	IS		Nzs	As	Js	IN	T	P	S	HK		Nzb	Nzs	Ab	As	Jb	Js
Q6. Do you personally believe genetic engineering is a worthwhile area for scientific research? Why?...																							
Yes	41	62	57	65	77	65	74		76	60	69	76	71	55	80	60		92	60	94	69	90	74
No	29	17	10	8	5	7	16		9	16	4	6	5	30	7	12		4	20	1	14	4	9
Don't know	30	21	33	27	18	28	10		15	24	27	18	24	15	13	28		4	20	5	17	6	17
N	321	197	334	523	682	456	50		95	108	423	314	231	158	249	105		204	95	250	113	554	378
Not stated	39.6	37.6	53.9	50.7	40.8	75.8	72.0		27.4	30.6	51.8	36.9	33.3	40.5	59.4	60.0		21.0	35.8	26.8	31.0	47.5	55.8
Science	5.3	9.6	6.0	4.6	19.4	4.8	4.0		4.2	1.9	9.5	3.8	23.8	3.8	2.0	1.9		8.3	6.3	10.0	8.9	16.3	9.0
Cure disease	7.8	8.1	9.0	9.0	2.1	0.7	10.0		27.4	25.0	12.8	15.0	2.6	11.7	9.2	15.3		18.5	6.3	18.8	11.5	8.5	4.5
Humanity	5.6	7.1	9.9	14.1	6.5	6.7	0		10.5	10.2	9.9	21.0	4.4	9.5	14.8	9.5		15.2	9.5	13.2	8.0	3.6	1.6
Good for Environment	0.6	1.5	0	0.4	0.6	0.9	0		1.1	2.8	0	0.6	0.9	1.3	0	1.0		1.0	0	0.4	0.9	0.7	0.5
Help if careful	7.2	11.2	2.4	3.1	5.0	1.7	10.0		9.5	3.7	1.7	3.2	2.2	7.6	3.2	1.9		14.6	12.6	15.6	18.6	13.2	12.4
Agr/economy	5.3	8.6	2.7	12.1	16.6	2.6	0		5.3	5.6	1.9	15.6	21.2	3.8	3.4	2.9		14.6	7.4	11.6	6.2	3.8	1.6
Misuse	5.9	3.5	5.4	0.4	1.7	1.1	0		6.3	5.6	2.6	0	2.6	1.3	0.8	1.9		2.4	7.4	2.0	7.1	3.3	6.1
Dangerous	4.0	1.0	1.2	1.0	1.5	1.7	4.0		2.2	3.7	1.4	0.6	0.8	1.9	1.6	1.0		1.0	6.4	0.8	1.8	1.3	2.7
Playing God	14.0	8.6	4.5	1.1	1.2	0.9	0		5.3	10.2	2.4	0.3	0.9	12.7	3.2	1.9		2.0	7.4	0.4	5.3	0.7	2.1
Don't need	2.2	0	0.6	0.2	0.6	0	0		1.1	2.8	0.7	0	0.9	0	0.8	1.0		0	0	0	0	0.4	1.1
Unknown	2.5	3.1	4.5	3.4	4.1	3.2	0		0	0.9	5.4	2.9	6.5	3.8	1.2	1.9		1.5	1.0	0	0	0.9	2.7
Q7. Do you have any worries about the impact of research or applications of genetic engineering? How much? Why?...																							
No worries	14	19	22	48	42	26	17		11	16	20	51	37	10	25	11		13	9	11	10	15	15
A few	23	21	39	23	32	23	17		27	19	44	23	38	25	23	29		34	11	23	12	44	34
Some	24	26	24	19	19	28	30		33	33	24	17	19	30	36	42		38	38	39	29	28	29
A lot	39	34	15	10	7	23	36		29	32	12	9	6	35	14	18		15	42	27	49	14	22
N	309	195	316	500	670	456	47		95	107	422	310	230	155	245	104		204	94	250	112	555	379
Not Stated	31.1	33.3	58.9	55.4	45.4	79.5	74.5		24.2	26.2	57.4	54.8	34.4	51.0	65.7	61.5		23.0	42.6	29.6	29.5	53.3	59.1
Don't know	2.9	3.6	1.9	6.0	5.7	1.7	0		0	0	4.0	3.6	10.4	0.7	2.0	1.9		0	0	0	0	0.7	1.9
Interfere Nature	13.3	9.2	2.9	3.8	1.8	0.9	2.1		10.5	11.2	4.7	1.9	1.7	7.7	3.3	3.9		2.9	5.3	4.0	6.3	1.3	6.1
Fear/feeling	5.2	4.6	6.7	6.0	8.7	5.8	0		0	0.9	6.6	5.8	5.2	5.2	3.7	3.9		4.4	4.3	3.2	7.1	3.4	2.1
Ethical	4.2	3.6	3.2	1.2	1.0	1.1	0		9.5	13.1	4.0	1.3	0.9	4.5	1.6	5.8		5.9	7.5	5.6	12.5	6.3	5.0
Social effect bad	1.6	1.0	1.0	1.0	0.3	0.4	0		0	0.9	2.4	0.7	0.4	0.7	0.8	0		0	0	0.8	1.8	2.0	3.7
Insuff. control	2.6	4.1	2.2	0.8	3.0	1.7	0		5.3	1.9	2.8	0.7	6.5	3.2	1.6	4.8		10.3	5.3	11.2	8.0	8.3	9.0
Bad health	1.0	1.5	1.0	3.0	1.8	0.4	2.1		2.1	0	1.0	3.2	1.7	2.6	1.6	3.9		1.0	2.1	0.8	0.9	0.9	1.6
Dangerous	3.6	2.6	2.2	0.6	2.1	1.9	0		3.2	5.6	1.4	2.6	3.0	3.2	0.8	1.9		1.5	1.1	0.8	1.8	1.4	1.1
Ecology	2.3	1.0	1.9	2.6	2.8	0.9	0		1.1	1.9	1.2	2.3	3.5	0.7	2.9	1.9		6.9	1.1	6.8	1.8	13.2	4.2
Waste	1.6	0.5	1.0	0.4	0.8	0.2	0		1.1	0	1.0	0.9	1.3	0.4	1.0	1.0		0.5	0	0.4	0	0	0
Human misuse	19.4	20.5	11.7	5.6	6.1	4.1	10.6		20.0	15.0	12.3	6.8	5.7	7.7	6.5	4.8		27.5	16.0	23.6	17.9	5.6	4.2
Eugenics	6.5	7.2	0.6	2.4	2.2	0	8.5		19.0	19.6	0	12.9	4.8	8.4	3.7	3.9		8.3	11.7	1.6	10.7	1.6	0.8
Can control	4.9	7.2	4.1	11.2	18.4	1.3	2.1		4.2	3.7	2.1	2.6	20.9	3.3	5.3	1.0		7.8	3.2	11.6	1.8	2.0	1.3

By dividing up the concerns that people have in such a way, we can form a better picture of what risk assessment means in their minds. The same type of analysis was done in 1990 in New Zealand (Couchman and Fink-Jensen 1990) and in 1991 in Japan among scientists, students, teachers, and the public (Macer 1992a). There is a trend for scientists to give more concrete concerns, though in related questions on the risks of genetic engineering of animals and humans in that survey, still 16% gave concerns that it was interfering in nature.

Therefore greater awareness of a technology may not mean that the perceived risks are only technical. Risk assessment in the minds of people includes aesthetic, religious and moral concerns which are often vague. Rather than saying that one class of risk perception is mature and another immature, we could actually say that to appreciate the wide range of risks is more mature than to only think of one or two.

We can expect that the awareness of both benefits and risks of products will grow with the increased use of biotechnology products, and about 70-80% were already aware that genetically modified organisms are being used to produce foods and medicines. In all countries of the International Bioethics Survey there was an overall positive view of science and technology. It was perceived as increasing the quality of life by the majority in all countries. Less than 10% in all countries saw it as doing more harm than good (Macer 1994a).

When specific details of an application are given there is generally greater acceptance, suggesting that people have some discretion, another indicator of bioethical maturity. It also suggests that if details of a technology are given, for example by the company or government related to the release of a GMO, the public will show greater acceptance of an application (Macer 1992b, 1994a; Macer et al. 1995). This is illustrated in questions looking at environmental release of genetically modified organisms (Q31) which were taken from the OTA (1987) survey, with comparisons to a question of Hoban and Kendall (1992). The results are in Table 3. The approval of the Calgene FlavrSavr modified tomato, which has delayed ripening, for general cultivation in the USA was given by the USDA in 1993. It was approved for general commercial food consumption by the FDA in 1994 and sold in the summer 1994 in some parts of the USA (Rothenburg and Macer 1995). This tomato is being marketed as a tasty tomato, "a tomato like those you ate as a child", and the results of Q31 for a tasty tomato suggest that people support this goal for genetic engineering.

The healthier meat question is relevant to efforts to make less fatty meat, both by hormones in pigs, and other animals. In the USA in 1992, 45% said "acceptable", 32% "unacceptable" and 23% "don't know" to a similar question (Hoban and Kendall 1992). In a related question on cows with increased milk, 36% said "acceptable", 41% "unacceptable" and 23% "don't know". This has become reality in 1994 with the general use of bovine growth hormone (BST – bovine somatotrophin) in the USA dairy industry, a hormone made by genetic engineering that can increase milk yield by 10-20%. It also received less support in the International Bioethics Survey than the goal of less fatty meat, which is consistent with the widespread questioning of the need, given the existing milk surplus in some countries.

Animals have long been used for agriculture, and are likely to continue to be used. The moral status of animals, and decisions about whether it is ethical for humans to use them, depends on several key attributes: the ability to think, the ability to be aware of family members, the ability to feel pain (at different levels), and the state of being alive. Causing pain is considered bad, and it is the major guiding principle for animal treatment. If we do use animals we should avoid pain. Animals are part of the biological community in which we live, and we have to consider the ethical implications of whether they possess autonomy. People will continue to eat animals, and practical ethics must improve the ethical treatment for all animals. This is a further area of risk assessment that applies to animal use, the risks of unethical treatment of organisms. People need to decide how much more they are prepared to pay for better treatment of animals, such as the costs of eliminating battery farming, or the costs in not using new animal treatments that produce cheaper milk or meat such as bovine growth hormone.

The highest degree of support among the applications of genetic engineering that were given was seen for disease-resistant crops, and bacteria to clean oil spills (see

Table 3). The sports fish is an example of genetic engineering for fun – and it is reassuring that many people reject such genetic engineering. The highest degree of support for the sports fish is in the USA where 53% approved in a 1986 survey, while 73% approved of bacteria to clean oil spills or disease-resistant crops (OTA 1987). The general support for products of genetic engineering seems to be high, especially if they are claimed to be more healthy. In the Canadian study comparisons between chemicals and genetically engineered organisms usually found less support for chemical methods (Decima 1994). In the 1991 survey in Japan an open question looking at awareness, benefits, and risks of genetic manipulation of microbes, plants, animals and humans, was asked (Macer 1992a; 1992b). The responses made by the public, teachers and scientists were compared with results from New Zealand (Couchman and Fink-Jensen 1990), and few differences were observed. As in the USA, human genetic manipulation is associated with the most risks, and plant genetic manipulation with the least, but unfortunately they didn't compare open comments (OTA 1987).

Table 3: Approval of environmental release of GMOs[*]

Q31. *If there was no direct risk to humans and only very remote risks to the environment, would you approve or disapprove of the environmental use of genetically engineered organisms designed to produce...?*

Yes: *Approve* No: *Disapprove* DK: *Don't know*

[percentages of total respondents]	NZ	A	J	J91	IN	T	R	IS	US86	NZ	A	J	IN	T	P	S	HK	Nzb	Nzs	Ab	As	Jb	Js
Tomatoes with better taste																							
Yes	49	54	69	-	73	83	35	40	-	54	53	71	77	88	68	74	58	67	51	60	47	67	55
No	35	35	20	-	20	10	45	44	-	21	36	15	17	5	27	17	32	22	35	25	40	21	29
DK	16	11	11	-	7	7	20	16	-	15	11	14	6	7	5	9	10	11	14	15	13	12	16
Healthier meat (e.g. less fat)																							
Yes	54	60	57	-	66	84	35	44	-	74	71	65	68	88	75	72	62	72	63	71	57	60	47
No	30	31	26	-	22	9	43	42	-	20	23	18	18	4	21	17	27	18	31	18	32	24	33
DK	16	9	17	-	12	7	21	14	-	6	6	17	14	8	4	11	11	10	6	11	11	16	20
Larger sport fish																							
Yes	22	19	22	19	48	58	13	20	53	28	23	24	50	64	54	44	42	26	16	22	22	19	16
No	61	65	54	50	27	25	61	58	43	63	65	52	31	20	40	39	37	59	68	64	67	64	67
DK	17	16	24	31	25	17	26	22	4	9	12	24	19	16	6	17	21	15	16	14	11	17	17
Bacteria to clean up oil spills																							
Yes	75	82	71	75	74	87	63	70	73	92	89	76	74	85	78	86	70	85	82	91	84	77	63
No	11	11	13	7	14	5	20	12	23	1	4	10	13	6	19	6	23	7	11	3	8	12	15
DK	14	8	16	18	12	8	17	18	4	7	7	14	13	9	3	8	7	8	7	6	8	11	22
Disease resistant crops																							
Yes	70	78	66	75	78	91	54	50	73	81	81	67	81	91	82	83	72	85	70	83	70	71	55
No	16	13	17	6	13	4	25	28	23	7	13	13	11	5	15	8	14	10	20	7	18	15	22
DK	14	9	17	19	9	5	21	22	4	12	6	20	8	4	3	9	14	5	10	10	12	14	23
Cows which produce more milk																							
Yes	36	39	44	-	75	84	23	38	-	55	44	49	72	86	70	57	54	59	49	57	43	56	38
No	45	42	32	-	19	7	38	40	-	31	35	29	19	5	26	25	34	28	37	25	39	26	35
DK	19	19	24	-	6	9	39	20	-	14	21	22	9	9	4	18	12	13	14	18	18	18	27

[*] J91 from Japan 1991 survey (Macer 1992a, 1992b). US86 – OTA 1986 survey published 1987.

2.5 Environmental concerns

Some environmental concerns were seen in the responses to the general questions on genetic engineering and biotechnology (see Table 2). In the 1991 survey in Japan (Macer 1992a) 49% of the public agreed that genetically modified plants and animals would help Japanese agriculture become less dependent upon pesticides, while 49% of teachers and 56% of scientists agreed. Of the company scientists 71% agreed with this statement. Only 7% of scientists and the public disagreed with this, while 13% of teachers disagreed. This is a major argument of those calling for the development of genetic engineering in agriculture, and the result suggests that it is supported by a majority of people, though still many people are not sure about how they feel. This statement was also supported by a majority of respondents in the countries in the International Bioethics Survey (Macer 1994a).

In 1990 a European public opinion poll was conducted in the UK, France, Italy and Germany, by Gallup for Eli Lily (Dixon 1991). The respondents were asked to choose the largest benefit that they saw coming from biotechnology, between one of four possible benefits from biotechnology. Over half rated cures for serious diseases as the most important benefit. Another option was reducing our dependence upon pesticides and chemical fertilisers, which 26% of Italians, 24% of French, 22% of British and 16% of Germans, chose as the largest benefit. The respondents were asked a similar question about their largest concern. 40% of French, 35% of Germans, and 25% of British and Italian respondents chose eugenics, and slightly lower proportions overall chose environmental harm: 34% in Britain, 33% in France, 22% in Italy and 21% in Germany. Potential health hazards from laboratory genetic research were named by 29% in Italy, 17% in France, 11% in Britain and 10% in Germany. Overall, one third of respondents feel that biotechnology is ethical and one third feel that it is unethical, and one third think it is in between, "neither".

Therefore, it appears that in all countries medical advances, and the ability to cure genetic diseases are the major benefits people see from genetic engineering and biotechnology. Environmental risks are a major concern, and this is consistent with the International Bioethics Survey. However, from the results of the open questions, we also see lower proportions of the public cite these concerns, and there are other common concerns including what is natural, or ethical, as discussed above (see Table 2). The perceived benefits are divided depending on the organisms that are considered. Microorganisms are seen for both medical use and general use to produce useful substances through fermentation. Plants and animals are seen for their obvious agricultural importance, and genetic manipulation is perceived for its ability to aid the breeding of new varieties, and to increase production of food (Macer 1992a).

There were also two open questions asking what images people had of life and nature. The question on nature followed several questions on genetic engineering, so it is not surprising that many (about one quarter) included a comment that nature is something not to be touched by human beings, and about one tenth mentioned ecological problems (Macer 1994a). The ethical limits of genetic engineering may in the end be decided by subjective perceptions of "nature" rather than objective environmental risk itself. Subjective concerns are very difficult to define and this survey is an attempt to begin a search among ordinary people around the world on what these limits might be. We all have some limit, whether it be blue roses or chicken with four legs – and we also realise these limits change through time. A simple definition of bioethics, as I said earlier could be *love of life*. It is essential to understand the images people have of life in order to develop understanding of the bioethics that people have. Public acceptance depends at least as much on these types of concerns as on ecological or health risk, which is an important point in discussion of risk assessment.

3. Risk Assessment, Bioethics and Trust in Authorities

One of the central issues of ethics is decision-making, that is, who should make decisions, and who do people trust? A question on the level of trust that people had in authorities for information on the safety of biotechnology products was asked in the International Bioethics Survey, as shown in Table 4. There was most trust in the government in Hong Kong and Singapore, and least in Australasia, Japan, and Russia. Despite the lower trust shown in the government in Russia, they had a high level of trust in medical doctors. The result is most striking when we compare it to Japan, in which doctors were not trusted. In fact it appears Japanese do not trust anyone very much, but the biggest difference with the other countries was that doctors and university professors were mistrusted, especially so by medical students. Whereas Russians show great trust in doctors, environmental groups, and professors. Companies were least trusted everywhere. Farmers were also not trusted (unlike the USA, where in 1992, 26% had a lot of trust, 68% had some trust, and 6% had no trust in farmers (Hoban and Kendall 1992)). In hindsight it would have been interesting to ask whether consumers or the public can be trusted, and do people trust such crude transparent democracy.

The lack of trust in companies or governmental regulators is also seen in European (Eurobarometer 1991, 1993) and North American surveys (OTA 1987; Hoban and Kendall 1992; Rothenburg 1994). This lack of trust is a concern. The most trusted source of information are environmental groups. The main source of information is the media in all countries (Macer 1994a), but people are becoming more selective in what they believe.

There are a variety of arguments calling for public involvement in policy making. If we respect autonomy of human beings we should respect their right to have at least some property, or territory, and control over their own body. In agriculture this means respect for freedom of growing what crops a farmer chooses, and eating what food we like, within social constraints (e.g. human flesh is a general taboo in most cultures). People's well-being should be promoted, and their values and choices respected, but equally, which places limits on the pursuit of individual autonomy. We want to give every member in society equal and fair opportunities, and equally share the risks in the application of technology, this is justice. Utilitarianism (the greatest good for the greatest number) is useful for general proportions, but it is very difficult to assign values to different people's interests and preferences. The concept of "society" includes the future of society; future generations are also an essential part of society, and ethically speaking we should protect the environment for the future generations.

One of the underlying philosophical ideas of society is to pursue progress. The most cited justification for this is the pursuit of improved medicines or increased stable food supply, which is doing good. A failure to attempt to do good, is a form of doing harm, the sin of omission. This is the principle of beneficence. It is a powerful impetus for further research into ways of improving health and agriculture, and living standards. It is therefore unacceptable to hold up the progress of a potentially useful technology, unless the harms it may bring are likely to be significant when compared to the benefits. Biotechnology is challenging because, like most technology, both benefits and risks will always be associated. A fundamental way of reasoning that people have is to balance doing good against doing harm. We could group these ideals under the idea of 'love'; love means to do good to others and not to harm others. We need to share benefits of new technology and risks of developing new technology to all people.

Table 4: Trust in authorities

Q29. *Suppose that a number of groups made public statements about the benefits and risks of biotechnology products. Would you have a lot of trust, some trust, or no trust in statements made by...?*

[percentages of total respondents] Trust..	Public								Students							
	NZ	A	J	IN	T	R	IS		NZ	A	J	IN	T	P	S	HK
Government agencies																
A lot	5	8	8	25	33	5	24		7	7	4	25	28	20	34	37
Some	52	61	48	47	63	39	38		65	68	37	49	66	62	58	55
No	43	31	44	28	4	56	38		28	25	59	26	6	18	8	8
Consumer agencies																
A lot	24	13	12	23	43	33	28		28	8	8	23	41	17	6	25
Some	58	61	65	57	54	44	42		58	54	60	51	55	68	63	58
No	18	26	23	20	3	23	30		14	38	32	26	4	15	31	17
Companies making biotechnology products																
A lot	5	4	6	21	8	6	20		3	4	5	25	13	15	7	8
Some	44	52	43	47	70	31	28		49	53	38	54	75	57	66	57
No	51	44	51	32	22	63	52		48	43	57	21	12	28	27	35
Environmental groups																
A lot	21	20	15	47	-	53	54		18	14	7	52	-	57	35	45
Some	68	64	60	44	-	37	36		73	73	52	37	-	42	60	50
No	11	16	25	9	-	10	10		9	13	41	11	-	1	5	5
University professors																
A lot	25	30	12	38	42	35	42		50	54	10	47	29	46	30	47
Some	65	60	61	53	57	50	48		48	43	62	39	69	52	65	47
No	10	10	27	9	1	15	10		2	3	28	14	2	2	5	6
Medical doctors																
A lot	33	30	12	48	60	55	46		55	58	10	55	55	68	42	48
Some	60	64	58	43	38	35	50		44	40	64	37	44	29	54	49
No	7	6	30	9	2	10	4		1	2	26	8	1	3	4	3
Farmers or farm groups																
A lot	6	9	6	-	7	-	28		6	6	7	72	7	18	6	6
Some	69	69	50	-	67	-	50		70	70	50	15	76	71	54	43
No	25	22	44	-	26	-	22		24	24	43	13	17	11	40	51
Dietitians or nutritionists																
A lot	24	21	6	-	25	-	40		28	21	5	68	25	42	20	20
Some	66	69	54	-	67	-	50		65	69	56	18	65	53	66	71
No	10	10	40	-	8	-	10		7	10	39	14	10	5	14	9

People in developing countries should not be the recipients of risks passed on to them by industrialised countries, despite the economic pressure to allow this. We can think of the dumping of hazardous wastes to developing countries, in return for financial reward, but the environmental and human health consequences of dumping toxic waste cannot be measured. Testing of GMOs is a similar case, though we must note the developing country that is growing GMOs over the largest area is China which is doing so for its own reasons. Industrialised societies have developed safeguards to protect citizens, and some of these involve considerable economic cost. While it may not be possible for developing countries' governments to impose the same requirements, they should not accept lower standards – rather, all can use data obtained in countries with strict and sufficient safeguards of health, with the aid of inter-governmental agencies. Any basic human right should be the same in all countries, and this is one of the roles of the United Nations. Ethically this would support the implementation of minimum international standards for regulation of biotechnology (Krattiger and Rosemarin 1994). This suggests that risk assessment methods should become systemised and standard, though as discussed in other chapters in this book, and as seen in international comparisons, how to effect a system is still contentious.

The precise outcome of interventions in nature or medicine is not always certain. It has taken major ecological disasters to convince people in industry or agriculture of the risks. Introducing new organisms to the environment is also associated with risk. If we introduce very different gene combinations into the environment they could have major consequences, which may be irreversible (Macer 1990; see other chapters in this volume). The new genes may enter other organisms, or the new organisms themselves may replace existing organisms in the ecosystem. The ecological system is very complex, minor alterations in one organism can sometimes have effects throughout an ecosystem. Field trials and experimentation are an ethical prerequisite before full scale use of new organisms, as is the scheme used by the USDA in the USA, and quarantine regulations used throughout much of the world.

In most interventions in life there are slippery slopes. The idea is that because we perform some action, we will perform another. Controls which were adequate for initial exploration may fail under increased pressure. While we may not do any direct harm with the application in question, it could result in progressive lowering of standards towards the ill-defined line beyond which it would be doing harm. The inability to draw a line is no measure of the non-importance of an issue – rather some of the biggest fundamental questions in bioethics and life are of this nature.

With precautionary laws to prevent risk because of insufficient scientific knowledge, like the regulations on field trials of GMOs, we could expect gradual weakening of control as experience is gained to support reduced controls. However, Jäger and Tappeser (Chapter 4 in this book) argue that the available data do not support a relaxing of guidelines, as has occurred in the USDA and is being called for in Europe. In this case it may be a slippery slope of increasing familiarity, combined with an absence of dramatic incidents, rather than maintenance of the same scientific objectivity as in the initial trials. It may also be led by bureaucratic overload, and pressures for commercial releases. In this case, there are differences in the interpretation of risk assessment data. It should also be noted, however, that the real safety test of GMOs is large scale commercial releases, and some releases could be justified if a substantial monitoring system was established to track the genes and ecological impacts. In this case, an intermediate phase between large experimental trials and full commercial release, over the period of several years would seem wise.

Some people, from all countries, say that some developments of science and technology such as genetic engineering are interfering with nature because "nature knows best". However, we have some good reasons to interfere with parts of nature. For example, we try to cure many diseases that afflict humans or other living organisms and we must eat. A negative science fiction image has been easily promoted and is appealing to the human imagination. The fascination with creating "new forms of life" is coupled to a fear of how far it might be taken. There are many movies which play on scary themes, from Frankenstein to the 1993 blockbuster movie *Jurassic Park*, which brought genetic engineering into the imagination of many. These are thought to be very powerful in shaping public acceptance and perceptions, though just how influential they are is a question for research.

4. A Future with Public Involvement in Risk Assessment

We must ensure that efficient and sustainable agriculture is encouraged, but recognise it is only part of a broader solution. Sustainable agriculture could be defined as the appropriate use of crop and livestock systems and agricultural inputs supporting those activities which maintain economic and social viability while preserving the high productivity and quality of the land. We need to improve agricultural efficiency to succeed. However, current research interests in biotechnology are not necessarily the best way to provide sustainable agriculture. Large corporations are developing new techniques that may require constant application. For example, biological weed control is more cost effective and has a higher success rate than that achieved in searching for useful agrochemicals. Yet, development is limited because it may not make commercial profits.

The consequences of these decisions on the different communities involved in agriculture also needs to be considered. There exists a variety of social risks of new technology, which could in the end be the greatest risk of manipulation of life, as it will shape future public acceptance about the limits of interventions humans can make in nature. This could be called social risk assessment, and it is an area that social scientists will have to explore, using the tools of descriptive bioethics.

Some of the criticism is against technology in general, and needs balanced consideration. For example, there are valid criticisms about the development of herbicide-tolerant plants (that biological control is better), but they do have immediate environmental advantages in some cases. For example, maize growers make 4-6 herbicide applications a season, but if the crop was tolerant to a broad-spectrum post-emergence herbicide only one application would be needed. Reducing herbicide use and switching to biodegradable products is consistent with sustainable agriculture and is an important practical step in that direction, as long as the powerful commercial interests do not prevent the eventual widespread use of the ideal, biological control.

The ethical role of scientists is defined by several levels of moral community: the scientific community itself, the local community, the national society, and the global society. Scientists are involved in a number of different relationships, but first they are participants in society, having the same responsibilities as any citizen. Scientists are also part of a profession, which includes some moral responsibility. If the scientific profession or community does not censor themselves others will do so. We can see the trend for different groups or professions to lay out their ethical codes, as written codifications of etiquette, if not always ethics. When scientists fail to regulate their activity, laws and regulations will be made stronger to ensure that they do, this is a risk that scientists take when they go beyond what is publicly acceptable.

Other groups are involved in the application of science in the world. Companies have been responsible for about 80% of the releases of GMOs in the world (Krattiger and Rosemarin 1994). The risks that companies take include investment into unprofitable products, risks of environmental and/or medical legal claims, and risks of unwelcome legal restraints. As commercial seeds and animals are passed on to farmers, the farmers will assume increasing responsibility for sensible farming practice, which is usually in their long term interests also (e.g. monitoring of pest resistance to insecticidal proteins). The risks to the farmers include, crop failure, unprofitable products, damage to their land or their health, and even possible legal claims against them.

Each of the groups, or players, involved in the release of GMOs also has its own set of benefits. Ideally, all may share the goal of human progress, but they also share the benefits of their own progress. All three have economic interests, perhaps scientists less than the other two groups if the scientists have the luxury of financial support unlinked to research application. The general public also shares these benefits, but may have a longer term economic and environmental framework, and has the benefit of being consumers. Variety or alternatives can give choice, if such a variety is available, and many people will also welcome the variety of lower cost. In fact, when we consider this factor the public may also have short term economic sights, when it enters the supermarket. Nevertheless, as discussed above, there are a number of ethical reasons to give the general public the major role in deciding what risks and benefits are acceptable for technologies which do have broad implications, in fact global implications in the case of genetic engineering. This means that risk assessment strategies need to be developed from public concerns as well as the concerns of specialists. The broad nature of a technology also suggests that social and ethical impact issues can be included as "risks", and methods to assess these types of risks would be needed. Genetic engineering is certainly not a special case, but it has made people wake up to the fact that many technologies have such broad potential impacts, and we need to think of risk assessment and technology assessment in general. In this respect the decision by the 1995 US government to virtually dismantle the Office of Technology Assessment is surprising and short-sighted.

However, unless the broader dimensions of applied science are taught, society will be unable to make balanced decisions about the use of technology. In all countries in the International Bioethics Survey there is strong support for teaching students about the ethical and social issues associated with science and technology (Macer 1994a). Such issues are already introduced into the curriculum to varying degrees in Australia, New Zealand and Japan, as measured in the International Bioethics Education Survey. The general attitudes to the teaching of bioethics were extremely positive. It is interesting that more biology teachers thought bioethics should be taught in biology classes, while social teachers thought they should teach it.

There is more inclusion in Australia and New Zealand teachers than in Japan. There is now some research into how these issues are being best taught, the most suitable issues, the suitable classes and the most effective delivery. They are relevant to both science and social studies classes. The next stage in the education project is the development of materials to aid the teaching of these issues. The responses obtained were used to make such materials. Teachers are testing some on-line materials, and developing them for use at appropriate times in existing courses.

Public education is a special responsibility of scientists, who have the best knowledge of the technology, even if they may not know of the impact so much. People who have high familiarity with such techniques, such as scientists and high school biology teachers, are also concerned about such technology (Macer 1992a). Rather than attempting to dismiss feelings of concern, society should value and debate these concerns to improve the bioethical maturity of society. The data suggest that the public is already informed enough to be trusted in the formation of policy, and there needs to be inclusion into policy making. Several countries including Denmark, the Netherlands and the UK have had public consensus conferences as new methods to involve the public in decision-making. Public forum, and public notification, and chance for response, are prerequisites of democracy that are still being excluded in some genetic engineering applications.

In some discussions of the impact of biotechnology, safety and risk are considered separate from bioethical concerns. However, as shown above, the origin of concern about safety and impact is the ethical principle of *do no harm*. People of various cultures, ages, educational training, occupation and outlook on life, perceive both benefits and risks from developments of science and technology. People in the countries surveyed do not have a simplistic view of science and technology and do show the ability to balance benefits and risks of science and technology. This calls for public involvement in the process of risk definition and assessment.

Note

I wish to thank Ad, the editor, for numerous useful comments on this paper.
On-line materials for teachers, books, papers, the *Eubios Journal of Asian and International Bioethics*, and up-to-date news are available from *Eubios Ethics Institute* (http://www.biol.tsukuba.ac.jp/~macer/index.html).

References

Alstad, D.N. and Andow, D.A. 1995. 'Managing the evolution of insect resistance to transgenic plants.' *Science* **268**, pp.1894-1897.
Couchman, P. and Fink-Jensen, K. 1990. *Public Attitudes to Genetic Engineering in New Zealand*. DSIR Crop Research Report No. 138. DSIR Crop Research, Christchurch, NZ: Private Bag.
Decima Research 1993. *Final Report to the Canadian Institute of Biotechnology on Public Attitudes to Biotechnology*. Ottawa.
Dixon, B. 1991. 'Biotech a plus according to European poll.' *Bio/Technology* **9**, p.16.

Dixon, B. 1994. 'Biotech in Thailand.' *Bio/Technology* **12**, p.954.

Eurobarometer, European Commission. 1993. *Biotechnology and Genetic Engineering: What Europeans Think About It in 1993, Eurobarometer Survey 39.1* (and 35.1) is available in French or English from M. Lex, DG XII/E-1 SDME 2/65, Commission of the European Communities, Rue de la Loi 200, B-1049, Brussels, Belgium.

Hamstra, A.M. 1991. *Biotechnology in Foodstuffs.* SWOKA Report 105, Institute for Consumer Research, Koningin Emmakade 192-195, 2518 JP 's-Gravenhage, The Netherlands.

――――. 1993. *Consumer Acceptance of Food Biotechnology.* SWOKA Report 137, Institute for Consumer Research, Koningin Emmakade 192-195, 2518 JP 's-Gravenhage, The Netherlands.

Hoban, T.J. and Kendall, P.A. 1992. *Consumer Attitudes About the Use of Biotechnology in Agriculture and Food Production.* Raleigh, NC: North Carolina State University.

Krattiger, A.F. and Rosemarin, A. (eds.) 1994. *Biosafety for Sustainable Agriculture. Sharing Regulatory Experiences of the Western Hemisphere.* Stockholm: Stockholm Environmental Institute.

Macer, D.R.J. 1990. *Shaping Genes: Ethics, Law and Science of Using Genetic Technology in Medicine and Agriculture.* Christchurch, NZ: Eubios Ethics Institute.

――――. 1992a. *Attitudes to Genetic Engineering: Japanese and International Comparisons,* Christchurch, NZ: Eubios Ethics Institute.

――――. 1992b. 'Public acceptance of human gene therapy and perceptions of human genetic manipulation.' *Human Gene Therapy* **3**, pp.511-518.

――――. 1993. 'No to "genethics".' *Nature* **365**, p.102.

――――. 1994a. *Bioethics for the People by the People.* Christchurch, NZ: Eubios Ethics Institute.

――――. 1994b. 'Perception of risks and benefits of in vitro fertilization, genetic engineering and biotechnology.' *Social Science and Medicine* **38**, pp.23-33.

――――. 1995. 'Bioethics and biotechnology: What is ethical biotechnology?' In: D. Brauer (ed.), *Modern Biotechnology: Legal, Economic and Social Dimensions, Biotechnology, Volume 12.* Weinheim, Germany: VCH, pp.115-154.

Macer, D.R.J. et al. 1995. 'International perceptions and approval of gene therapy.' *Human Gene Therapy* **6**, pp.791-803.

Martin, S. and Tait, J. 1992. 'Attitudes of selected public groups in the UK to biotechnology.' In: J. Durant (ed.), *Biotechnology in Public.* London: Science Museum, pp. 28-41.

[OTA] U.S. Congress, Office of Technology Assessment. 1987. *New Developments in Biotechnology, 2: Public Perceptions of Biotechnology – Background Paper.* Washington, DC: U.S.G.P.O.

Rabino, I. 1991. 'The impact of activist pressures on recombinant DNA research.' *Science, Technology and Human Values* **16**, pp.70-87.

――――. 1992. 'A study of attitudes and concerns of genetic engineering scientists in Western Europe.' *Biotech Forum Europe* **9**, pp.636-40.

Rothenburg, L. 1994. 'Biotechnology's issue of public credibility.' *Trends in Biotechnology* **12**, pp.435-438.

Rothenburg, L. and Macer, D. 1995. 'Public Acceptance of Food Biotechnology in the USA.' *Biotechnology and Development Monitor* **24**, pp.10-13.

Schomberg, R. von (ed.) 1995. *Contested technology. Ethics, Risk and Public Debate.* Tilburg/Buenos Aires: International Centre for Human and Public Affairs.

Suzuki, D. and Knudtson, P. 1989. *Genethics: The Clash Between the New Genetics and Human Values.* Boston: Harvard University Press.

Zechendorf, B. 1994. 'What the public thinks about biotechnology.' *Bio/Technology* **12**, pp.870-875.

About the Authors

Susan Carr – is a lecturer in the Systems Department of the Open University, where she writes on environmental, agricultural and management related courses. Her main research interest is in environmental perceptions. Her current research includes a study of the role of NGO advocacy on global environmental policies, as well as this study of biotechnology regulation. She maintains an interest in tropical agriculture through her involvement in the editing of the journal *Experimental Agriculture*.

Address: Centre for Technology Strategy, Open University,
            Milton Keynes MK7 6AA, United Kingdom
E-mail: S.Carr@open.ac.uk

Ad van Dommelen – studied philosophy and science dynamics at the University of Amsterdam and the New School for Social Research in New York. From 1989-1992 he has been working in the Department of Applied Philosophy at the Agricultural University in Wageningen, the Netherlands. Since 1992 he is doing research on the methodological status of background theories in applied biotechnology research in the Department of Theoretical Biology at the Free University of Amsterdam.

Address: Department of Theoretical Biology, Free University, De Boelelaan 1087,
            1081 HV Amsterdam, The Netherlands
E-mail: avando@bio.vu.nl

Brian Goodwin – was born in Canada in 1931. He studied biology at McGill University in Montreal (B.Sc.1953, M.Sc.1954), then won a Rhodes Scholarship to Oxford where he read Mathematics (B.A. 1957). From 1957-60 he worked towards a PhD in Edinburgh on the dynamics of embryonic development under the supervision of C.H. Waddington. The degree was awarded in 1960, and the thesis was developed into a book, *Temporal Organization in Cells*, published by Academic Press in 1963. After research fellowships at McGill (1960-61) and MIT (1961-64) he returned to Britain to take up first a lectureship at Edinburgh University (1964-1965) and then a Readership in Development Biology at the University of Sussex, where he remained until 1983. He was then appointed to a Chair in Biology at the Open University. His research interests cover the areas of development and evolution, understanding how biological form (morphology and behaviour) is generated and making biology more of an exact and less of an historical science. The main focus of his current work is to understand biological processes in terms of the transformations of organized wholes (organisms, communities, ecosystems) and their natural (generic) states of order, using the sciences of complexity and theories of emergence. This work is linked to applications in the study of health and environmental issues.

Address: Department of Biology, The Open University,
            Milton Keynes MK7 6AA, United Kingdom
E-mail: B.C.Goodwin@open.ac.uk

Dr. Manuela Jäger – born 1964, mother of one son, studied biology at the University of Ulm, Germany, with microbiology, virology and molecular genetics as her main subjects. Since 1992 she is applied at the department for Risk Assessment of Genetic Engineering at the Institute for Applied Ecology, Freiburg, Germany.

Address: Öko-Institute e.V., Institute of Applied Ecology, P.O.Box 6226,
            D-79038 Freiburg, Germany
Fax: +49-761-475437

Soemini Kasanmoentalib – born 1949, studied biology and philosophy at the University of Leiden, the Netherlands, with mathematical biology, animal ecology and philosophy of biology as her main subjects. In the seventies she worked at the University of Amsterdam to set up an educational programme 'Biology and Society', on ethical and social aspects of biology in the biology curriculum. In the eighties she worked at the University of Nijmegen on a research project in philosophy of medicine which resulted in a doctorate thesis on Viktor von Weizsäckers concept of the organism and its implications for psychosomatic medicine. Since 1990 she teaches statistics and research methods at the Faculty of Kinaesiology of the Free University of Amsterdam. Since September 1992 she is also associated with the department of Theoretical Biology as a post-doc researcher on a research project on ethics in applied biotechnology. She is mother of a teenager son.

Address: Department of Theoretical Biology, Free University, De Boelelaan 1087,
            1081 HV Amsterdam, The Netherlands
E-mail: soemini@bio.vu.nl

Sheldon Krimsky – is professor of Urban & Environmental Policy at Tufts University. He received his bachelors and masters degree in physics from Brooklyn College, CUNY and Purdue University, respectively, and a masters and doctorate in philosophy at Boston University. Professor Krimsky served on the National Institutes of Health's Recombinant DNA Advisory Committee from 1978-1981. He was a consultant to the Presidential Commission for the Study of Ethical Problems in Medicine and Biomedical and Behavioural Research and to the Congressional Office of Technology Assessment. He also served on a special study panel for the American Civil Liberties Union that formulated a policy on civil liberties and scientific research. Professor Krimsky served as chairperson of the Committee on Scientific Freedom and Responsibility for the American Association for the Advancement of Science for 1988-1992. Currently he serves on the Board of Directors for the Council for Responsible Genetics. Professor Krimsky's research has focused on the linkages between science/technology, ethics/values and public policy. He is the author of five books: *Genetic Alchemy: The Social History of the Recombinant DNA Controversy* and *Biotechnics and Society: The Rise of Industrial Genetics*. He is co-author of *Environmental Hazards: Communicating Risks as a Social Process* and co-editor of a collection of papers titled *Social Theories of Risk*. A forthcoming book is titled *Agricultural Biotechnology and the Environment: Science, Policy and Social Values*. Professor Krimsky has published over 85 essays that have appeared in many books and journals.

Address: Department of Urban & Environmental Policy, Tufts University,
            Medford, MA 02155, USA
E-mail: SKRIMSKY@Pearl.Tufts.Edu

Les Levidow – is a Research Fellow at the Open University, where he has been studying the safety regulation of agricultural biotechnology, colloquially known as 'the real Jurassic Park'. He is co-editor of several books, including *Anti-Racist Science Teaching* and *Cyborgs Worlds: The Military Information Society* (Free Association Books, 1987 and 1989, respectively). He has been Managing Editor of *Science as Culture* since its inception in 1987, and of its predecessor, the *Radical Science Journal*.

Address: Centre for Technology Strategy, Open University,
             Milton Keynes MK7 6AA, United Kingdom
E-mail: L.Levidow@open.ac.uk

Darryl R.J. Macer – was born in New Zealand in 1962, and completed a Bachelor of Science with first class honours in Biochemistry from Lincoln College, University of Canterbury. He completed a PhD in Biochemistry at the MRC Laboratory of Molecular Biology, and Trinity College, University of Cambridge, U.K. He has since researched bioethics, as a senior research scholar at Trinity College, University of Cambridge, U.K; and as a consultant scientist to the Department of Scientific and Industrial Research, and the Ministry for the Environment, New Zealand. He was the founder, and is the director of *Eubios Ethics Institute*, Christchurch, New Zealand & Tsukuba Science City, Japan (http://www.biol.tsukuba.ac.jp/~macer /index.html). Since September 1990, he has been a Foreign Professor, and since April 1995 an Associate Professor, in the Institute of Biological Sciences, University of Tsukuba, Ibaraki 305, Japan. He is a member of the UNESCO Bioethics Committee and HUGO Ethics Committee; the coordinator of the International Association of Bioethics Genetics Network; and editor of *Eubios Journal of Asian and International Bioethics*. He has authored 6 books (1 in Japanese), edited 2 books (2 in Japanese), and has written about 50 academic papers and articles.

Adresses: Institute of Biological Sciences, University of Tsukuba,
             Tsukuba Science City 305, Ibaraki 305, Japan
             Eubios Ethics Institute, 31 Colwyn Street, Christchurch 5, New Zealand
E-mail: Macer@Zobell.biol.tsukuba.ac.jp

Ruth McNally – is a Director of Bio-Information (International) Limited and Visiting Lecturer, Sociology Department, University of the West of England, Bristol. She has a Bsc Hons in Genetics, an MA in Socio-Legal Studies, and is doing a PhD in Sociology using a Foucauldian perspective to examine abortion for foetal handicap. As Director of Bio-Information (International) Limited, she has undertaken a number of consultancies for the European Parliament, the European Commission, and the BBC. With Peter Wheale, she has published three books and approximately twenty papers, articles and reports on the social relations of genetic engineering. Recent publications are on bioethics in Europe (STOA 1992), European biotechnology policy (Wheale and McNally 1993), genetic engineering in modernity (Wheale and McNally 1994; McNally and Wheale 1994), animal genetic engineering (Wheale and McNally 1990b, 1995), biopatenting and new social movements (McNally and Wheale 1995), and abortion for foetal handicap (McNally 1995c). (See chapter 7 of this book for the references.)

Address: 14A Elthorne Road, Uxbridge, Middlesex UB8 2PS, United Kingdom
E-mail: Ruth.McNally@brunel.ac.uk

Philip Regal – is a Professor of Ecology, Evolution, and Behavior. Much of his research has concerned trends in the physiological, morphological, behavioral, and genetic adaptation of plants and animals to the environment. These interests led him to an interest in delineating the principles by which the adaptive potential of various types of genetically engineered organisms might be estimated and their safety and effectiveness predicted. He has been the author of key papers on this subject, the organizer of key scientific workshops, and he has consulted for a number of government agencies, industries, and public interest groups. His current interests include the history and philosophy of science, and science policy.

Address: 100 Ecology Building, University of Minnesota,
             St. Paul, Minnesota 55108, U.S.A.
E-mail: regal001@maroon.tc.umn.edu

Christoph Rehmann-Sutter – is lecturer of Philosophy of Nature and Bioethics in the Faculty of Natural Sciences of the University of Basel, Switzerland. As a molecular biologist and philosopher he specializes in ethical aspects of biotechnology and ecology. His recent research and writing interests have focused on the practical aspects of biological theory formation, foundations of general bioethics as ethics of relationships with human and non-human beings, and risk ethics. He is author of *Leben beschreiben: Über Handlungszusammenhänge in der Biologie* (in press), co-author of *Sinnengegenwart. Essays zur Wahrnehmung* (1993), and *Ethik und Gentherapie* (1995).

Address: Biozentrum der Universität Basel, Abteilung Mikrobiologie, Klingelbergstr. 70,
             CH-4056 Basel, Switzerland

Piet Schenkelaars – has a background in molecular biology and philosophy of science. After his studies at the Agricultural University in Wageningen, the Netherlands, he has worked for Dutch NGOs in the area of biotechnology for several years. From 1991 to 1993 he was employed by Friends of the Earth Europe in Brussels, Belgium, as coordinator of the Clearinghouse on Biotechnology. At the moment, he works as biotechnology consultant at Schuttelaars & Partners in The Hague, the Netherlands. His working areas entail international and national biosafety regulations, risk assessment and risk management in biotechnology, and communication of biotechnology related issues.

Address: Rembrandtlaan 68, 2251 HA Voorschoten, The Netherlands

Dr.ir. René von Schomberg – agricultural scientist, PhD in Philosophy and Science and Technology Studies, based at Tilburg University, director International Centre for Human and Public Affairs, major recent books: *Science, Politics and Morality. Scientific Uncertainty and Decision Making* (Kluwer Academic Publishers, 1993); *Der rationale Umgang mit Unsicherheit. Die Bewältigung von Gefahren und Dissens in Wissenschaft, Wissenschaftspolitik und Gesellschaft* (Peter Lang, 1995); *Contested Technology. Ethics, Risk and Public Debate* (1995).

Address: Faculty of Philosophy, Tilburg University, PO Box 90153,
             NL-5000 LE Tilburg, The Netherlands
E-mail: R.vonSchomberg@Kub.nl

Dr. Beatrix Tappeser – born 1954, studied biology at the University of Bonn with plant physiology, molecular biology and immunology as main subjects. A postdoctoral fellowship in the field of molecular developmental biology (regulation of gene expression during early embryonic development) followed at the University of Berlin. In 1985 she became scientific adviser of the Green Party at the German Bundestag. Since 1987 she coordinates the working group on Risk Assessment of Genetic Engineering at the Institute for Applied Ecology, Freiburg, Germany.

Address: Öko-Institute e.V., Institute of Applied Ecology, P.O.Box 6226,
             D-79038 Freiburg, Germany
Fax: +49-761-475437

Adrian Vatter – is self-employed, working as a political scientist in Berne and as lecturer at the University of Berne, Switzerland. He specializes in environmental politics, in development planning, in the evaluation of participation-procedures and in the analysis of elections and referenda. He is the author of *Eigennutz als Grundmaxime der Politik?* (Haupt Verlag, Bern/Stuttgart 1994) and co-author of *Gewissen in der Politik* (1995).

Address: Politikforschung & -beratung, Schwanengasse 4, CH-3011 Berne, Switzerland

Christine von Weizsäcker – is a biologist, freelance researcher, writer, lecturer and mother of five children. She developed the concept of "error-friendliness" as an evolutionary principle and analyzed its implications for a "technology policy worthy of democracy". As a researcher-activist she advises many environmental NGOs, foundations, consumers' organizations and churches on the national and international level. To her own surprise she keeps being invited to lecture at many universities in Europe and the United States.

Address: Postfach 130165, 53061 Bonn, Germany
E-mail: CVW@mail.isd.de

Dr. Peter Wheale – has a degree in Economics from Manchester University and was awarded his doctorate for studies on the conduct, structure and performance of the cereals industry. He also has a Msc in the Structure and Organisation of Science & Technology from Manchester University and an MA in Medical Ethics and Law from King's College, London. He is the co-author of *People, Science & Technology: A Guide to Advanced Industrial Society* (Wheatsheaf, 1986); *Genetic Engineering: Catastrophe or Utopia* (Wheatsheaf, 1988); and the co-editor of *The Bio-Revolution: Cornucopia or Pandora's Box?* (Pluto, 1990) and *Animal Genetic Engineering: Of Pigs, Oncomice and Men* (Pluto, 1995). He currently holds a Visiting Fellowship in the Department of Philosophy at Tilburg University in the Netherlands and will shortly take up a post at Surrey University, England.

Address: Surrey European Management School (SEMS), University of Surrey,
             Guildford, Surrey GU2 5XH, United Kingdom
E-mail: P.Wheale@surrey.ac.uk

David Wield – directs the Open University's Centre for Technology Strategy. His main research interests lie in the areas of the regulation and shaping of technologies, the management of innovation, and industrialization and development.

Address: Centre for Technology Strategy, Open University, Milton Keynes MK7 6AA, UK
E-mail: D.V.Wield@open.ac.uk

Index

Words that are frequently used in this book, such as *biotechnology, environment, release, risk, safety,* and *technology,* are not included in this index.

Acceptability 11, 81, 82, 91, 95, 98, 99, 149, 150, 151, 153, 160, 162-164, 173, 174, 212
Acceptance 8, 11, 47, 94, 131, 160-164, 167, 171-174, 201, 202, 214, 227, 231, 236, 239, 242, 245
Actor-network 103, 104, 106-114
Advisory committee 27, 86, 96-98, 100-102, 122, 124, 125, 133, 149, 150, 151, 154, 155, 165-167, 169, 170, 172, 173, 175, 248
Agriculture 26, 32, 37, 44, 52, 61, 62, 68, 70, 73, 77, 83, 84, 90, 92, 96, 100, 101, 102, 107, 108, 114, 117, 122, 131, 133, 143, 144, 146, 149, 150, 153, 160, 164, 172, 175, 201, 228, 230, 236, 238-242, 245, 247
Analogy 35, 48, 53, 82-84, 86, 99, 143, 213
Antibiotic-resistance 92, 101
Argument 17, 19, 25, 29, 32, 38, 41, 50, 51, 56, 58-60, 64, 84, 95, 142, 148, 155, 181, 213, 214, 238
Asilomar 19, 20, 31, 140, 159
Attitude 26, 139, 153, 171-173, 182, 195
Attitudes 75, 160, 173, 176, 214, 231, 232, 243-245
Autographa californica 122, 133
Autonomy 139, 180, 213, 214, 216, 225, 227, 236, 239
Bacillus thuringiensis 58, 69, 71, 72, 146, 228
Baculovirus 7, 11, 121-127, 129-131, 133-135, 166
Behaviour 10, 17, 35, 39-42, 48, 73, 74, 82, 127, 128, 142, 148, 149, 211, 219, 227, 247
Beneficence 139, 213, 227, 240
Benefit 29, 35, 43, 86, 131, 132, 137, 139, 154, 160, 177, 183, 184, 203, 212, 227, 232, 234, 235, 238, 243
Biochemistry 28, 249
Biodiversity 84, 91, 138, 145, 202, 205, 224, 227
Bioethics 11, 118, 139, 194, 224, 227-230, 232, 234, 236, 238, 239, 241-245, 249, 250
Biological containment 64, 123, 125, 133
Biological control 58, 127, 142, 144, 229, 242
Biology 5, 17-23, 28, 31, 32, 57, 61, 62, 73, 74, 75, 78, 163, 176, 200, 205, 226, 227, 232-235, 237, 243, 244, 247, 248-251
Biosafety 10, 20, 25-27, 30, 53, 73, 75, 77, 78, 100, 116, 134, 166, 170, 172, 173, 186, 197, 199, 201, 245, 250
Biosafety protocol 75, 77, 78, 199, 201
Boloria euphrosyne 125
Brassica napus 77, 88, 95, 96, 98, 128
Burden of proof 139, 140, 144
Bureaucracy 180, 183
Case-by-case 25, 56, 57, 88, 141, 142, 149, 152, 154, 163
Causality 82, 83, 98, 131
Cause 9, 15, 20, 25, 28, 33, 34, 54, 56, 58, 59, 81-83, 96, 98, 107, 111, 122, 126, 129, 130, 132, 150, 170, 184, 189, 195, 217, 220
Communication 8, 11, 67, 114, 128, 133, 153, 163, 169, 176, 181, 183, 193, 203, 207, 208, 210, 212, 214, 215, 217-220, 223, 225, 226, 250
Community 15, 17, 19-23, 25, 26, 29, 32, 54, 60, 63, 69, 83, 86, 101, 105, 110, 116, 117, 121, 127, 131, 134, 140, 141, 143, 146, 160, 168, 170, 171, 174, 176, 181, 184, 186, 193, 194, 202, 204, 212-215, 223, 228, 231, 236, 242, 243
Competitiveness 33, 42, 85, 86, 101, 110, 116, 141, 160, 161, 176, 179, 193
Consensus 15, 49, 50, 55, 56, 87, 94, 131, 138, 142, 154, 182, 193, 219, 225, 230, 244
Conservation 32, 129, 131, 134, 153, 167
Containment 9, 20, 64, 84, 121, 123, 125, 126, 128-130, 132, 133, 187-191, 198
Controversy 7, 11, 31, 50, 51, 55-57, 81, 82, 115, 121, 122, 126, 128, 130, 131, 132, 140, 142, 148, 150, 248

Cosmology 27, 28, 30
Cost 15, 43, 49, 106, 154, 203, 217, 241-243
Cost-benefit 43, 154, 203
Cyborg 104, 110, 114, 115, 183
Danger(s) 43, 48, 58, 73, 83, 143, 182, 207-
     209, 212, 219, 222, 230, 235
Decision-making 77, 102, 137, 139, 161, 167,
     169, 173, 191, 198, 202, 215, 217,
     219-223, 231, 239, 244
Deletion 38
Democracy 8, 114, 178, 180, 181, 193, 194,
     196, 199, 205, 207, 216, 217, 239,
     244, 251
Deregulation 26, 27, 63, 64, 69, 162, 198, 201
Determinism 18, 30, 36
Dioxin 36
Discourse 17, 18, 49, 137, 181, 187, 195, 196,
     202, 204, 210, 212, 215, 225
Disease 20, 39, 58, 59, 108, 112-214, 232,
     235-237
Disease-resistant 236, 237
Dispersal 33, 35, 41, 42, 189
Dormancy 65
Ecology 16, 17, 21, 25, 27, 28, 30-32, 35, 38,
     42, 45, 57, 62, 72, 95, 116, 134, 141,
     142, 146, 151, 163, 186, 201, 205,
     216, 235, 248, 250, 251
Economy 21, 163, 164, 235
Ecosystem 39, 40, 45, 61, 116, 227, 229, 241
Ecotoxicology 43, 61
Epistasis 36
Epizootic 122, 124, 126-129, 132
Escape 20, 126, 129, 130, 183, 187-190, 228
Escherichia coli [*E.coli*] 64, 65, 68, 71, 72
Essentialism 16, 25, 26, 30
Ethics 61, 62, 118, 144, 181, 194, 210, 213,
     215, 224-226, 232, 236, 239, 243-245,
     248-251
Eugenics 18, 118, 235, 238
European Commission 8, 10, 11, 69, 81,
     83-87, 94, 97, 100, 101, 103, 105,
     106, 109-114, 116-118, 121, 127, 131,
     134, 135, 140, 144-146, 159-162, 164,
     165, 168, 169, 171, 173, 174, 176,
     177, 179, 183-187, 189-191, 193-195,
     197, 201, 207, 231, 238, 239, 244,
     245, 249, 251
Evidence 10, 18, 25, 26, 47, 48, 54, 57, 68,
     70, 84, 85, 89, 90, 96, 99, 108, 112,
     113, 115, 121-123, 127, 128, 130,
     131, 138, 140, 191, 203, 220
Evolution 16, 17, 27, 28, 31, 32, 39, 57, 73,
     76, 78, 134, 194, 200, 201, 205, 244,
     247, 250
Exotic (introductions) 32, 35, 37, 38
Experiment 9, 33, 39, 55, 101, 122, 128, 167,
     169, 199
Explanation 87, 214

Familiarity 28, 48, 234, 241, 244
Fault tree analysis 34
Field test 37, 39, 55, 134
Field testing 32, 33, 36, 44, 45, 52, 62, 146
Field trial(s) 90, 105, 113, 116, 119, 121, 122,
     124, 130-132, 134, 135, 161, 169,
     190, 229, 241
Fire ants 37
Fitness 39, 50, 52, 56, 57, 63, 64, 199, 200
Gene therapy 68, 116, 118, 234, 245
Generality 15, 57
Genetics 21, 31, 35, 36, 45, 57, 71, 72, 92,
     133-135, 145, 232, 245, 248, 249
Global warming 37, 207
Greenhouse 36, 39, 41, 43, 143
Guidelines 84, 88, 89, 121, 138, 172, 213,
     224, 230, 241
Gypsy moth 127
Harm 56, 58, 81, 82, 84-86, 88-92, 95, 96, 98,
     107, 111, 112, 122, 125, 129, 130,
     132, 138, 139, 143, 151, 152, 154,
     155, 167, 172-174, 177, 184, 185-187,
     189, 190, 207, 208, 209, 211, 213,
     215, 227, 229, 234, 236, 238, 240,
     241, 244
Harmonization 174
Hazard 34, 42, 44, 81, 87-89, 91, 93, 130, 209
Herbicide 7, 10, 67, 77, 81, 83-88, 90-99,
     101, 150, 151, 153, 242
Herbicide-tolerance 88, 90, 95, 99
Host 10, 20, 33, 36, 38, 39, 41, 50, 58, 59,
     60, 62, 103, 107, 112, 115, 122,
     123-127, 129-131, 174, 189
Host organism 33, 36, 38, 39, 50, 189
Host range 41, 59, 60, 62, 103, 112, 115, 122,
     123, 125-127, 129-131
Hybrid 35, 89, 93, 95, 96, 103, 110, 115, 183,
     194, 229
Hybridization 88, 91, 95, 96, 98, 99, 101, 102
Ice minus 35-38, 45
Idealism 18, 19, 28, 30
Ideology 7, 15, 16, 18, 30, 43, 182
Ignorance 11, 27, 69, 82, 137, 139, 144, 172
Indeterminacy 11, 128, 131-133
Induction 34
Information 4, 8, 11, 18, 30, 33-36, 39, 43,
     63, 69, 73, 76, 106, 113-115, 117,
     126, 127, 134, 137, 138, 139, 143,
     149, 150, 152-154, 159, 161-174, 179,
     210, 213, 214, 218, 219, 220, 222,
     231, 232, 239, 249
Insect 24, 40, 58, 69, 122-124, 126-128, 134,
     135, 142, 228, 244
Insecticide 45, 69, 76, 77, 124, 125, 127, 134,
     135, 228
Introduction 7, 9, 15, 32, 33, 37, 45, 47, 54,
     58, 62-65, 69, 73, 81, 89, 103, 117,
     121, 137, 141, 143, 144, 146, 147,

159, 177, 183, 194, 195, 201, 202, 207, 211, 220, 223-226, 229
Jumping genes 76
Klebsiella planticola 39, 70
Knowledge 8, 16-19, 24, 28, 33-35, 40, 47, 49, 52, 58, 60, 64, 66, 69, 70, 82, 86, 90, 99, 116-118, 128, 132, 133, 135, 137, 139, 141-143, 147-150, 163, 164, 167, 173, 176, 181-183, 191, 195-197, 202-205, 212, 214, 215, 220, 233, 241, 244
Kudzu 35, 37
Laboratory 17, 20, 21, 28, 36, 38, 40, 44, 45, 63-67, 70, 71, 111, 116, 122, 124, 125, 127, 128, 131, 133, 134, 142, 143, 225, 238, 249
Latour 103, 104, 114, 117, 177, 182, 193
Law 75, 86, 103, 106, 116, 117, 126, 131, 138, 144, 145, 154, 166-169, 196, 199, 203, 212, 234, 245, 251
Legislation 81, 83, 84, 98, 102, 121, 134, 140, 145, 149, 153, 154, 159, 161, 167, 168-171, 184, 186, 199, 203
Machiavelli 115, 177, 178, 191, 192, 194
Maize 67, 141, 242
Mamestra brassica 128
Mass-media 122
Medicine 21, 73, 103, 212, 216, 222, 227, 241, 245, 248
Metaphysics 7, 15, 30
Methodology 40, 47, 49, 104, 162, 222
Microcosms 10, 33, 36, 39-45, 65, 71, 72, 148, 230
Microorganisms 7, 33-44, 58, 59, 63, 65, 66, 70-72, 134, 135, 193, 202, 238
Model 7, 10, 17, 25, 30, 32, 39, 42, 44, 45, 47-55, 57, 58, 60-62, 65, 70, 72, 74, 75, 82, 83, 93, 104, 123, 124, 127, 131, 132, 151, 163, 203
Modeling 7, 33, 43
Molecular biology 17-23, 28, 31, 57, 249, 250, 251
Monoculture 129, 131, 132
Moratorium 7, 37, 63, 73, 77, 78, 159
Morphogenetic fields 74
Mycorrhizae 39
Natural history 35, 57, 62
Nature 9, 15, 17, 18, 20, 23, 27, 28, 30, 31, 32, 36, 38, 49, 53, 54, 56, 66, 67, 73, 75, 76, 78, 104, 116, 117, 123, 129, 133-135, 137, 139, 141, 150, 151, 153, 163, 164, 167, 168, 172, 177, 181, 183, 186, 191, 196, 198, 205, 206, 208, 210, 212, 225, 227-229, 232, 234, 235, 238, 241-243, 245, 250
NGO(s) [Non-governmental organisation(s)] 8, 11, 73, 81, 92, 94, 98, 164 166-169, 172-178, 182-187, 189-191, 247, 250,

251
Non-target species 41
Objectivism 21
Oilseed rape 10, 77, 86-92, 95, 102, 141, 151
Paradigm 32, 38, 135, 181, 182, 208
Pathogen(s) 42, 45, 55, 58-60, 84, 103, 112, 185, 188
Pathogenicity 42, 57-60, 70, 116
Persistence 10, 41, 64, 66-71, 124, 125, 133, 141
Pest 58, 84, 95, 122, 131, 134, 135, 141-143, 185, 211, 215, 230, 243
Pesticide 24, 44, 94, 130, 134
Phenotype 35, 38, 39, 51, 142
Philosophy 5, 7, 15-19, 21-24, 27, 28, 30, 31, 42, 62, 117, 118, 145, 194-196, 210, 214, 216, 223-225, 247, 248, 250, 251
Physical containment 17, 19, 40, 64, 74, 84, 88, 109, 121, 123, 125-129, 132, 133, 153, 154, 185, 187, 189, 207, 209
Pleiotropy 36
Policy 8, 11, 16, 18-20, 22-28, 30-32, 35, 44, 49, 51, 53, 61, 71, 72, 81, 85, 86, 97, 100, 102, 118, 134, 135, 137, 139, 144, 145, 147-156, 159, 160, 162, 164, 168, 170, 175, 179, 194, 196-198, 205, 207, 218, 227, 231, 239, 244, 248-251
Politics 11, 16, 18, 32, 49, 62, 63, 64, 70, 72, 100-102, 114, 145, 179, 180, 184, 195, 196, 207-209, 216, 223, 250, 251
Pollution 135, 138, 145, 172, 190, 194
Popper 18, 30, 32, 42, 45, 197, 205
Potato 211, 215
Precautionary 8, 11, 37, 77, 81, 83-86, 96, 98, 100, 102, 121, 123, 125, 133, 134, 137-142, 144, 145, 148, 149, 152, 154, 196, 202, 241
Predictability 34, 82, 140
Prediction 22, 34, 75, 227
Promise(s) 10, 21, 22, 29, 77, 148
Protocol 73, 75, 77, 78, 130, 199, 201, 205
Pseudomonas putida 65
Pseudomonas syringae 37
Public information 8, 11, 153, 159, 161, 164, 165-167, 169, 171, 173, 174
Public opinion 163, 167, 172, 178, 238
Public participation 10, 11, 77, 159, 161, 165, 166-168, 171, 173, 198, 208, 216, 217, 219, 224, 225
Public perception 160
Public understanding 160, 179
Quality 5, 7, 16, 23, 25-28, 30, 31, 35, 47, 49-52, 54, 61, 92, 113, 143, 159, 163, 170, 173, 185, 199, 203, 210, 212, 215, 216, 218, 236, 242
Rabies 7, 10, 103-119, 184, 194
Rationality 21, 102, 181, 182, 203, 209, 212,

216
Reality 19, 29, 76, 104, 115, 151, 177, 181, 182, 197, 207, 211, 218, 227, 236
Reasoning 10, 16, 21, 48, 53, 55, 58, 94, 141, 166, 230, 231, 240
Recombination 54, 56, 68, 70, 129, 159
Reductionism 7, 17-19, 21, 23, 24, 30, 31, 33
Regulation(s) 10, 11, 15, 21, 23, 25, 26, 31, 38, 41, 43, 45, 47, 48, 50, 55-58, 61-63, 69, 77, 78, 81-83, 84, 86, 90, 92-94, 97, 98, 100-102, 127, 130, 131, 133-135, 138, 140, 141, 145, 147, 151, 152-156, 159-164, 167, 176, 177, 183, 184, 190, 201, 207, 212, 220, 225, 230, 231, 241, 243, 247, 249-251
Regulatory framework 48, 55, 56, 86, 159, 160, 161, 168, 176, 179, 185
Relativism 51, 52, 181
Resistance 20, 60, 67, 68, 71, 72, 75-77, 82, 84, 87, 88, 90, 92, 93, 95, 96-98, 101, 112, 119, 143, 159, 217, 219, 228, 243, 244
Responsibility 32, 82, 92, 97, 98, 133, 160, 180, 195-197, 208, 210, 214, 224, 243, 244, 248
Rhetorical 48, 129, 187, 190
Risk analysis 29, 33, 37, 149, 177, 183, 184, 225
Risk assessment 2-4, 7, 8, 10, 11, 13, 15, 16, 22, 23, 26-45, 47-58, 60-63, 66, 70, 71, 77, 79, 81-85, 89, 92, 94, 95-97, 99, 100, 104, 111, 121, 122, 123, 127, 129, 131, 132, 135, 141, 142, 145, 148, 149, 151, 153, 155, 157, 159, 162, 163, 166, 169, 170, 172-174, 177, 183-191, 196, 198, 203, 204, 208, 209, 210, 225, 227-229, 235, 236, 239, 241-243, 248, 250, 251
Scientism 30
Scorpion toxin 24, 121, 124, 125, 128, 130, 131, 134, 135, 166
Simulation 40, 131, 132, 228
Society 5, 9, 10, 16, 18-20, 25, 29-32, 38, 40, 44, 45, 53, 60-62, 71, 101, 102, 104, 114, 117, 118, 122, 129, 131, 132, 134, 145, 147, 170, 172, 176, 177, 184, 194, 204, 207, 213, 214, 223, 226-231, 234, 239, 240, 242-244, 248, 249, 251
Speculation 37, 49, 53, 147
Spread 10, 15, 27, 39, 41, 54, 58, 62-64, 66, 69, 76, 77, 90-92, 95, 96, 107, 109, 111, 150, 210, 230
Stability 63, 68, 70, 71, 76, 77
Step-by-step 84, 123, 130, 141-143, 149, 152, 177, 187, 190, 191
Survey 11, 171, 230-239, 243, 245
Survival 10, 33, 41, 42, 58, 59, 63-72, 88,

128, 189, 212
Sustainability 10, 137, 144, 168, 174
Sustainable development 138, 144, 151, 163, 174
Technological fix 164
Technology assessment 11, 43, 45, 101, 118, 179, 196, 203, 204, 223, 243, 245, 248
Teleology 11, 131, 132
Tomato 236
Toxicology 34
Trade-off 127, 219
Traditional breeding 24, 47, 48, 53, 56, 77, 229
Transfer 10, 35, 38, 54, 57, 61, 63, 65, 66, 68-73, 76, 77, 88, 90, 95, 102, 141, 142, 160, 172, 179, 205, 211, 228
Transparency 169, 170, 177, 187, 189, 190, 223
Transposons 54, 76
Trichoplusia ni 124, 128, 124
Trust 70, 160, 182, 202, 230, 239, 240
Uncertainty 11, 62, 75, 88-90, 99, 102, 125, 128-130, 132, 135, 137, 139, 143, 144, 145, 151, 152, 172, 174, 194, 209, 212, 218, 250
Unpredictability 73, 75-77, 86, 123, 141
Utilitarianism 28, 30, 239
Vaccine 34, 103, 105-108, 110-119, 184, 228
Vaccinia virus 103, 111, 112, 116-118
Validity 47, 53, 133, 161, 169, 209
Value(s) 10, 30, 43, 54, 55, 60, 75, 78, 82, 117, 122, 131, 135, 139, 144, 145, 165, 181, 182, 187, 190, 193, 194, 203, 212-214, 216, 219, 227, 230, 239, 244
Vector 9, 70, 89, 115
Virus 9, 10, 68, 103-105, 108, 111, 112, 115, 116-118, 121-135, 228
Weediness 57, 68, 91, 141
Weeds 39, 90, 91, 95, 101, 102, 230
Wheat 25, 39, 70, 229
World view 16, 172, 196